M000211006

Tekdem

51 — Le Commandant Berhanou Métcha

52 — Le Capitaine Mola Wakéné

Catégorie C — Ceux qui ont tenté de diviser les différentes unités de l'Armée et de créer la discorde entre le peuple et l'Armée:

53 — Le Capitaine Demessié Chifferaou

54 — Le Capitaine Belaye Tseguayé

55 — Le Capitaine Wolde Yohanes Zerguaou

56 — Le Caporal Teklé Haïlé

57 — Le Soldat Bekele Wolde Guihorguis

Catégorie D — Les membres du Conseil Militaire Provisoire coupables d'avoir tenté de diviser l'Armée et de jeter le pays dans le chaos:

58 — Le Lieutenant Général Aman Mikaél Andom

59 — Le Lieutenant Tesfayé Teklé

60 — Le Caporal Yohanes Fetoui.

Les autres personnalités toujours détenues seront très prochainement jugées par la Cour Martiale, précise le Communiqué du Conseil Militaire Provisoire qui appelle le peuple à l'ordre et à la discipline ainsi qu'à une participation active dans l'oeuvre de construction de l'Ethiopie de demain.

(ENA).

Appel de Siad Barré à l'unité africaine

Prétoria et Lusaka poursuivraient des négociations secrètes depuis deux mois

LUSAKA — Des entretiens secrets se déroulent depuis deux mois entre l'Afrique du Sud et la Zambie, apprend-on dimanche à Lusaka de source informée.

Ces conversations, par émissaires spéciaux, viseraient à tenter de résoudre les problèmes régionaux y compris éventuellement la Rhodésie, le Sud-Ouest Africain (Namibie), et à améliorer les relations entre pays à minorité blanche et majorité noire de l'Afrique Australe.

Le même jour en Afrique du Sud, le *Johannesburg Sunday Times* rapporte qu'un responsable zambien de haut rang, envoyé par le président Kaunda est venu la semaine dernière en Afrique du Sud, mission qui pourrait ouvrir la voie à une rencontre entre le président Kaunda et M. John Vorster, premier ministre sud africain.

M. Vorster, premier ministre sud-africain, dans un discours récent, avait demandé à ses voisins africains de coopérer avec son pays plutôt que de recourir à la confrontation, et avait également demandé que le monde donne six mois à l'Afrique du Sud pour améliorer son image de marque. Le président Kaunda avait alors qualifié ce discours de «voix de la raison que l'Afrique attendait».

Le journal sud-africain, se référant à des sources non-nommées à Prétoria et Lusaka, ajoute que les relations entre les deux pays pourraient se normaliser et aboutir éventuellement à une rencontre des deux chefs d'Etat, si l'Afrique du Sud

Il y a quelques jours, le *Times* de Zambie avait rapporté que Lusaka avait présenté à la Grande-Bretagne un plan en cinq points pour résoudre le différend sur l'indépendance rhodésienne.

Un règlement de cette question serait une étape majeure dans l'amélioration de la situation en Afrique Australe.

En Namibie, l'Afrique du Sud qui administre sa région sous un mandat très controversé de la défunte Société des Nations, prépare l'évolution du territoire, qui selon certains observateurs, pourrait accéder à l'indépendance dans les dix années à venir.

Prétoria prévoit selon sa politique de développement séparé, de diviser le Sud-Ouest Africain en régions dominées respectivement par les Blancs et les Noirs. Dans cette optique, le territoire obtiendrait l'indépendance sous la forme d'une fédération d'Etats ou cantons noirs et blancs.

On indique encore la forme des changements intérieurs qu'entend mener à bien le gouvernement de M. Vorster. Mais, M. Hilgard Muller, ministre sud-africain des Affaires étrangères, a déclaré récemment: «Nous pouvons nous éloigner du racisme et d'une discrimination inutile sans voiler notre politique et sans sacrifier ou mettre en danger notre identité de Blancs».

Aucun changement ne doit cependant être attendu de la politique fondamentale selon laquelle la

Meskel

An Ethiopian Family Saga

1926–1981

Mellina and Lukas Fanouris

Jacaranda Designs Ltd. *Publishers*

About the Authors

Lukas and Mellina Fanouris were both born in Addis Ababa. Their parents were Greek immigrants who had made a new life in Ethiopia, settled, prospered and instilled in their children an enduring love and respect for the culture and people of Ethiopia.

Gabby, their only daughter was also born in Addis Ababa, but was forced to flee with her mother when Emperor Haile Selassie was overthrown.

Lukas was not permitted to leave and had to survive as best he could in the military regime that followed.

Despite danger, hardship and prolonged separation, their love has survived and the family lives today in Nairobi, Kenya.

First published in Kenya by
Jacaranda Designs Ltd. 1995
P.O. Box 76691, Nairobi, Kenya

Copyright ©

ISBN 9966-884-26-2

Typeset in Palatino. Printed in Singapore.

Dedicated to

MANOLI and EVANGELIA
*their children, grandchildren and
great-grandchildren*

NESTOR
*a wonderful father who left behind the gift of love
and who inspired us to document this in print*

NICHOLAS G. HAMAWI
*in memory of the one who offered unfailing
support, but modestly chose to remain silent*

TYRONE
who risked his life to unite two families

and to

THE PEOPLE OF ETHIOPIA

Acknowledgements

We wish to express our deep gratitude to a rare breed of people whom we have been privileged to know, and who offered not only their time, love and understanding when it was most needed, but their true friendship which will be eternally treasured.

Among them are Ed and Linda Telles who implanted the initial idea that our story had to be documented; Brigitte Hillen-Ogutu who, for four years patiently listened, encouraged and gave up endless time to guide us to perfection; Claire Taylor who had a look at the first shabby draft and had positive comments to make; our enthusiastic and efficient editor, Sue Williams, whose grasp, professionalism and inquisitive mind wrapped up our story and turned it into something worth reading; Susan Scull-Carvalho and Bridget King who believed in the book enough to publish it; and last but not least our Ethiopian friends and colleagues who yearned to have 'their' story told.

Contents

Meskel

Meskel—the Amharic word for 'cross', became the symbol of burden, sacrifice, faith and hope in the half century that the Fanouris family lived in Ethiopia. At the most tragic and crucial time of their lives, when all hope was lost of surviving one of the cruelest revolutions on African soil, a tale related by one of their forefathers gave them the strength to hold on for a better tomorrow:

> *Stricken by poverty and hardship, a mother once expressed her indignation that the Son of God had given her the heaviest of crosses to shoulder. Hearing her complaint, Christ guided her to a vast mountainside carpeted with a bright blaze of yellow daisies and dotted with a multitude of crosses. Some were large and solid like the one He was crucified on—others as small as the gold emblem hanging around her neck. He asked her to select the cross of her choice. Identifying the tiniest she could lay her eyes on, she pointed it out. Our Lord smiled. "But, that's the one you are already carrying," He answered.*

Foreword

Meskel is an illustration of the history, culture and traditions of an ancient Empire that lived through the dynasties of the Queen of Sheba, Tewodros, Menelik and Haile Selassie. Ethiopia is one of the most ancient countries on earth, where the Ark of the Covenant is believed to be kept and where "Lucy" and the fossils of human ancestors dating back 4.4 million years were found.

In the 1950s and '60s the Fanouris Bookstore served as a library for those who could not afford to buy books and a meeting place for intellectuals and the younger generation who, for the first time, discovered the joys of periodicals such as *Time*, *Newsweek*, *L'Express*, *Paris Match* and *Le Monde*. It was a time when you could pick what you wanted and pay later; a time when one's word was sufficient.

Meskel is the true and poignant story of the Fanouris family who survived the suffering and humiliation of an artificial Marxist-Leninist regime in Ethiopia when the country was totally destroyed by the incredibly brutal and bloody military regime of the tyrant, Mengistu Hailemariam. Armed with goodwill and determination— and protected by Saint Gabriel of Kulubi—they were forced to flee their homeland and build a new life in Kenya, awaiting their return to the promised land.

In recalling the tragedy of the Fanouris family, Lukas and Mellina record an authentic testimony of their times, something which most exiled Ethiopian intellectuals failed to do.

Fekrou Kidane
Coordinator International Olympic Committee
Lausanne, Switzerland

INSERT; LETTER IN GREEK WITH
TRANSLATION

The Omen

The sight of the bird had disturbed him. He began to feel uneasy.

Lukas, he rebuked himself, stop the superstition. So what if it was a black bird? The azure sky was dotted with them. But the emotion persisted. His throat was dry; a vein on his temple began to throb. He frowned as his gaze concentrated on a knuckle-shaped rock on the horizon. That was it. The old woman. What had she predicted so many years ago? When was it? His memory was hazy but slowly fragments of the puzzle began falling into place.

It began when he was a teenager walking home from school. An old beggar woman, squatting in the dirt, had stopped him with outstretched hands. He had pulled out a small coin and was about to toss it into the jagged tin she held when, raising her head, she fixed him with a penetrating stare. As if in a trance, she cleared her parched throat and whispered, "Turn that coin into a paper note and I'll tell thy fortune."

He had accepted the bargain.

Swatting the hungry flies feasting on the mucous globules at the corners of her eyes, she took the green bill from his hand and held it up, blocking out the sun. It became translucent with his future engrained upon it.

"Thy destiny shines brightly, lavished with riches and expensive objects. But be warned, my son. Sinister clouds are gathering, awaiting the moment to smother our beloved land. When this country's strongest tree falls and the sun scorches its roots, many nests will drop to the ground crushing newly-hatched eggs. Blood will flow in the streets and the shrieks of mother birds will chill the air.

"When this," she said, scooping up a handful of dust, "has quenched its thirst, forcing the seed of the Meskel flower to crack the earth and burst its buds, reawakening the dead earth with garlands of yellow, birds in cages will be free to fly to their mates. Beware the feathers of black crows. Only the ones white as hail, fluffy as dove down, will lead the way to freedom."

Prologue

Addis Ababa, 12 August 1978

"Get your head down! They're shooting at you—you, Mellina!"

My numbed limbs slowly absorbed the message. Thoughts tumbled in a crazed kaleidoscope. A voice somewhere in my head screeched: Oh God, my baby... and Lukas... How will they cope without me? How will my baby survive without a mother?

"Help me, dear Lord!" I groaned.

I sank to my knees as bullets ricocheted off the white-washed stone walls. A prickling sensation ran down my spine. Unable to move, I crouched, awaiting a fatal shot. Around me, I was vaguely aware of doors and windows slamming shut, of screaming mothers behind flimsy shutters flinging their children to the ground and covering them with their bodies. In the dead-end street, there was no way out, no escape.

Suddenly, a pair of shaking arms began dragging me to safety. They had drawn miraculous strength from the sound of the gunfire. Exhausted eyes scrutinized mine as gentle hands stroked my face.

"The Virgin has saved you, my child," whispered Mama Askala hoarsely, choking back the tears. "And it would have been all my fault. What a waste it would have been to have given your life for mine, an old woman who's on the point of death anyway. What a sin!"

In a dream, I crawled over the freshly scrubbed threshold, slamming the door behind me. Trembling from the effort, the old woman fell back on her bed. Her wrinkled face, pale and drawn, twisted into a painful grimace; beneath the traditional, handwoven dress, her chest heaved as she strained to breathe.

Shots whistled through the open window. I staggered to pull the shutters closed, fumbling with the latch. Through a crack in one of the slats, my eyes focussed on a figure zigzagging between unyielding walls with the speed of a panicked gazelle. With murder in their eyes, a dozen khaki-clad raw militia men, toting guns for the first time, closed in on him, tugging at their triggers. Random bullets cracked tin roofs, shattered windows, splintered wooden fences. Obviously a university student, his tweed jacket sliding off his shoulders as he struggled to keep the fluttering silk tie from blocking his vision, the young fugitive jerked his head from side to side in a desperate search for a means of escape. His eyes still darting, he froze for a second as a door creaked open. A hand beckoned him.

"Quick in here," whispered a woman's voice. I recognised it instantly; only a few nights before her blood-curdling cries had stung our frail nerves like the lashing of a whip. It was Turunesh, whose fifteen-year-old daughter, sent by the authorities into the interior to teach the illiterate, had returned home in a coffin—her youthful body and innocent features disfigured by ugly red abrasions and purple bruises. Blind to the consequences, her maternal wounds raw from the loss of her child, Turunesh stretched out a helping hand. Spurred on, the student glanced back at the militia. Their leader was levelling his rifle, fixing the sights on him.

A young girl, panting and gasping in her bid to keep pace with the marksman, tugged at his sleeve imploring him to spare the boy's life. Irritated, he whacked her across the cheek with his rifle butt. Her hand flew up, touching the wet gash. Undaunted, she knelt to grasp his legs, to kiss his feet. She screeched in a desperate supplication, but shaking his leg free, the militia leader booted her in the ribs, and sent her sprawling across the hard ground. Unhampered now, he took careful aim and fired. The crack of the discharged bullet echoed in the empty street. With fatal precision it embedded itself in the boy's spine. Seized by uncontrollable reflexes, arms flew up, legs turned to rubber, a juvenile face crashed on to the gravel. Granted a second more, he would have crossed the threshold of the half-open door. The girl ran towards the limp figure and threw her body over his. Rolling him over, she screamed out his name. Placing her hands under his head, she shook him hard in a desperate bid to revive him. Her tears drenched the motionless face.

Now the shooting had ceased, doors creaked open and heads peered out. A small crowd gathered around the body. Some, relieved that the dead youngster was not known to them, drew back. One bystander, touched by her grief, came forward and tried to lift the girl to her feet. "He's gone, little one." His voice quivered, fearful of being overheard. "Go now. Now—before they take you as his accomplice."

"We were to be married next week," she sobbed, shaking herself free. "I don't care what these dogs do to me!"

"Watch your tongue, *usha*," the khaki-clad marksman spat at her, his youthful features contorted with hate. The crowd shrank back at the use of the word "bitch". The girl froze beneath his icy glare. The time for reasoning, pleading and begging were gone. She stared helplessly at her blood-drenched white dress. Finally accepting the loss of all hope, she stripped the *shamma* from her shoulders and with trembling fingers bent down to close her loved one's eyes. "Rest in peace, my love," she murmured, spreading the shawl over his face. "You don't have to run any more."

The sound of choking from Askala's bed drew me away from the window. I delved in my bag for the oxygen container, which was the reason for my visit, and with shaking hands began spraying it into her mouth.

"Don't die, Mama Askala!" I pleaded, stroking back her snow white hair. The old woman had worked for us for so long, she was as dear to me as my family. I prayed I hadn't arrived too late. "Breathe deeply. Please don't give up. Don't fight the oxygen!"

As the rasping grew softer, an agonized shout reached my ears from the street outside. "Mellina. Mellina. Where are you? For God's sake, has anyone seen my wife?"

I rushed to the door. "Lukas. Here… in here." But the pent-up anguish was so intense he never heard my call. A small boy, hidden behind a wood pile while the bullets flew, ran after him, tugging at his trouser leg.

"*Geta* Lukas, she's safe," he yelled, pointing to where I was standing.

Lukas strode over and clasped me in his arms. "Thank God!"

"Mama Askala's asthma…," I tried to explain. Together we gave the old woman a few more sprays of oxygen. When the blue faded from her lips and the ashen pallor left her face, we decided to walk back home.

Once there, he was cruelly logical. "You must take Gabby and get out. I'm a national. They won't let me leave—not for a long while—but we have to think about our child. Next time, we may not be so lucky." Why, I agonized, had Lukas ever renounced his Greek passport for an Ethiopian one? Was it only two years ago? It seemed like a lifetime away.

"Look," Lukas had said, "the law states one member of every foreign family business must become a citizen. That's fair enough. I love this country, this is my home. I want to serve the Emperor. I may as well throw in my lot, for better or worse."

There was no point now in regretting the decision. Could our love survive what might be years of separation? Could either of us survive without the other? We had waited so long to hear the cries of a child in our home. Now our prayers had been answered, that precious life was ours to protect and care for. Here, death surrounded us, eating away both our logic and our dreams.

Choking back the tears, I tried to put him off. "We're both upset. Let's not discuss this now. Put it to rest—at least for tonight."

"Don't you understand, Mellina. Those ignorant, trigger-happy louts were firing at random. Men, women, children—it's all the same to them, as long as they get target practice. They've been given a fine new uniform, big boots and a gun. They're important men. They don't give a damn who gets mowed down in their crossfire. Today, you might have been their target." I shuddered, pressing my body against his. "There's nothing more to discuss," he said. "Gabby needs you more than me."

Dumb, I nodded. The terrifying reality of the situation suddenly struck me. The Revolutionary Government had at first been lauded for its bloodless coup, which the majority saw as deliverance from an era of imperialism and the crumbling rule of a frail, ageing despot. The rebels had gained the support of the people by uncovering and publicizing the horrors of a hitherto hidden famine in the province of Wollo. Heart-rending pictures of skeletal, pot-bellied babies had incensed the nation. The enlightened vowed justice and equality for a criminally-abused country.

Within a few months, those promises had become dead letters. The revolution began devouring its children. The country was divided into *kebeles*, which had absolute life-and-death powers. Firing squads replaced the courts as the means of dispensing 'justice' and innocent people, branded as 'anti-revolutionaries', were shot in public. The prisons overflowed with political detainees and police stations were pressed into serving as makeshift jails. The secret police were busier and more sinister than ever. People of all classes of society were affected. And now, this senseless violence had thrust itself into the peace of our home and family.

Thankful for being spared, I began to plan our resettlement. It would be difficult. The new military government had nationalized all our assets. We had no foreign account to rely on, despite the authorities' conviction that we had regularly smuggled money out of Ethiopia. My income would be our sole means of survival. I worked for the United Nations. Could I present a strong enough case to my office to persuade them to reassign me to a job in another country?

Silently I gazed down at the lines on my hands seeking my destiny. Why did our families ever choose to come to this country? How did it all start?

PART ONE

Chapter One

The year was 1926. Greece, like the rest of Europe, was suffering an economic depression. Hundreds of emigrants were leaving their homeland to seek a better future for their families.

In Djibouti on the coast of tropical French Somaliland, the SS Elpitha—Greek for 'hope'—had just docked. As she stepped onto the gang plank and surveyed the steamy, strange, bustling world below, Evangelia Fanouris locked her fingers between her husband's.

"This is it, Manoli."

Travellers' dust already covered them and a long, hot train journey lay ahead. With their infant son, they were to travel into the interior, through Dire-Dawa, to the capital of Abyssinia, Addis Ababa. The thrill of adventure filled their eyes.

Abyssinia, as Ethiopia was then known, was still a wild and unpredictable country. Although Ras Tafari, soon to be crowned the Emperor Haile Selassie, had for ten years been regent and heir to the throne, he had diehard enemies who ceaselessly plotted against him. At the same time, the country was surrounded by territories occupied by countries with colonial interests—the British in the Blue

Nile area, the Italians in Eritrea and Italian Somaliland and the French in their Somali protectorate. The future, especially for immigrants, was uncertain.

Evangelia looked up at her husband's strong, determined face. He had been one of the most sought-after bachelors on Karpathos, courteous and soft-spoken, but it was his deep olive skin and black curls that had captured the young girls' hearts. Standing over six feet, lean and well-muscled, he had been nicknamed *"o psilos"*—the tall one—by the burly island Greeks who envied his extra inches. His love of life, his sense of humour, his gift for inspiring hope and laughter simply overwhelmed Evangelia. She fell so deeply in love that she had vowed to follow him to the ends of the earth. And she had. To her, Africa was it.

"Let's cross ourselves and Pavlos and go on," she said with a smile.

Manoli drew her to him, wiping away the thick trickle of sweat which ran down his face and neck. "We may regret this. We may look back on Karpathos as a paradise, but with you beside me, I can't be a pessimist."

She turned her face away, fearing he might see the tears that suddenly filled her eyes. Settling in this new land would be much more difficult if he sensed her qualms. Soon, she reminded herself, she would be embracing the brother she had not seen for over a decade. It was Logotheti, with his tales of Africa, and Abyssinia in particular, of emperors, kings and fortunes to-be-made, who had inspired their journey. But she couldn't help feeling homesick and a little afraid; so much of her heart had remained behind in her native land. Karpathos, with its white-walled churches and brilliant blue skies, its holy day celebrations with all-night feasting and dancing in the

4

churchyards. Wonderful, carefree days. Admittedly, they were poor and, happy as they were with the simple Greek way of life, she understood that the temptation to improve their life-style and that of their children was too strong to ignore. Evangelia sighed, then she remembered the icon safely packed in her trunk; it was her most valued possession and its presence gave her renewed strength. Only a year ago her faith had been put to the test. Her unborn baby was in a breach position and doctors had told her it would not survive a caesarian operation. Evangelia had prayed fervently to the Virgin Mary to save her child and, in return, vowed to celebrate an all-night vigil on the Madonna's Feast Day for as long as she lived. As the surgeon's scalpel was poised to rip her flesh, the baby turned and was born naturally.

A sharp cry from Pavlos, impatient for his midday meal, cut into her reverie. Her breasts ached with milk: hastily she unbuttoned her white blouse and guided the searching mouth to her dripping nipple. The baby's vigorous sucking brought relief and contentment bolstered her resolve.

The heat of Djibouti was unbearable. It was worse than the blast from an inferno. The harbour water stank in the sun like rank fish soup. Somali men, wearing only a piece of diaphanous white cloth pulled up between their legs and loosely twisted round their waists like a baby's napkin, rushed about unloading cargo. Their chocolate-brown skins seemed oiled. They slowed their pace only to wipe away the sweat blurring their vision.

The weekly train to Addis Ababa was due later that day. Fellow travellers flopped on their belongings, some even too exhausted to seek shade. Manoli, anxious to look up some of the Greeks who had already established themselves in Djibouti, settled Evangelia and Pavlos under the meagre shadow of a stunted palm and went about his business. Cristos Nomikos, an old family friend, was among the first he visited. Cristos owned a thriving bookstore and was well known for lending newcomers a helping hand. He and Manoli hit it off like a house on fire. Manoli had barely crossed the threshold before Cristos offered him a job. Manoli hesitated, momentarily toying with the idea, but as he slapped a mosquito on the sticky nape of his neck, his mind was made up. Drained by the heat and humidity, with his shirt sticking to his back and the soles of his shoes smelling of melted rubber, he decided he couldn't wait to get out of that hole.

The sun had climbed to its zenith. Evangelia had followed the tree's shrinking shadow until she was backed up against its trunk. Surreptitiously, she had rolled down her stockings and tossed them to one side. "If only I could strip off to my skin," she sighed. Oozing with perspiration, she tugged at the knot which secured her black, rose-bordered head scarf with its paper-thin gold coins. "So what if they see my long hair!" she told herself, peeling the wet charms from her forehead.

It was with a certain envy that she watched the black, velvet-skinned women in their flimsy, colourful *kangas*, swinging their hips through the heavy air. Then shame closed her eyes. Their breasts were naked. She could not understand how proud they were of their female beauty. They thrust out their chests, swaying from side to side, displaying every curve. Opening one eye, then the other, she could not resist the temptation to take another glimpse. It was unheard of in Karpathos for any young girl to parade in public in a state of undress. She imagined what a stir would be created by her first letter home, describing this nakedness.

* * *

Laboriously, the clanking steam engine set its wheels squealing against the metal tracks, jerking a dozen heavily-loaded wagons into life. Leaving a thick slash of black soot behind it, it eased its way out of the station. Passengers who had been hanging out of the carriage windows, anxiously awaiting the movement of the iron snake, collapsed thankfully into their seats, fanning themselves with newspapers and pieces of torn cardboard. The journey would be tediously slow, but lethargic limbs slowly regained their vigour as a welcome breeze gently refreshed flushed faces and filled jaded lungs.

The trip from Djibouti to Addis Ababa, the Abyssinian railhead, took three days with two overnight stops at Dire-Dawa and the Awash station. Mile upon mile of featureless desert slid by. The only signs of life were the occasional vultures circling ominously overhead or perched on some carrion, ripping at scorched flesh.

In the failing light, little could be seen of the flat-roofed mud huts that surrounded the rest-house at Dire Dawa as the train, screeching and hissing, pulled in to the station. Grateful for the interlude, passengers hurriedly climbed down from the carriages and were ushered into the huge white-washed mud and wattle house, where a hot meal and canvas camp beds awaited them.

Manoli, keen to explore, left Evangelia and Pavlos sleeping while he took a walk. It was a pleasant, moonlit night. He strolled towards the first group of huts, their black shapes quite distinct against the lightened sky. It was too early for the local inhabitants to have retired, yet

7

the town was deserted. He couldn't understand it. Then he froze in his tracks. A maniacal cackle followed by eerie whooping noises came out of the darkness surrounding him. Heart pounding, he raced back to the safety of the rest house. There he learned it was quite common for packs of hyenas to throng the town at night, scavenging for left-overs and frequently running off with lambs and goats. Shamefaced, Manoli never mentioned the incident again.

Early next morning, everyone boarded the train for the second leg of the journey. As the track slowly snaked up towards the Abyssinian highlands, Evangelia noted with relief a marked change in both the temperature and the scenery. The hot-air breeze of yesterday, which served only to dry the beads of sweat as they formed, was now refreshingly cool, while the dull brown, arid landscape was increasingly enlivened by patches of vegetation which became greener and lusher as the day progressed. Her bliss, however, was short-lived. As the train screeched to a halt at Erer, she saw with terror a mob racing towards it. "Manoli, what's going on?" she screamed, gripping his arm. "Are we being attacked?"

Peering out of the window, Manoli watched the growing commotion. "Yes," he said suppressing a smile, "we're being stormed by bare-bosomed natives with nipples as large and as black as olives." Seeing her panic-stricken face, he smiled. "Relax, my little one." He winked. "They don't compare with yours. But I have to admit, I've never seen breasts like these before. Now, if I can just force myself to move my eyes a bit…" he teased, "ah yes, now I can see a bit more clearly… perfectly-shaped bodies with narrow waists and bulging hips, swathed in flimsy flowered cotton, and elegant legs… little left to the imagination."

Evangelia kicked him, her cheeks gradually losing their flush. "If all you can give me is a description of how generous our Creator was in moulding these creatures, I shall look for myself," she huffed. She moved to the window and looked out. "So these are the descendants of the Queen of Sheba. They certainly don't look dangerous. They're smiling," she exclaimed.

The station—if a ramshackle hut and a rusty water tank could be called such—was milling with nubile, honey-skinned women, most of them carrying babies strapped to their backs while they balanced gaudy, intricately-designed baskets on their heads. Their hair fell in innumerable tiny braids, each decorated with beads or cowrie shells, while their slender necks were festooned with brightly coloured beads, which served to enhance the simple beauty of their naked breasts. Some had tattoos on their cheeks; all had inquisitive, almond-shaped eyes, which searched the carriages for prospective buyers.

"What are they selling?" yelled Evangelia, trying to make herself heard above the commotion. She had been squeezed to one side as other passengers jostled for window space.

"Fruit," shouted Manoli. "Oranges, tangerines, lemons, anything you like."

"Buy as many oranges as you can get. We need the fresh juice for Pavlos. Logotheti warned us not to drink any water without boiling it. It could be polluted. He said…" Her words were lost in the hubbub.

Manoli was busy studying some of the strange and wonderful fruits being peddled; some prickly and uninviting, others smooth and mouth-watering. He was particularly fascinated by a curved, yellow finger-like fruit, which appeared to grow in clusters. Registering his

9

interest, one young woman, nodding and smiling, broke off one of the fingers and offered it to him, smacking her lips to reinforce her sales pitch.

"Don't touch it, Manoli! It could be poisoned," cried Evangelia, as he stretched out his hand. Sensing Evangelia's alarm, the woman picked another specimen from her basket, peeled it, broke off the top and placed it in her mouth. A broad smile revealed there was no need to shrink from the exotic.

"Do you know what these are?" Manoli asked a fellow passenger, waving the yellow object.

"We call them bananas," he replied.

"So these are what the Italians were boasting about," Manoli mused aloud. The man looked puzzled. "We had some Italian soldiers on Karpathos who had served in Somalia," Manoli explained. "No matter what fruit they tried, no matter how delicious, they always said the same thing, 'Tasty, but nothing like a banana'. We called them the banana bunch. I didn't realise at the time, but it was appropriate, eh?" Manoli chuckled to himself. He turned to Evangelia. "It seems this lady is determined I should taste one of her, er, bananas. I can't disappoint her." So saying, he peeled the fruit and bit off the soft stem as the woman had shown him.

"Saint George from my mother's land, place your hand on this rash man!" Evangelia prayed to her family's protector.

Manoli laughed and finished the banana with relish.

"The sun of Africa has already boiled your brain," cried his wife. "If you get sick, who do you think will help—the local witch doctor with his concoctions of lizard eggs and spider's blood? He'll certainly be the only one you can call in the middle of this God-forsaken wilderness."

Ignoring Evangelia, Manoli leaned out of the window and gestured to the woman that he wanted to buy the whole basket. "Now what about these. Has anyone any idea what these are like?" He pointed to a peach-coloured, oval fruit, taking boyish delight in his wife's discomfort.

"Those are mangoes," someone behind him volunteered. "When ripe, they're like European peaches, but more tangy. You suck the core until every last morsel of flesh has gone."

"I'll try them," said Manoli. The woman was delighted. She smiled her gratitude; few passengers on the Djibouti train were as generous as this white man.

Next morning, brief glimpses of circular native huts, built of a typically arched framework of poles overlaid with bark and dry hides, indicated that they were travelling through the Awash region, land of the Danakil. It was hot, dusty and swarming with flies. Barely visible against their bleached surroundings, herds of camels stirred the fine sand into clouds of dust while flocks of goats raced from one shrivelled shrub to another, searching out the tender shoots.

The Danakils, wearing a formidable curved dagger strapped across their stomachs and carrying their rifles like yolks across the back of their necks, stood guard over their animals beneath the fierce sun. Naked but for their loin cloths, their mops of hair were twisted into thick ringlets half-hiding their finely-chiselled features. Evangelia stared in fascination at their beauty, ignorant of their murderous custom of castrating any male they killed or maimed and wearing their trophies dangling from their wrists. The women were equally impressive. Like the women of Erer, they wore layer upon layer of brightly-coloured bead necklaces which hung upon their proud

11

breasts in vivid contrast to their smooth dark skins. A wrap-around skirt slit on one side revealed the supple grace of their bodies.

Evangelia had adamantly refused to even look at the contents of the baskets Manoli had bought, but as the day wore on she began to feel a craving for the 'forbidden' fruit. When the train eventually stopped at Awash Station and the same basket-toting crowds began to descend upon them, she finally admitted defeat.

"If all these plump children are nourished on bananas," she said, looking at the chubby native toddlers, "then Pavlos and I are ready to try them."

Manoli sighed deeply. "Thank God and all his saints," he murmured to himself. Perhaps settling in this land would not be so difficult after all.

* * *

The rhythm of the iron wheels lulled Manoli into reverie as he speculated how it might feel to become a wealthy exporter of gold and silver, a merchant so successful and influential that even kings and emperors would ask to meet him. But, he sighed, there was a long and difficult bridge to cross before he would see the gates of any palace.

As their journey's end approached, Manoli hung out of the carriage window to catch a first glimpse of the town which was to be their home. A smooth, golden carpet of flowers stretched across the plain as far as the eye could see to the foothills of a distant mountain range. The sweet smell of honey filled the air. Peering beyond the narrow-gauge track as it looped in a series of hairpins, he could just make out, amid densely-forested hills, clusters of native thatched huts interspersed with a few stone buildings.

Brakes screeched; the carriages rumbled to a halt. Through open windows, the crisp fragrance of eucalyptus trees gently wafted into the wagons, dispelling the stale air. Like caged birds fretful to fly the coop, passengers fought their way to the exits. Some shoved bundles and baskets through windows into the arms of waiting porters, others crawled under seats frantically searching for misplaced socks and shoes.

"Let's wait a little," Manoli suggested. "The baby might get hurt in the crush."

Adolescent boys swarmed upon the train from all directions, seizing luggage thrown down onto the platform or rushing to relieve travellers of their loads. "*Getoch, getoch*," one youngster shouted, pushing his way through the melee. "Please choose me. I have no mother, no father. I have to feed three brothers and sisters," he implored. Another, taking a more direct approach, grabbed the two bags and ran towards the exit. It was the surest way of earning a few cents.

Manoli and Evangelia clambered down from the train. The 'Chemin de Fer', built by the French just 13 years earlier, was more impressive than either of them had imagined with its glass-roofed platform and elegant arched porticos. They stood, a little overwhelmed, as the broiling stream of traffic gradually thinned. What now? Here they were, but where was Logotheti? Evangelia squatted on one of the bags with the baby in her arms.

"Dear Mother of God," she prayed, "don't let him get the date wrong." As she raised her head to look down the platform once more, she saw a tall, lean young man with ginger hair and a neatly-cropped beard striding purposely

13

towards them. "Logotheti," she whispered to herself. "Logotheti." She leapt to her feet. "Manoli, it's Logotheti. It must be. That shade of hair runs only in my family." Thrusting the baby into her husband's arms, she ran down the platform. Logotheti locked her in a tight embrace.

"Evangelia! I knew it must be you when I saw you. My, but you were just a child when I left Greece. Can it be so long ago? Look what a fine woman you've become! And this must be Manoli, of whom I've heard so much." Logotheti gripped Manoli's hand as he approached. "So, you're here at last."

Logotheti's portrayal of the land he loved with its ancient history of Christianity and its magnificent churches hewn out of solid rock, its breath-taking landscapes and almond-eyed beauties was finally a reality. Outside the station lay a bustling town of narrow dirt streets bordered by white-washed wattle huts and tin-roofed shacks. The roads swarmed with people—men swathed in white with rifles slung over their shoulders, travellers on horseback, mule trains, limbless beggars, long-skirted, barefoot women trudging under back-breaking loads of firewood and clay pots. The smell of rancid butter and burning cow dung permeated the air.

While the men supervised the luggage, Evangelia eagerly absorbed the scene. Glancing towards the setting sun, she focused on the faint black outline of a church on the hill opposite.

"That must be Mariam on Entoto Hill!" she exclaimed, delighted to be able to identify the shrine that Logotheti had built for the Emperor, so often described in his letters. At the beginning of Emperor Menelik's reign the hill was on the southernmost border of his empire; when he died, it was at the empire's heart. Menelik had originally planned to build his capital on Entoto Hill overlooking the sweet-smelling, bluish-grey valley of eucalyptus so admired by Taitu, his wife. But after bathing in some hot springs at the foot of the hill, he had changed his mind. He found the waters soothed his inflamed arthritic joints, giving him renewed strength and vigour. It was a good omen. He built a church on the hill and founded his city at its foot, next to the life-giving spring. He named his capital *"the new flower" — "addis ababa"*.

"I was hoping to pick you up in a taxi," Logotheti's voice interrupted. "Unfortunately, they're all being used by the Palace tonight, so we'll have to settle for a *gari*" He pointed towards a horse-drawn carriage. "Better cover Pavlos up," he said, handing Evangelia a blanket. "At eight thousand feet, the nights get pretty chilly."

A single tarmac road stretched from the railway station to Menelik's palace. Elevated on a grassy mound, the royal residence, the only building with electricity, shone in the darkness like a lighthouse in the middle of an ocean with the city at its feet resembling dark waves settling after a storm. Once night fell, total darkness descended upon the capital. The deserted streets were given over to packs of screaming hyenas and hundreds of savage, howling dogs.

Shivering, Evangelia snuggled close to her brother. "If we don't reach your house soon, we'll freeze to death."

"It's not far now," he comforted her. "Now, tell me your news from home."

"Anna misses you terribly. She's built a house with the money you've been sending her, but she's desperate to start a family. She isn't the seventeen-year-old you left behind, you know."

Logotheti nodded. He felt rising pangs of guilt and frustration. They had been married less than a month when he had been offered a year's contract to build lighthouses in the Red Sea. It seemed like only yesterday when he had hugged his young bride, kissing away the tears as he bid her goodbye. "With what I'll earn we'll be able to afford anything money can buy," he had promised her.

Then one morning a messenger had arrived from Menelik's palace demanding the presence of the "one with the hair the colour of fire".

"I'm just a simple contractor. What could the Emperor want with me?" he had questioned the Imperial bodyguard sent to escort him, but his only answer was an impatient shake of the head. The journey along narrow dirt tracks had to be negotiated by mule, a troublesome and dangerous form of transport in the rainy season. The animal was fine until it reached the approach to the palace, then it refused to budge. No amount of heaving, tugging, coaxing or cajoling could shift it, until, losing patience, Logotheti twisted its tail. This had the required effect, but only after the beast had kicked up its hind legs spattering filth all over its master's white trousers. Already nervous, this did not increase Logotheti's confidence.

Menelik was probably the most powerful ruler the country had ever known, directly descended—so his subjects believed—from Solomon and Sheba. Determined to unify and modernise his country, he had driven out the Italians who claimed a protectorate over the country, defeating them ignominiously at the Battle of Adoua in 1896. He had conquered the Ogaden, Harar, the lands of the Galla tribes, the Gurage country and the ancient kingdom of Kaffa. He had even subjugated the Anuak and other tribes on the borders of the Sudan. By the 1890s, all the rulers of the ancient provinces of Abyssinia had accepted him as Emperor. But he was not just a warrior. After founding the capital, he introduced the country's first currency and postage stamps, granted a concession for railway and telegraph links with Djibouti and sent several students abroad to be educated. He established the first cabinet, bank, school, hospital, printing press and modern road system. Now he sat before Logotheti in autocratic splendour, a glittering velvet cloak embroidered with gold thread intertwined with scarlet silk draped majestically about his person. A cluster of dark rubies formed the clasp which drew it together at the throat.

With penetrating, almost glaring eyes, Menelik addressed Logotheti. "I've heard of the towers of light that guide ships to safety. The beam of true faith must now attract our Coptic Orthodox followers to the house of Mariam." He paused. "I want you to build a shrine on Entoto Hill which I shall dedicate to the Virgin Mary."

Logotheti could not refuse this all-powerful monarch. He was also excited by the challenge. Some time after he had completed the church, Menelik summoned Logotheti once more. This time the Emperor asked him how much it would cost to build a wall around the Palace. Logotheti told him he didn't know: he would have to ask his assistant to measure the surrounding compound and do his calculations. Menelik burst out laughing and addressing his entourage, said, "This young man doesn't know how to steal by himself. He needs an assistant to help him." Turning back to Logotheti, he clapped him on the back and said, "Let me help you, son." Handing his walking stick to an officer of the court, he ordered him to use it to measure the Palace periphery. When the measurements were brought to him, the Emperor did some quick calculations and made Logotheti a fair offer. After that, Logotheti became Menelik's favourite constructor. His next assignment was to erect a monument to commemorate the Emperor's magnificent victory against the invading Italian forces at the Battle of Adoua in 1896. With all the skill he could summon, Logotheti created Saint George's Cathedral, where Haile Selassie was soon to be crowned. Years later, when the Italians finally succeeded in taking Addis, they attempted to blow up the cathedral, but the building was so carefully constructed that only the cupola was slightly damaged by the blast.

Logotheti found himself passing from one project to another as the Emperor called upon him to build roads, bridges, schools, hospitals. And so the months turned into years and dreams and hopes of returning home to Karpathos began to diminish and eventually fade away.

Chapter Two

Inching her way through the market-day crowds, her progress slowed by the perpetual exchange of greetings, Evangelia made her way towards the large, open market square. Despite Logotheti's detailed descriptions, Abyssinia was still totally different from anything she or Manoli had imagined. An alien culture warred with their deep-rooted beliefs, but they soon came to realise that survival depended upon their ability to adapt themselves to a new way of life.

This was her first venture alone into the heart of the city. Bobbing in rhythm to their mincing steps, donkeys weighed down with top-heavy loads of dried cow dung, brushwood and hay, led the way. Bleating herds of goats and sheep milled around weather-beaten men and ragged boys, carrying cane baskets stuffed with squawking chickens. Through this boiling stream of people and animals, the occasional automobile swerved and honked.

Plump *woizeros* in long, hand-woven dresses with brightly-coloured scarves covering their fluffed out hair, swayed with the serenity of Egyptian princesses towards the market place. Each was attended by young retainers holding fanned umbrellas over their heads, not only to protect their silken skins and long aristocratic faces from the sun's darkening rays, but also—when necessary—to politely screen their hunched forms from view while relieving their bladders.

Men and women with creased, sun-darkened faces squatted in the dirt screeching at customers to buy their wares; mounds of green and scarlet chili peppers, onions, heaps of ginger and garlic, earthen pots, skins, cartridges, beer and lengths of cloth. Tribesmen, wrapped in flowing white *shammas* worn over long tunics and jodhpurs, bargained and argued over the price of grain and bars of salt. Covering themselves with patches of sheep skin stitched together with ribbons of dry gut, monks roamed around begging for scraps of food, fulfilling a self-inflicted vow to deprive themselves of dignity in order to feed illegitimate children.

Timidly at first and then with growing confidence, Evangelia made her purchases, fast learning the art of bartering. As the earth began to bake beneath the midday sun, heavily-laden, she made her way home. With the passing of time, Evangelia also came to terms with living without running water and electricity. Lighting her petromax lamps and continually burning her fingers on charcoal stoves became a daily routine.

For several months the couple toyed with various schemes for making a living. Finally, with Logotheti's financial support, they decided to open a Greek restaurant. After endless searching, they found the ideal place—a double-storey house close to the city centre. When word got about that Greek national dishes and island specialities were on the menu, the restaurant rapidly became a focal point for Addis Ababa's Greek community. In the evenings, the simple, white-washed room with its potted, creeping vines, overflowed with young and old, sipping *ouzo*, nibbling *meze*, battling over backgammon and reminiscing about their Mediterranean homeland. As they savoured Evangelia's *moussaka* and *dolmades*, her home-made feta cheese and yoghurt dips, the nostalgic twang of a *santuri* would float from some corner. Tables would be pushed to one side and before long, the room would vibrate to the sound of men clapping, stamping and dancing, slowly at first, then faster and faster as the music reached a crescendo.

Evangelia would watch from the kitchen door, leaning against the jamb, her foot tapping to the beat of the music. Back home, she had always loved these gatherings. These were the times when she felt most content. She would look at Manoli, laughing and joking or buried in some heated debate, and know they had made the right decision. But above all, she loved to watch Manoli dance. His big, lumbering frame would suddenly be transformed into an object of grace as he surrendered himself totally to the music.

"Come, Evangelia. Come, my little one," he said to her one evening, taking her hand and leading her to the floor. "I know how you love to dance. Come and show these foreigners," he waved his hand, jokingly, at the room full of expatriate Greeks, "how a real island girl can perform."

The *bouzouki* struck up her favourite tune *"O skopos tis nihtas"*. Her cheeks burning but unable to resist the music, she falteringly began. Manoli smiled encouragement. As she danced, she began to feel a sense of relief, almost abandon. All the pent-up emotions of the past few months seemed to be released by the movement. She began to spin round the room, dipping and twisting as the music reached a frenzied climax. Manoli was laughing and clapping. Suddenly spots of light flashed before her eyes. She steadied herself against a table. Manoli rushed to her side and as he slid his arm round her waist, her knees gave way.

"Give her air. Give her air," said a woman briskly stepping from the crowd. "It's alright. She's just fainted," she reassured Manoli, holding a limp wrist to take the pulse. "Get her upstairs to bed and I'll come and take a look at her. I'm the midwife for this area."

"Well, it's as I suspected," the midwife told Manoli later. "Your wife is pregnant."

"Pregnant!" Manoli exclaimed. It was the one thought he had not entertained. His mind had been racing with imagined fears of malaria, yellow fever, blackwater fever, hepatitis and a dozen other equally nasty and potentially fatal tropical diseases which were rife in this primitive land. But pregnant!

He strode into the bedroom. "How are you feeling, little one?" he asked, stroking a wisp of hair back from her forehead. "And how is our little girl?" He gently patted her stomach.

"Manoli, I'm so scared. What if something goes wrong? Look what happened with Pavlos. What if it should happen again? There are no hospitals here. We don't even have a doctor. I don't know if I want any more children here. I already have to watch Pavlos like a hawk in case he goes near any beggars with leprosy or tuberculosis. With two, it will be a nightmare."

Manoli clasped her hand. "Don't worry. Everything's going to be alright. That midwife who was just here seems to be very capable. A bit bossy and domineering, but what good woman isn't. She certainly seems to know her job. Come on. Cheer up. We're having a baby and she's going to be a beautiful girl, just like her mother."

The restaurant continued to flourish, but Evangelia found it increasingly tiring to supervise the running of the kitchen and even more difficult to stay awake long enough to participate in the nightly debates. Reports of current events in the outside world were rare, but any snippet of news served to spark off heated discussions of political issues.

"We need foreign newspapers," Manoli announced one night. "Apart from what we glean in letters from home, none of us know what's happening in the world."

While the regulars continued to argue as their fingers flashed across the backgammon board, Manoli was lost in a world of his own. Everyone was desperate for a newspaper stand—a constant flow of information. Why hadn't he thought of it before? The idea started to take shape. He would import daily gazettes, magazines, books...

A sharp shriek from above drew Manoli up the stairs two at a time.

"Quick, Manoli, the midwife," panted Evangelia. Her body bathed in cold sweat, she was trying desperately to control the urge to push. Manoli fiddled with a curl at the nape of his neck. "Don't just stand there, Manoli. Run!" she screamed.

He turned and shot past Logotheti. "I'm in labour," he mumbled. "Going to fetch Jenny."

Logotheti placed his hand on her stiffening belly, then quickly withdrew it. "There's no need to panic, sister," he said with a nervous grin. "If this woman doesn't get here in time, I know exactly what to do."

"Dear Mother of God and all the saints," Evangelia muttered to herself.

"She's here," a voice called from below.

Purposeful, flat-footed steps were heard on the stairs. "Now then, stop shaking man," the midwife said, brushing Logotheti aside. "Fetch me boiling water and clean bedsheets, will you? Men!" she exclaimed, wiping the perspiration from Evangelia's forehead. "They're neither use nor ornament when it comes to having babies. Your husband nearly drove me mad with his jabbering. If I were not saving my strength, I would have given him a right hook there and then to bring him to his senses. Now, let's see. Yes," she said, examining her patient's dilated cervix. "One strong push and I think your troubles will be over."

As the tiny being slithered into the world and was slapped into life, Evangelia fell back on her pillow, exhausted.

"It's a beautiful girl," announced Jenny, wrapping the baby in a towel. "With ten fingers and toes and a cute little nose. Just hear her scream!"

Evangelia was no longer listening. With a deep sigh of relief, she allowed her heavy lids to close and surrendered herself to sleep. She awoke to subdued chatter and stifled giggling. Out of habit, she placed her hands on her abdomen and in momentary panic, felt the emptiness. Alarmed, she sat up. "Jenny. Where are you?"

The midwife's face appeared at the door. "I'm finished washing and smartening her up. I'll bring her to you in a few moments," she replied.

A smooth diminutive face turned searchingly towards its mother. Placing her lips on the silky head, Evangelia kissed her baby lovingly. "My Sophia," she murmured. Her fingers gently traced the delicate features, halting suddenly when they touched her ears. "What have you done to her," Evangelia cried, examining the turquoise studs which adorned the tiny lobes. With a shudder, she imagined the gold pin piercing her baby's flesh.

"She didn't even cry," Jenny boasted. "You can't leave a pretty girl without any protection against the evil eye, now can you?"

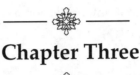

Chapter Three

"I'm taking the train to Djibouti on Monday," Manoli announced at the breakfast table. "I'm going to see Cristos Nomikos. You remember him? Remember how hard he tried to get me to work for him when we first arrived? I hear he has good connections with publishing firms: I've been thinking about it and I want to see if it's possible to get newspapers sent up every week."

"I can't understand you," cried Evangelia. "Why are you forever looking for something new? The restaurant is doing well. Why can't we keep all our eggs in one basket?"

Manoli shuffled in his seat. "The restaurant business is okay, but with another child on the way, you can't keep working like you do. It's time you retired from cooking for others. Besides," he added, "I want to build up a respectable business for the future for our kids."

While Manoli was away, Matina Skouros, a compatriot and close neighbour became a regular visitor, dropping in for coffee and a taste of Evangelia's speciality—*baklava*; a paper-thin pastry stuffed with nuts and soaked in syrup. Matina was a gossip. She thrived on revealing other people's intimate secrets, sadly unaware of rumours about her own husband and his affairs with local native women.

Evangelia was always careful to restrict their chats to innocuous topics like recipes and knitting patterns. Matina's habit of drawing odious comparisons between Sophia and her own daughter especially irritated her.

One day, Evangelia had had enough. She was secretly glad Sophia was sleeping and relieved when Matina packed her crochet away and stood up to leave. At that moment, Logotheti, who was staying with the family while Manoli was away, walked into the room with the child in his arms.

"I think she's ready for a meal," he said, handing the infant to Evangelia.

"What do you stuff her with, my dear?" demanded Matina. "You can't attribute that pot-belly just to breastmilk," she smirked. "Why, my Elizabeth is half her size and they're the same age."

She moved towards the door and was halfway through, when she turned back and said casually, "Incidentally, I found Sophia sucking her fingers while you were out shopping the other day, so I thought I would do you a favour and put her on my breast until you got back. I soon curbed that appetite of hers."

Her words struck Evangelia like a whiplash. How dare she touch her child! She felt like slapping the woman. She fought to control her feelings, but as she closed the door on her she swore to herself she would never let that woman cross the threshold again.

* * *

The day had been damp and dreary. The rainy season was in full swing. Torrential downpours often continued throughout the night as electric storms rumbled back and

27

forth across the sky, sometimes so close that the lightning illuminated the icon on the wall, while deafening cracks of thunder overhead threatened to shatter the precious wedding photograph on the dresser. Night after night the storms had woken one or both of the children, who had run for comfort to the safety of their mother's bed.

Evangelia was six months' pregnant and beginning to swell. It was market day and, as usual, she had done her weekly rounds. The rain held off until she was half way home, then the heavens opened. Within minutes the streets were flooded as the drains failed to cope with the deluge. Paddling through swirling, muddy streams, she struggled home. Logotheti, thankfully, had fed the children and put them to bed before going out to visit a friend. Soaking her feet in tepid, salty water, Evangelia sank wearily into a chair. There was still the ironing to do, but that could wait.

Her thoughts flew to Djibouti. It was over a month since Manoli had left and still there was no news of him. Knowing how proud he was, she knew she would hear nothing until he had achieved what he set out to do. If only this weather would improve. She couldn't wait for the end of September when the rain miraculously ceased and the *meskel* flower bloomed. She remembered how Logotheti had explained that the bloom was so named because its brilliant yellow petals were shaped like a cross and its appearance exactly coincided with the Christian feast of the Finding of the True Cross—Meskel. This year, she would take both children to the Meskel procession. They would enjoy seeing the priests in their colourful, shimmering robes carrying their sparkling brass crosses through the streets with the young deacons running beside them, juggling huge, patriotic red, green and

28

yellow umbrellas in an effort to protect the holy scriptures from the scorching sun. The church choir would also be there, chanting and singing their thanks to the Almighty and praying for peace, health and a good harvest to feed the nation. She could take the children to the service in Holy Trinity Church and then follow the procession to Emperor Menelik's palace. They would particularly enjoy the bonfire which ended the celebrations. She was also curious to see which way the fire would topple, for it was said to predict whether the coming year would be prosperous or whether troubles lay ahead.

Evangelina had almost dozed off to sleep when a cry from one of the children woke her with a start. She rushed to the bedroom. Pavlos was sleeping soundly but bending over Sophia's crib she saw with horror that the child was burning with fever. Her cheeks were livid and her breath came in short, sharp pants. In a panic, her mind went blank. What did her mother do to reduce fevers? Running to the balcony, she scraped the frost from the railings and ran with it to the kitchen to mix in some vinegar. Stripping Sophia naked she swabbed the tiny body over and over with the cooling liquid. Within minutes, her temperature had subsided and her breathing returned to normal.

"It's probably just flu," Evangelia told herself.

By daybreak, it was raining heavily again. The din on the corrugated tin roof muffled Sophia's whimpers. The rain turned to hail and the noise became deafening as the frozen droplets hammered on the roof and bounced off the windows to form a white carpet in the muddy street below. Leaning over the crib, Evangelia listened anxiously to her baby's feeble cries. Feeling her tremble, she tucked the covers closer round the plump little body. Suddenly the trembling developed into uncontrollable jerking.

29

"Dear God. It's pneumonia. Don't let her die. Please don't let her die," she cried, distraught. Snatching up the baby, she hastily wrapped the covers around her and ran out into the street. Wildly, she looked about for some means of transport. Seeing none, she raced down the hill. Within minutes, the rain had soaked through her flimsy dress. Oblivious, all she could feel was the burning child in her arms.

Panting and coughing, she picked up a stone and hammered on the doctor's iron gate. "Dr. Zaphirakis... please," she sobbed.

For what seemed like an eternity, there was no reply. Then there was the scraping of a window being unlatched. "What brings you here at this unearthly hour?" a groggy voice enquired.

"Please, please, open the gate!" she screamed.

The relentless rain was still coming down. In the grey light, the doctor peered out at the bedraggled figure hunched behind the railings.

"Calm yourself. I'll be down in a moment." His head disappeared inside the window and a flickering light slowly descended the stairs. Evangelia feverishly rocked the baby, muttering to herself, "Don't let her die. Don't let her die."

"Now then," said Dr. Zaphirakis, unbolting the gate and gently guiding her into the surgery. "I can't handle hysterical mothers before a cup of coffee." Taking the baby from her, he handed her a blanket. "Wrap this round you," he said, "and just relax. It's probably nothing serious."

Two paraffin lamps cast a bright glow on the couch where the doctor now laid Sophia and began his examination. It was as though her child were on stage and Evangelia was simply an onlooker, part of the audience lurking in the shadows, with no power to alter the script. With experienced hands, Dr. Zaphirakis gently pressed and probed. Finally, a look of growing concern on his face, he took a sample of blood from the infant's earlobe and disappeared into his laboratory. Evangelia waited, her heart thumping. Why was he taking so long? She stood helplessly by the baby. Sophia's forehead was cooler and she had dropped off into a troubled sleep.

The doctor reappeared, his eyebrows pinched together, his face flushed with anger. "You stupid woman!" he barked. "Has no-one ever warned you about trusting local help. Employing a wet nurse left you more time for socializing, did it?"

An excruciating pain hit the pit of Evangelia's stomach. Tears gushed down her cheeks. "What do you mean? I've never left my baby with a maid. Are you saying I've given my child some sickness?"

Dr. Zaphirakis took off his glasses and studied her closely. Regretting his outburst, he spoke with a gentler, more sympathetic tone. "No," he murmured, "I see no signs of syphilis in you."

Syphilis! The words resounded in her head like hammer blows. She swayed, feeling the floor rushing up to meet her.

"Sit down. I'm sorry. You've had a terrible shock. I'm afraid I was rather angry. I should have broken it to you more gently. Come, put your head between your knees." The doctor's voice seemed far away. Was it all a terrible dream? Syphilis! Her innocent child. How could it be? She felt cold.

"Tell me, doctor. What does it mean? What will it do to her? Will she die?" she cried with pleading eyes.

The old doctor sat down beside her. "Of course, I'll

have to carry out further tests, but I'm 99 per cent sure. If the results are positive, then we'll have to try her on a new medicine that's available in Cairo, but," he said, "you must prepare yourself for the worst."

A week later the diagnosis was confirmed. The disease had attacked Sophia's spinal column, damaging the top vertebrae. She would develop a hunch back, restricting the movement and control of her head.

"If you love your child, pray she dies now at nine months," Dr. Zaphirakis whispered. "Let's hope her suffering is not prolonged."

* * *

The train from Djibouti slowly pulled into the station. With relief Evangelia spotted Manoli, hanging out of his compartment window. Unable to contain his excitement, he shouted and waved exuberantly, impatient for the locomotive to stop.

"I did it, my darling," he yelled. "I have the very first consignment of French newspapers with me." Jumping down, he ran towards her. Suddenly he stopped, his eyes searching hers. She tried to smile.

"You're drained!" He touched her face. "Have you miscarried?" he asked, full of concern. Cold and immobile as a marble statue, she stood there unable to speak. "For the love of Christ, tell me what's happened!" he shook her.

In anguished tones, as they were bumped and shoved by the stream of traffic, she told him of Sophia's fate. He listened, the muscles in his jaw twitching as he fought to control the rising anger and pain. He clenched his fists. He wanted to crush the life out of whoever had done this to his child.

A boy, staggering beneath the weight of half a dozen bundles of newspapers, stopped beside him. These yours, *getoch!*" he yelled. Manoli stared at him, uncomprehendingly.

"What? Uh. Oh, wait for me at the exit," he said distractedly. He turned to Evangelia, all the anger suddenly dispelled. He took her in his arms, tears involuntarily welling in his eyes. "We'll beat this, my little one. We won't let our little girl die. We'll scour the earth for a cure."

Through Dr. Zaphirakis' connections in Cairo, the new drug was sent for Sophia. For weeks the child screamed in agony at the painful injections, but finally, her temperature dropped. The disease was under control, but there was no cure for the damage already done.

Chapter Four

Evangelia was baking for the New Year and the restaurant was filled with tantalizing smells. In one corner, Manoli, dressed in a brown three-piece suit, was busy arranging and rearranging newspapers on a little-used billiard table, when the door opened and a young boy with a beret perched on his freshly-shaven head entered shyly.

Removing the beret and twisting it nervously in his hands, he spoke in rough Amharic, "Mr. Fanouris, Sir. My father, he would like to buy one of your newspapers. Could you give me please?" He pulled money from his pocket and held it out.

Manoli looked up. "Come in. Come in. Bless you, son. I shall frame this coin and treasure it as a good luck charm for my future shop. This is my very first sale."

The boy's face suddenly brightened with an idea. "My father has many friends. I am sure they also like to buy. You give me. I sell them, okay? I come back with money." His voice rose with excitement.

Manoli studied the boy, his patched clothes and bare feet, but mostly the eager, ambitious look in his eyes. The sight stirred memories of his own youth, of an equally ragged urchin trying to sell poorly-printed journals in the narrow streets of Athens. "Here," he hurriedly placed a pile of his precious journals in the boy's arms. "Go, son. I'll give you something for your labour when you come back."

It was strange how things came full circle. His thoughts flashed back to a seven-year-old boy leaning over the deck rails of a huge freighter, his face glowing with excitement as it plunged and rose, the spray soaking him to the skin. The ship was bound for America. His father, Pavlos Senior, with ambitions of educating his son amidst lawyers and doctors, had traded the family property for the fare and decided to emigrate. Then disaster struck. Reaching Ellis Island, a suspicious cough contracted in the ship's stuffy cabins, denied him his medical clearance. Financially ruined, his dreams shattered, Pavlos died of a broken heart soon after being shipped back to Greece, leaving his son destitute and illiterate.

But Manoli did inherit one gift from his father— ambition, coupled with a dogged determination. Though he worked from dawn to dusk selling newsprint to fill his belly, he devoted every precious free minute to teaching himself to read. It had been a long, hard struggle, but— unlike his father—he had made it. Here he was in a new land full of promise, starting a venture which he prayed would ensure his own children never had to scrape a living off the streets. Manoli was still reminiscing when the boy burst through the door, his face beaming. He slid a grubby hand into his pocket and pulled out a handful of coins.

"They sell like ripe bananas, Mr. Fanouris. I take more, okay?"

The billiard table was almost empty when the regular *ouzo* drinkers sat down for their evening gossip.

"Where are these famous newspapers of yours, Manoli?" asked Stefanos Georgiadis.

"Come on, Manoli. Let's have them. Let's start the ball rolling for you," chimed in Dimitris Papadopulos.

Manoli grinned. "You're too late, my good friends. Sold out by lunchtime. When word got out that Fanouris was dealing in daily news, there was a stampede. If it were not for Evangelia, here," he said, as she poked her head round the kitchen door, "I should surely have been trampled to death. You could have inscribed on my headstone, 'Here lies Manoli Fanouris, a brave man who died struggling to bring enlightenment to a nation kept in the dark.' As a matter of fact, Omar Balcha's son took them round the streets and sold the lot for me this morning. However," continued Manoli, raising his hands to allay the growing protests, "I did not forget my good friends and true." With a flourish he produced half a dozen newspapers from beneath the billiard table. "These, gentlemen, I reserved for your delectation. Please, help yourselves."

* * *

Every week, Manoli collected his packages of newspapers and magazines from the Djibouti train. As the months went by, he noticed more and more new arrivals were speaking his mother tongue. Many were skilled men with a valuable knowledge of vineyards, oil refining, soap-making and trading. Usually they came alone, hoping to bring their families later, so Manoli would expansively invite them to his home, telling them what a wonderful cook Evangelia was and somehow turning the conversation to what newspapers they preferred to read.

By the time Kostas, their third child, was born, Manoli's newspaper venture had brought them undreamed-of wealth. With it came a position of honour within Addis Ababa's burgeoning immigrant Greek community. But always overshadowing their success was the cloud of Sophia's illness and the lingering fear of the inevitable.

Sophia was growing up to be a bright, intelligent, sensitive child and her parents tried their utmost to make her life as normal and happy as possible. But it was hard. As the child's delicate frame grew bowed and twisted, her drooping head having to be perpetually supported, children in the street would shun her or shout cruel remarks. It made their hearts burn with sorrow.

Evangelia was dressing Sophia one morning, when Manoli called excitedly from below. "Evangelia, come quickly. I've found a wonderful double-storey house right in the middle of the *piazza*. It's got four bedrooms for the children and one for Logotheti—and there's a large room downstairs which I can turn into a bookstore. Hurry. I'm sure you'll love it, but I want to hear your opinion before I sign the contract with *Ato* Makonnen."

Manoli held the door open for her as Evangelia stepped into the spacious ground floor room. It was certainly very conveniently placed. People could buy their newspaper or magazine and read it in comfort, sitting on one of the benches in the square. She tried to picture the grey walls lined with book shelves and magazine wracks.

Evangelia began to climb the creaky, wooden staircase leading to the top storey. Suddenly a cold chill ran down her spine. Was the place haunted? She was sure she could feel the presence of a sinister force. "Don't be silly," she told herself. All empty houses were cold and uninviting. Once her hand-crocheted curtains were hung and the chairs and tables decorated with her delicate embroideries, the house would be as cosy as a nest. She thought of the boxes stuffed with linen, mats and bedspreads which Manoli had brought back from Djibouti—all imported from China. "They're for our daughter's dowry," he had said. But Evangelia knew—as Manoli did in his heart—that little Sophia would never be given away as a bride.

"Dear God, please hear my plea," she prayed, as she lifted her eyes to the bare ceiling. "I know you've got your eye on my little one, but crippled as she is, she brings us joy and makes our life worth living. I'm thankful for my healthy boys, but a mother needs a daughter. Please don't take her away before granting us another."

A few weeks after settling into their new home, Evangelia conceived again.

* * *

Easter was approaching and the whole family was looking forward to the annual outing to the Saris vineyards at Akaki, twenty kilometres south of the capital. For the Abyssinians, Easter was not only a feast to commemorate Christ's resurrection, but a time for helping those in need. Prime bulls were slaughtered by the wealthy and distributed to the multitudes who customarily gathered outside their homes. The best cuts, the fillet and rump of the beasts, would be left to mature and then served raw at the breaking of the fifty-day fast which preceded Easter. The meat was cut into long strips, which the diner clenched between his teeth, pulling it taut with one hand while hacking free a bite-size piece with the other. The flashing blade of the razor-sharp knife often passed within a hair's breadth of the diner's nose. Any left-over meat was sliced into thin ribbons, dipped in a pungent paste of hot peppers, garlic and salt and hung out to dry. This *kuanta*—beef biltong—made a tasty appetizer, which was nibbled while drinking *tej*, an intoxicating amber-coloured wine made from wild honey.

Injera, the traditional bread, made from a gritty cereal which had been allowed to stand and ferment for several days, always accompanied the meat. Baked in large, round pancakes it was soft and flexible, making it easy to tear. *Injera* had a slightly sour taste, but when soaked in *wat*, a thick chillied meat stew, it softened the burning sensation and stimulated the palate.

Generous and hospitable by nature and tradition, no Abyssinian would close his door to the poor on this religious festival. Even in the shanty towns, beggars were given a piece of *dabo* and a glass of *tella*, the local barley-brewed beer that momentarily transported them to a world free from hunger and degradation.

Evangelia took down a large tray, covered it with a clean, embroidered napkin and carefully arranged a couple of her best plaited rolls together with the bright red eggs she had rubbed with fat to make them shine. She was satisfied with her dye this year. She had boiled the eggs in beetroot water and Sophia had helped her drop in a few wild mulberries to give them a deeper colour.

It would take them at least an hour to reach Akaki, but it would be worth it. The children loved the music and the merry-making and so did she.

"Sophia, carry this basket for me, Darling," said Evangelia. The six-year-old skipped across the room, her small bent figure two-thirds the size of other children her age.

"Will you dance with me today, Mummy? All the children run away from me and I so want to dance." Her eyes shone with excitement.

"Of course I will darling, and so will Papa and Pavlos."

The road wound through mile upon mile of brown, sparsely-vegetated bush. Sometimes, rounding a bend, a spectacular view of rolling barren hills would confront them. Then, suddenly, acres of neatly cultivated land came into sight. Giant steps were carved out of the hills, each dissected by precision-planted parallel rows of healthy, green sprouting vines.

"It looks like there's going to be a bumper harvest this year," shouted Manoli. "Maybe we're all going to have a fruitful year," he said, placing his hand gently on Evangelia's swollen belly.

Some families had already arrived and smoke from the barbequed lambs was filling the air. Evangelia unrolled a thick, woven rug she had brought from Karpathos and sat down heavily to watch the festivities. Sophia, clasping her knees, leaned against her. The *kalamatianos* was being danced by a group of men in traditional costume. Sophia's eyes followed the white handkerchief as it passed from hand to hand, being twisted and twirled in time to the music. Gradually, more and more people joined in as the excitement mounted. A group of curious Ethiopian villagers, drawn by the music, were motioned to enter the throng.

Some elders in white jodphurs and loose shirts sent boys running back to their huts to fetch their *masenkos*, while others followed with kettledrums and hand-crafted wind instruments. Making themselves comfortable on camel-skin cushions, they began to beat out rythmic native tunes. As the tempo quickened, shoulders jerked, muscles rippled, heads shook madly from side to side, feet pounded the ground. Ceremonial swords swung high above their heads, sometimes slicing the air within inches of the bass drummer before performing a graceful pirouette and returning to the grasp of their owners.

Shrieks of delight accompanied by piercing ululations came from the nearby native *tukuls*. Men and women in glittering, ornate national costumes, specially woven and embroidered for the festival, emerged from the huts and ran to join in the merrymaking. Full, voluptuous breasts swung heavily beneath the thin material of their dresses as they performed sensual native dances. An enthusiastic crowd gathered around cheering and applauding. Some of the more ebullient Greeks, fascinated by the rythmic movements, leaped to their feet and mingled with the natives, imitating their shoulder-shaking and attempting to follow their footsteps. Even more timid onlookers, tying their *shammas* around their waists, were eventually persuaded to join in.

"Can I dance? Will you dance with me, Mummy?" pleaded Sophia. The child struggled to her feet, extending a helping hand to Evangelia.

"I don't think I can manage this dance, Darling. It's a bit too energetic," said Evangelia, as she watched the flushed faces glistening with perspiration.

"Oh, please, please, Mama." Sophia paused. A lone tear glistened on her wan, freckled cheek. Brushing it away, she said in a steady, matter-of-fact tone. "I might never come here again."

Evangelia pressed the child to her breast. "Of course I'll dance, but don't expect anything too lively, mind," she said, attempting to be flippant.

The child pulling, the mother following, they entered

41

the throng. An unexpected drizzle, capturing the sun's rays, dropped like strings of glistening beads onto the gyrating circle of dancers. Some droplets clung to Sophia's bobbing dark tresses as she skipped and jumped in the strange, diffused light. For a moment, she appeared to hold her head straight, her eyes gleaming with excitement. Then it drooped again.

"Are you tired, Darling," asked Evangelia anxiously.

"Yes," answered Sophia heavily. "I think I'm ready to go now."

Chapter Five

It was 1933. The year was drawing to a close. With a feeling of satisfaction, Manoli leaned back in his heavy armchair and pondered over the events of the past six years. Business had been good. The steady increase in newspaper sales had enabled him to plough his profits into more books and stationery. He'd even branched out into school equipment. He loved to see the store swarming with noisy, happy children. Glancing across the room he smiled at Sophia, busily colouring a drawing book he had just given her.

"Look, Papa. Do you like my picture? It's a butterfly. Don't you think it's pretty? I've given it beautiful coloured wings. Now it can fly away."

"It certainly is. But it's not as pretty as you, my little dove," said Manoli, bending over and kissing her hair.

"Hello, anybody home?" a familiar voice called from downstairs.

"It's Jenny," cried Sophia.

"Come up, Jenny. Evangelia's out shopping, but I think I'm capable of brewing a reasonable cup of coffee," said Manoli.

Breathing heavily, the midwife appeared at the top of

the stairs. "What is Evangelia up to now, rushing around in her state," she scolded. "She's almost due and she goes dashing off to the market. I'm certainly not running down there to deliver this baby."

"You know what Evangelia's like. She's been washing and ironing everything in the house for the past month—curtains, bedspreads, tablecloths, even brand-new nappies straight from the trunk. I've been warning her to take it easy, but all she says is how could she face her neighbours if she died in childbirth and they didn't find everything clean and tidy. Now there's island logic for you. So, what can I do?" Manoli held up his hands in mock despair.

Jenny nodded: "Well, you know these island girls. They all have the same mentality and it's hard to knock anything into their obstinate heads."

"I heard that, Jenny. Making fun of me, eh?" teased Evangelia as she eased herself through the door and plumped herself heavily into a chair. Sophia ran to greet her.

"Evangelia, my dear girl. I have delivered two of your children so far and each time I've begged you to reserve a little of your strength for me and your labour. I have yet to see you obey my words," the midwife admonished.

"And who do you think would care for three children, a husband and a brother, who need food and clean shirts every day? It's easy for you to talk, Jenny. You don't have anyone to look after. Maybe we should try to find you a husband," Evangelia retorted.

"All right, I give up, but don't start yelling, 'Jenny, help! I can't push. Jenny, do something!'" she mimicked. "I shall wash my hands of you and walk out. Believe me, I will."

44

"Oh no, you won't! You've got to see me through this one. If God grants me a girl, I'll have no more," said Evangelia firmly.

"Don't you have any say in the matter, Manoli?" Jennny turned to him. "You can't put me out of business."

"It's funny you should say that. I had this friend who…" Manoli began recounting an anecdote, which he had been told the night before. One story led to another until the three of them were convulsed with laughter.

"Oh, Holy Mother," Evangelia cried, clutching her stomach. "My contractions have started."

"Don't go pulling anything on me tonight," said Jenny, wiping her tears. "You're not due for a couple of days and this is just a social call. I've two other babies to deliver tonight. Have pity on me."

"I'm not shamming, Jenny," Evangelia gasped.

"Can I do anything?" asked Sophia anxiously.

"Yes, darling. Help Daddy boil some water," said Evangelia.

The delivery was the easiest she had experienced.

"May I see my sister?" A pale anxious face appeared by the bedside. Leaning over to look in wonder at the tiny fingers and toes, Sophia opened her clenched fist to expose a pair of turquoise earrings. She bent and kissed the infant.

"I want Angeliki to have them," she whispered. "I won't be needing them any more."

* * *

Rumours of fighting over the wells at Walwal on the border between Abyssinia and Italian Somaliland reached Addis Ababa in early December 1934. Some said it was only a tribal dispute, blown up out of all proportion.

45

Others were convinced it was a clash between Italian and Abyssinian troops, engineered by Mussolini who had for years been looking for an excuse to incorporate Abyssinia into his new Roman Empire.

Logotheti was among those who believed it was only a tribal spat. "These nomads are always fighting each other for grazing land. It's nothing unusual. They've been doing it for years and nothing has come of it," he assured Manoli when the topic came up for discussion over the dinner table.

"True. It could be nothing, but I don't like the sound of things," said Manoli, serving himself a slab of *moussaka*. "Evangelia, there's enough food on this table to feed an army. You'll never learn to cook just for our family."

"Well, Manoli, next time you just happen to bump into an old friend and invite him home for one of your wife's island specialities, don't expect there to be enough to go round," she retorted in a huff.

Manoli winked at Logotheti. "She's not in the mood today, so I'd better shut up," he whispered, continuing aloud. "I heard from a very reliable source this morning that there were more skirmishes in the Ogaden last week with quite a number of casualties. I just hope these disputes don't escalate into something more serious. The problem is the Somalis are aggravating the situation by abusing the privileges they've been given. Okay, I know there's always been an understanding that the nomads can use the wells and graze their animals on either side of the border, but the Somalis are taking advantage of the situation. Each time they cross, they penetrate deeper and deeper into Abyssinian territory."

"Will there be a war?" asked ten-year-old Pavlos, eager to participate in the conversation.

"Bite your tongue, son!" Evangelia interposed, popping her head round the kitchen door. "You just pray there'll be no blood shed."

"The trouble is the border itself has been in dispute ever since Adoua back in '96," said Logotheti, helping himself to soup. "Walwal is supposed to be 60 miles inside Abyssinian territory, but Mussolini insists the border runs right through it."

"What disturbs me are these rumours that the Italians have built huge military bases and aerodromes in Eritrea. It must be true because only a couple of weeks ago the Emperor despatched a huge contingent up north. I just hope these border incidents don't spark something off." Manoli sighed.

"The Italians have never forgiven us for Adoua," Logotheti reflected. "They're a proud lot. They've never got over the humiliation of being sent packing by what they regard as a bunch of savages." He gulped down his last spoonful of broth. "If Mussolini's thirst for revenge can't be curbed, I suppose he might be just crazy enough to invade."

The possibility made both men reflect grimly. Karpathos had been under Italian occupation for many years. Logotheti clenched his fist as he remembered being forced to wear the dreaded *camicia nera*—the black shirt of the fascists.

"My God," he said. "Did I go through all that and survive only to have to relive it again. I tell you now. If the Italians occupy this country, I don't care what they do to me. I'll not wear the black shirt again."

"There's an article in one of the French papers carrying the Emperor's photograph. It must be about the border situation, but I've studied it and I can't make any sense out of it," said Manoli. Excusing himself from the table, he went down to the bookstore to fetch the newspaper, but none of them could decipher it. "I think I'll take it down to Dr. Zaphirakis. He speaks fluent French. He can translate it for us," said Manoli.

At the doctor's house, Mrs. Zaphirakis told Manoli her husband had been summoned to the palace to treat one of the royal children.

"Will he be long," asked Manoli. "I can wait."

"I'm afraid I don't know," said his wife. "The Emperor loves his chats with Jacob. He likes to talk politics with him," she confided. "Their sessions sometimes go on until the early hours. There's no knowing what time he'll be home."

Manoli was disappointed. He was eager to know what the article had to say. "I could leave it with you," he said, handing her the newspaper. "I've circled the article. If the doctor should be back early, I'd be grateful if you would send for me."

"Certainly, I will," said Mrs. Zaphirakis. "I only wish I spoke a little French myself. We're all anxious to know what's going on. But don't look so concerned, I'm sure it's nothing serious."

Night had fallen and a cold wind was chilling his ears. Evening temperatures dropped rapidly after the rains—sometimes to below freezing point. Pulling his collar tightly round his neck, Manoli slowly began to climb the steep hill towards the centre of the city. Stopping to catch his breath, he noticed a large crowd gathered outside the Ras Makonnen bar. Renowned for its good coffee and hot rolls, the bar was always packed, but this gathering was different. As he drew closer, Manoli could hear them chanting slogans and pledging their loyalty to the

Emperor.

"What's going on?" he asked Ilias, a fellow Greek who had also been attracted by the commotion.

"Reports from the Ogaden are bad." He shook his head sadly. "The bloody Italians are dropping poison gas on our army. They don't stand a chance."

"Are these volun…" Manoli's words were drowned as the crowd burst into an enthusiastic rendering of a patriotic song. "They're all going to sign up, are they?" he began again as soon as there was a lull in the uproar.

Ilias nodded. "What chance do these poor devils stand against the Iti's," he said. "We've got no aircraft, none of their fancy modern weapons. Our lads are using museum pieces from Adoua, stuff that went out with the Ark."

Manoli's heart sank. War was just around the corner. He had to make provision for his family. He hurried home.

* * *

A loud knock on the front door woke Manoli from a troubled sleep. Someone was calling him and from the tone of his voice, it was something urgent. Pulling on his trousers, he leapt down the stairs and unbolted the door. Dr. Zaphirakis barged in, almost knocking him over.

"Manoli, you're in serious trouble. The Emperor's Secretary on Educational Matters, *Ato* Sahle Sedalu, came to my house this morning to tell me to warn you that your life is in danger."

"What!" Manoli gasped. "What have I done? Is it something to do with the article I left you."

"Not particularly that one, my friend," said the doctor. "Listen, Manoli, it's not directly your fault, but the

Emperor is furious about the number of articles being carried by the foreign press which are offensive to him personally and to the nation. As the importer of these newspapers, you're responsible for their circulation. He, therefore, regards you as a subversive. He's given the order to hang you."

Manoli's head buzzed. A sudden hot flush produced a prickle of sweat on his brow. He loosened his collar. He couldn't have heard right. Was this the end of his dream? His mind raced with visions of a public execution, Evangelia pleading for mercy, his children reduced to roaming the streets in rags, and Sophia. Who would care for his loving, crippled Sophia? It had never crossed his mind that he was doing anything that was harmful or offensive to the Emperor. Half of the journals he imported were in a foreign language of which he had no understanding. How could he have known their articles were offensive?

Manoli straightened his shoulders. "Well, I have nowhere to run, doctor and I'm certainly not abandoning my family. So, I'll just have to wait for the knock on the door."

"I'll intervene, Manoli. I have a little influence. I can't promise anything, but I'll speak to the Emperor and beg him to reverse his decision."

"What's going on?" Evangelia asked sleepily from the landing. "Who's with you, Manoli? Why don't you bring them up for breakfast. I've got some freshly baked bread and…"

"For God's sake, woman. Can't you talk of anything but food. This is a matter of life and death and you want to socialize!" Manoli exploded with sudden rage.

"Come now, Manoli. Don't take it out on your poor

wife. She doesn't even know what's going on." Dr. Zaphirakis walked up the stairs and put his arm round Evangelia's shoulders. "We can all do with a strong cup of coffee."

Ashamed of his outburst, Manoli squeezed his wife's hand as he explained the situation.

"Now, I'd better be on my way." The old doctor stood up, adjusted his glasses and smoothed the creases in his suit. "I'll join the Emperor in his early morning walk and plead with him. I am his personal physician, after all," he said with the glimmer of a twinkle in his eye, "so he should heed my advice."

"God be with you, doctor." Manoli's throat was dry. It was the longest day in Manoli's life. For what seemed like hours, he discussed with Logotheti and Evangelia what they should do in the event of his arrest. The children, sensing a heavy atmosphere, kept out of sight. When everything had been said that had to be said, Evangelia went calmly about her chores.

Hours passed and still no news. Manoli paced up and down. Logotheti produced a pack of cigarettes. "I know you don't smoke, but maybe an odd one will calm your nerves." Manoli took one and walked to the window for the hundredth time that day. Still no sign of the doctor. He inhaled deeply and was overcome by a fit of coughing.

"You want to kick that habit, my boy. It's bad for your health. After all, you've got a long and happy life ahead of you." Dr. Zaphirakis beamed from the open door. The old doctor was flushed and out-of-breath and Manoli rushed across the room to help him to a chair. "I came as fast as I could. It was a close shave, my boy. He took some persuading, but when I convinced him you were just a harmless blockhead, he finally conceded."

Manoli grasped the doctor's hand: "I owe my life to you, my good friend. You know what that means."

Dr. Zaphirakis squeezed Manoli's arm. "Now, you'd better look after this good woman of yours." Evangelia had flopped into a chair, her face ashen, now that the worst was over. "No time for fainting," said Dr. Zaphirakis briskly. "You must bake your best pie for *Ato* Sahle Sedalu. Without his warning you wouldn't all be here."

Chapter Six

Logotheti had been out of town on business for a few days and, by chance, had finished his work a day early. He'd heard disturbing news of heavy fighting up north. The Italians were said to have taken Adoua and it was rumoured the Emperor's son-in-law, Haile Selassie Gugsa, had defected. Logotheti was eager to find out what the latest reports were in the capital. Approaching the outskirts of Addis Ababa, he stopped on the brow of Entoto Hill to stretch his legs and admire the spectacular view.

"It's all downhill now, Kora," he told his horse, gently patting her neck. "It won't be long before you're fed and brushed down for the night. We've both had a long ride. I can't wait to have some of Evangelia's hot soup and slide into some fresh, sweet-smelling bedsheets."

Mounting his horse, he turned to take a last look at the sleeping city. He stopped for a second and blinked. Was it his imagination or could he see sparks of light dancing about among the dim, black shapes of the *tukuls*. And wasn't that smoke? Suddenly, a thatched roof burst into flame, illuminating a group of scurrying figures wielding lighted torches. Within seconds, another *tukul* was alight—and another and another. Logotheti watched with horror as the city turned into a roaring, spitting inferno before his eyes.

"Go, girl!" He dug his heels into his mount's belly, sending her racing down the hill. Half-a-mile away he could smell the smoke and feel the heat, as the angry flames shot twenty feet into the air. Swerving and jumping to avoid collapsing beams and fallen pieces of flaming thatch, he reached the bookstore. The front door had already burnt down and the blaze, feeding on huge stocks of newspapers and books, was leaping high and licking the wooden staircase. It would only be a matter of minutes before it penetrated the upper storey, where everyone was sleeping.

"For God's sake!" he shouted hoarsely. "Manoli, Evangelia. Someone wake up!" Leaping from the horse, he picked up a handful of stones and threw them at the bedroom window, smashing the glass. "Fire, Manoli. Fire," he screamed.

Manoli woke with a start at the sound of the shattering glass. By now smoke was billowing in through the window and seeping through the floorboards. He dashed to the window and saw Logotheti below. In the street, all hell was let loose. Women were wailing, children were screaming, people were running in panic not knowing which way to go.

"Pass the children down to me," yelled Logotheti. Together, Manoli and Evangelia hurriedly snatched the children from their rooms.

"I'll ease you down first, son," said Manoli, lowering Pavlos out of the window. "You're the eldest. You can help your uncle with the others." Pavlos dropped into Logotheti's waiting arms.

"Where's the ladder?" he asked the shivering boy. "We're done for if it was left in the store."

Holding up his arm to shield his face from the intensity of the blaze, Pavlos led Logotheti to the back of the house. The ladder was still intact but pieces of fallen debris had fallen across it and had set the surrounding grass alight. With a branch ripped from a nearby eucalyptus tree, they beat the flames and rescued the wooden structure. The lower rungs still smoking, they rushed to prop it against the wall. Before Logotheti had climbed half-way up, Manoli was handing out the first of the children. Clad only in her pyjamas, Sophia leant her fragile head on her uncle's shoulder, encircling his neck with her thin arms. A terrified Kostas followed. Logotheti eased the boy's bare foot onto the first rung, urging him to keep his eyes forward and not look down. Engrossed in Kostas' nervous descent, Logotheti himself forgot about the burnt crosspieces. His foot had barely touched the charcoaled rung when it crumbled under him. Losing his balance, he fell on his side, crushing Sophia with his body. The child let out a feeble cry. Logotheti scrambled to his feet.

"Sophie, my little Sophie. Are you alright?" he asked anxiously.

"I'm alright, uncle," she whimpered, concealing the extent of her agony. "Are you hurt?" She gently stroked Logotheti's face.

"Nothing can be as painful as hurting you, my darling," he replied, gently lifting her in his arms. Limping, he guided the two boys and their sister to a safe corner of the garden and returned to help Manoli and Evangelia.

The bedroom was full of smoke. Coughing, a cloth held over her nose, Evangelia was cautiously climbing down the ladder. She had wrapped Angeliki in a small red rug and strapped the newborn tightly to her back.

"Watch out for the bottom rungs," yelled her brother. "They're giving way."

"Logotheti, what would have happened if you hadn't arrived in time?" gasped Evangelia.

Manoli ran from one room to the next stripping blankets from the beds and flinging them down into the street. They would need coverings to keep them warm or they would all freeze to death. Ignoring Evangelia's urgent pleas to jump, Manoli ransacked the house for the few items which were too precious to leave behind. Piling them into a tablecloth, he quickly knotted it and flung the bundle out. Satisfied he'd got everything that mattered, he took one last look at his home and abandoned it to join his family. Clinging to each other, they stood helplessly in the street and watched it burn. No longer able to hold back her tears, Evangelia began to sob uncontrollably.

Manoli pressed her to him. "At least, we've all been spared, my darling."

"But our home, your books. Everything we've worked to build up…" she cried.

"We can start again. We've done it before and we'll do it again—with the Virgin's help," Manoli comforted her.

"Our icon!" screamed Evangelia, cupping her hands over her mouth. "Who'll protect us now?"

"All's not lost." Manoli untied the bundle he had salvaged. There, on top of the pile staring at them with eyes of sympathy and compassion, was the sacred image. Evangelia picked it up, lovingly stroking the gentle face inside the silver-encrusted frame. Never before had the image seemed so real and serene. The smile, melancholy but tender, imbued Evangelia with a feeling of calm and determination.

"Look what else we've got!" Manoli forced a thin smile. Safely embedded in a wooden slab was the coin from his first newspaper sale. "This," he swallowed, "will help us start again... But come, we've got to get out of here before we're cut off. This whole section of the city seems to be alight."

"I think we should make for the Hotel Imperial," said Logotheti. "As far as I could see from Entoto Hill that part of the town seems to have escaped the flames."

Carrying Sophia, Manoli led them through the burning streets, yelling warnings as buildings collapsed on either side. Already many of the mud and wattle *tukuls* had burnt to the ground. Everywhere groups of people just stood, wailing children clinging to their mother's skirts, staring in disbelief at the smouldering remains of their worldly possessions. In the distance, war drums were beating the alert and bellows of *zeraf, zeraf* sent shivers down Manoli's spine. It signified that the Italians were closing in on the capital and the Abyssinian army had been given instructions to burn and destroy everything in their path.

"It looks like we've lost the war," Manoli said grimly to Logotheti. "Thank God the Emperor got out before it was too late. He left while you were away—just two days ago. He's going to appeal to the League of Nations. We can only pray that this time they'll listen to him and do something. But who the hell set the city on fire? Did you see? Why didn't they give us any warning? Was it the Italians or our own people?"

"I don't know," said Logotheti, still limping from his fall and feeling suddenly weary. "I just saw some figures running around tossing firebrands, but I was too far away to make out who they were. And you never did get your oats and your brush down, did you, old lady?" Logotheti patted his horse as he led her, prancing and jibbing nervously through the smoking ruins.

"Ilias was right," sighed Manoli. "He said our army never stood a chance. Of course they didn't. I saw them leave full of patriotic valour, singing and laughing—and do you know what weapons they were carrying to defend themselves and this nation against a modern, twentieth century power? Swords and spears! That's what they were carrying. Oh, and an odd musket, probably the family heirloom handed down by their grandfathers, who fought at Adoua." Manoli shook his head.

"The Emperor has been begging the British to give him the arms they promised, but God knows they seem to be aiding and abetting Mussolini. They won't sell us arms, yet they're allowing the Italians to ship in as many as they like through the Suez Canal. Where's the justice in this world? Does no one care what's happening here? Our boys are having their flesh stripped from their bones by chemicals which every sane nation has banned. They're being…"

A muffled cry interrupted his ravings. It was Sophia.

"What's the matter, my little one? Am I carrying you too roughly?" asked Manoli.

"No, it's my tummy, Papa. It's hurting. Can you put me down for a little while?"

Manoli gently lowered her to the ground. Her face was grey. "Why didn't you say something before, Baby," said Manoli, wrapping her in one of the salvaged blankets. Evangelia rushed over.

"What is it, Darling?" she said, taking the child in her arms and checking her for cuts or bruises. Finding nothing

58

visible, she pressed her close to her body, rocking her gently. "Just rest a little while. You'll soon feel better. Do you remember last Easter when we went to the vineyards at Akaki? You made me dance and we had such a wonderful time. I think we might go again next year. I may even make you a dress with frills on it, so that when you twirl round the skirt will ripple like the waves on the sea."

"You'll all be there, Mummy," Sophia replied faintly. "I'll be watching you from heaven."

"Nonsense." Evangelia hugged her closer. Panic-stricken, she felt the child's heartbeats losing their regularity. "Manoli, we need a doctor."

Manoli looked around him in despair. Now the fires had died down, a dull glow illuminated streams of homeless figures wandering aimlessly to and fro. "It's hopeless." He leant over and pushed the dark locks back from Sophia's delicate face.

Sophia stared up at her father and then her eyes glanced up at the crystal stars hanging in the sky. "Look…," she turned feebly to her mother, "they're lighting lanterns to show me the way… I'm not scared, Mummy," she whispered, "…promise you'll wave to me…"

"Of course I will, my darling… Oh God," Evangelia bit her hand hard. She pressed the child closer, nuzzling and kissing her. "Dear God, don't take her away," she whispered to herself. "Not now. Leave her with us a while longer. Don't let her die out in the cold."

"Mummy, I'm-m fr-eezing…" Sophia trembled, her teeth chattering. "P-please h-hold me."

Manoli took off his coat and wrapped it round her. He took each hand in turn and rubbed it vigorously to stimulate some warmth, but to no avail. A creeping coldness gradually took over her body. The lips, so ready to implant a kiss, turned slowly blue and a cloudiness tarnished the eloquent expressiveness of her eyes. With a small sigh, her lips parted and Evangelia felt the small body go limp.

Evangelia clasped the child to her breast, rocking her back and forth. Tears flooded her cheeks. "You're free at last, my baby. Your suffering is over. No one can tease you any more, my poor, brave, misshapen little soul. You've gone to join the stars, where there's no pain or suffering, only peace."

Pavlos and Kostas began sniffling. Manoli hastily wiped his arm across his eyes. "Dear God. Why now? Why do you take everything from us at once?" he cried bitterly. "Come, Evangelia, give her to me. Let me carry my little Sophie. We must go on."

They stumbled on, until the lights of the Hotel Imperial finally came into view. At the main entrance, a young British army officer, barred their entry. "I'm sorry, Sir," he told Manoli. "The hotel has been commandeered by a contingency of the King's African Rifles. There's no way we can accommodate you." His words were decisive. Then his eyes fell on the lifeless child clutched in Manoli's arms. "However, I suppose, er—considering the circumstances, you could sit in the lobby until you can contact someone who can assist you. Allow me to help." He extended a hand.

"Don't take her away from us," Evangelia flung her arms protectively round her child. "We must find our priest and give her a Christian burial."

The officer drew back. "I understand, Madam. You can stay here until you have made your funeral

60

arrangements."

The crowing of a lone rooster heralded the dawn of the aftermath of the destruction. Manoli and Logotheti slowly picked their way through the still burning wreckage. Hundreds of people stood helplessly among the smouldering ruins, mourning their dead or scavenging through the rubble in an effort to salvage their meagre possessions. Barely a building remained standing. Luckily St. Frumendios, the Greek Orthodox Church, was intact.

The two men breathed a sigh of relief. Manoli tried the iron gate and found it locked. He called out, but the noise from the courtyard behind the temple drowned his words. He rattled the gate frantically. Eventually, someone heard the banging and ran to summon the priest. Father Irothion hurried out, clutching his robes with one hand and searching his pockets for the key with the other.

"Manoli," he panted, "so your home has been destroyed too?"

"We've lost much more, Father," said Manoli, fighting to control his voice. "It's Sophia. She was taken from us last night."

"You must be brave, my son," the priest gripped his shoulders. Sighing heavily, he raised his eyes to the heavens. "It's your will, Oh Lord, but it couldn't have happened at a worse time."

A crowd of people gathered around Manoli, offering words of sympathy. Some wept. Many were neighbours, who had themselves lost all and had come to seek refuge at the church.

"You'll be safe here," Father Irothion assured the clamouring congregation as he prepared to leave with Manoli. "I'll be back before dark. Marcos!" he called out to the Deacon. "Pick oranges from the orchard and offer them round. Leave the tangerines for the little ones; they're sweeter," he instructed.

Walking back to the hotel, Logotheti related the sequence of events. Father Irothion listened intently. "Now then," he said, when Logotheti had finished. "After the funeral, you must all come back to the church. Evangelia and the children can use my bedroom and we men can move into the downstairs storeroom." As the men began to protest, the priest raised his hands, commanding silence. "I won't take 'no' for an answer."

The hotel lobby was packed with mourners who had already heard of the tragedy. Neighbours and acquaintances, forgetting their own misfortunes, formed a silent vigil around the small, still figure. Thin, woven shawls, tied at the waist were pulled up to cover bowed heads and partly screen their faces in a cultural expression of mourning. At Father Irothion's entrance, a plaintive cry broke the silence as the mourners realized the time for departure was near. The cry evoked an eerie high-pitched wail which was taken up by all the mourners until it filled the room. The British soldier standing guard shuddered. Evangelia slowly released her grip on the small, hunched figure. Gently laying her down, she looked at the smooth, innocent face. Traditionally, Greek virgins were dressed as brides in death. Tears started in her eyes once more. No flowers, ribbons or veils would adorn her child. She didn't even possess a shroud to cover her body.

A young Abyssinian woman, sensing Evangelia's torment, softly tapped her on the shoulder. Unknotting the white shawl from her waist, she folded it neatly and knelt before her, offering it with both hands. "I would be honoured if thou would use it for thy little one," she whispered, bowing her head.

Evangelia looked into a pair of dark, fathomless eyes. "Thank you," she whispered. "Thank you *woizero*…?"

"A-Askala Gebrejesus," the woman replied softly, giving her name.

The drive to Gulele—the burial ground for Orthodox Christians—was long and slow. The procession moved like a caterpillar up the rugged hillside as carriage wheels spun and slid on the winding mud road. Eventually the grey walls of the cemetery came into sight.

Using oil from the church lamps and wine reserved for communion, Father Irothion anointed Sophia's body. Then, in a coffin hastily fashioned from pieces of discarded wood, she was lowered into the ground. She had reached her final resting place.

The sun was low in the sky as the returning cortege approached the outskirts of the city.

"Isn't that singing I can hear," asked Manoli, cocking his head on one side. They quickened their pace. The strains grew louder. It was the sound of hundreds of triumphant voices singing in unison.

"It's the Italians," cried Logotheti. "That's *La Giovinezza* they're singing. They're here already. They've occupied the city."

Turning a corner onto the main highway leading to the palace, they saw them, goose-stepping with precision through the ash-blown streets in their gleaming leather boots, rifles glittering in the fading sunlight. Riding at their head was the hated General Pietro Badoglio. It was Badoglio who had ordered mustard gas to be dropped on unsuspecting Abyssinian troops as they crossed the Takazze river the previous December. The gas had left the soldiers writhing and screaming, totally bewildered by what was happening to them. Saluting triumphantly,

Badoglio paraded his troops through the city ensuring the local populace was suitably impressed by the might of Italy.

"Let's get off the streets before we run into any more trouble," said Logotheti. He led them through a number of twisting alleys until they emerged in the square where their house and store used to stand. Kostas nudged Pavlos's arm.

"Look," he said, pointing to the blackened frame of their parents' wrought iron bed, standing among the rubble. "That's all that's left."

"Don't say anything," Pavlos whispered. "Just keep your eyes to the front. Mother's been through enough for one day."

They reached the church just before dusk. Father Irothion took Evangelia and the children up to his own quarters, where some mattresses had been arranged on the floor.

"I don't think it's correct for us to occupy your room, Father," said Evangelia, her voice barely a whisper. "We could just as easily stay in the storeroom downstairs."

"Nonsense, my child. I don't want any arguments. You've had more than your share of suffering. I don't even want to discuss it," said the priest, raising his hands adamantly. "I'm not offering you comfort—just a warm room to sleep in. It's a small crumb compared with the kindness you showed me when I arrived in this country. You took me in and looked after me like a member of your own family. So, not another word."

Evangelia sank wearily into the priest's threadbare armchair. She felt drained. Thankfully the baby was sleeping. She didn't even know who had been caring for her during the day. People had been very kind, bringing her when she needed feeding and then whisking her away again. It had been like a dream, a long, terrible nightmare. Gratefully, she accepted a cup of steaming coffee. The sound of sniffling made her look up. With a pang of guilt, she regarded her boys, standing before her like two forlorn waifs, feet shuffling, noses running, yearning for comfort but fearful of disturbing her grief. She opened her arms. "Come here," she whispered. "We will all have to be brave for one another now. It has been a terrible blow for us all, but life continues and we must be strong. Your father has a heavy burden on his shoulders and we shall have to help him, each in our own different way."

Kostas began to sob, burying his head in her shoulder.

"Don't cry, darling. You've been such a brave little man." She stroked the hair back from his face. "Now listen to me both of you. I don't know what your father will do now that the bookshop is gone. I don't know how he will start again. I'm sure he's got plans, but we shall all have to sacrifice our time and effort to pull our family together. I shall ask Father Irothion if he will give you lessons in the evening, but I'm afraid we must try to find jobs for you both during the day."

"But I don't know how to do anything, Mama," cried seven-year-old Kostas with alarm.

"Well, maybe you can sell newspapers on the street like your father did when he was your age," said Evangelia with a sigh. "It's the last thing we wanted, son, but we have no choice."

"Don't worry, Mother. I can do anything. Just give me a chance. You watch, I'll earn a fortune. We'll soon have the bookshop going again," said Pavlos, full of excitement at the prospect of becoming a wage earner and an honorary adult at the age of ten. Voices could be heard from the churchyard below. The children ran to the balcony to see more people of all ages, colours and creeds pouring in off the streets. Father Irothion had opened the gates wide and was hurriedly ushering people in. The Italians had already imposed a curfew and these homeless refugees were in danger of being caught in the open.

"God bless you, *Abuna*," some called, using the Amharic for 'Father'. "We were told you wouldn't turn anyone away. Can we stay here till morning? We have nowhere to go."

"As long as there is room in our church to keep you out of the cold, no one shall be turned away," shouted the priest. "I'm only worried that we have no food to offer you, only a little fruit from the trees."

An elderly man pushed his way through the crowds clutching a bundle. He offered it to the priest. "I have some *injera* and would be honoured to share it with you. It's not much, but it will satisfy our hunger tonight. After that, God will provide."

Inside the dimly-lit church, young and old crowded together for warmth. Meagre belongings were unravelled and children bedded down. Nursing mothers finally found time and space to suckle their infants. One old man drew out a backgammon board he had saved from the flames. Beneath the cross, a circle of candles cast a dancing shadow of the crucifix which stretched up the wall and half way across the vaulted ceiling, as though Christ were hovering with open arms over his flock.

Outside the men pulled blankets tightly round their shoulders and huddled round glowing braziers. It was going to be a long, bitter night.

* * *

The days that followed were filled with terror and uncertainty. All weapons had to be surrendered within twenty-four hours of the occupation; anyone found carrying a weapon was summarily shot. Troops would burst into houses at any time of day or night, dragging women and children screaming from their beds as they made their searches. Then came an order to round up and execute all the youths who had been educated abroad at the Emperor's expense. The invaders considered they might present some future threat to the regime. Parents caught trying to smuggle their sons out of the city were slaughtered too.

For some inexplicable reason, the sanctuary of St. Frumendios was never violated. Each day the refugees waited with trepidation for the onslaught which never came. The sole victim was an eccentric old man who insisted on marching up and down the street outside, an ancient sword strapped to his waist with which, he boasted, he had fought at Adoua almost half a century before. Inevitably, one day he met a patrol. A sympathetic trooper, in deference to his age, asked him to hand over the weapon. The old man hesitated. Then, with a sudden strength, he drew the sword and uttering some long-forgotten battle cry lunged at the soldier. Taken by surprise the trooper fired. The old man staggered and fell, the sword clutched proudly in his hand.

Not long after the occupation, Badoglio returned to Italy and was replaced by General Rodolfo Graziani as Governor-General and Viceroy of Abyssinia. Graziani had already earned a 'butcher's' reputation in previous campaigns; now he adopted similar methods in Abyssinia. It was reported he had said, "The Duce shall have Abyssinia with or without the Abyssinians, as he pleases."

One hot February day in 1937, there was a sudden commotion in the church courtyard. Pavlos raced up the stairs and burst into the room where Evangelia was feeding the baby. "Mother," he panted. "Have you heard the news? Someone tried to kill General Graziani!"

It had happened at an outdoor celebration of the Italian invasion. Two young Abyssinian patriots had attempted to assassinate the General by throwing hand grenades at his entourage. No one was killed, although several Italians, including Graziani, were wounded. In retaliation, an infuriated Graziani turned his Black Shirts loose on the streets of Addis Ababa with orders to kill, destroy and "do all you want to the Abyssinians" for three days. In the massacre that followed between five and ten thousand people were killed in the capital and thousands more in the provinces. Survivors described how the Black Shirts in full dress uniform set fire to *tukuls* and then slaughtered men, women and children with their ceremonial daggers as they tried to escape the flames.

Days and nights were filled with the sounds of gunfire, crashing masonry, agonizing screams and pitiful pleas for help, while the nauseating stench of burning flesh floated on the air. All around the city, bodies lay in mud-soaked piles prey to the tearing jaws of dogs and ravenous hyenas.

Secure in the priest's room, Evangelia clasped and unclasped her hands. "Surely, there's something we can do, Manoli. We can't just sit here while those poor people are butchered. I can't bear to hear their screams for another night. Holy Mother of God," she exclaimed, crossing herself. "Why is this happening?"

"Evangelia, what can we do? If we go out there, we'll be cut down before we cross the street. Then what use are we to anyone? No, we must just pray that we live through it. No one can stop this slaughter. It's hard, but survival is the name of the game."

At noon on the third day, an eerie stillness descended on the city. Nothing stirred. Scattered plumes of smoke rose from among the smouldering ruins.

"It's over."

Manoli put his arm round Evangelia.

An army truck came rumbling down the road and stopped where a mother and her three children lay in a bloody heap. Two soldiers leapt out and together threw the bodies on the back. The truck moved on.

* * *

Sporadic resistance to the occupation continued despite an intensified campaign of terror to cow the Abyssinians and exterminate the rebels. Executions continued daily. During one 'flushing' operation, over four hundred monks and clergy were butchered at the monastery of Debra Libanos in the south.

For Manoli, and everyone like him, the survival of his own family was of paramount importance. Manoli realised, for the time being at least, he had to accept the regime and work within it. If he wanted to launch another bookstore, he had to break into the Italian market.

Chapter Seven

"Manoli!" Logotheti shouted, opening the gates of the churchyard and running towards the priest's house. "You're wanted down at the station. There's a package for you from Djibouti."

Wagon loads of Italian foodstuffs were congesting the platforms when Manoli arrived at the station. Cases labelled red wine, grappa, caneloni and parmesan cheese were stacked everywhere.

"*Ato* Kidane. Good morning," Manoli greeted the station master. "I hear there's a package for me. I've come to collect it."

"A package! That's an understatement, Mr. Fanouris. Come, I'll show you, but I think you may need a little help with your 'package'." The station master led Manoli to the last freight car. "This is it,'" he said, pointing to the wagon. "It's all yours."

Manoli looked bewildered. "You mean the whole wagon is mine?"

"That's correct. Take a look. It's stuffed with books and newspapers and judging from the date on them, they're not too old."

Manoli glanced at one of the bundles. He slapped his

forehead, threw his head back and for a second was undecided whether to shout with joy, laugh or cry.

"Oh, before I forget, there's also a letter for you," said *Ato* Kidane, reaching into an inside pocket. "It was in the pouch and there were strict instructions that it be handed to you personally."

Manoli took the letter and opened it quickly. It began: "I heard with great sadness of the loss of your darling Sophia and I cannot find words that would be of comfort to you both. The loss of a child is the greatest pain any parent could suffer. I heard also of the terrible fire that destroyed your home and bookstore. After meeting you in Djibouti and seeing for myself the zeal, energy and enthusiasm with which you are trying to promote literacy—something which I hope to see in my own two sons one day—I have taken the liberty of sending you enough stock to start you up again. I don't want you to worry about paying me back. I am confident the money will be forthcoming in due course when you are back on your feet. I have faith in you, Manoli. You're a capable man and with hard work you will regain all that you lost. In return for what I am sending you, I want you to give me the honour of being godfather to your second daughter, Angeliki. I want nothing more than to be considered a member of your family."

The letter was signed by Cristos Nomikos.

"Cristos, you old rogue. We couldn't ask for a more worthy man to be godfather to our little Angeliki. If you were here, I would embrace you," cried Manoli. A few sidelong glances were cast at the big, lumbering Greek, as he waved the letter excitedly. "This," he said, slapping the station master on the back, "is the answer to my prayers. A new life, a new beginning—a future for my children.

All through the generosity of a true friend. Here, boy!" Manoli yelled to some passing porters. "I need your help."

"Does this mean you're back in business, *Geta* Manoli," grinned one of the youngsters.

"It certainly does."

The wagon proved to contain not only books and newspapers but food, bedding and clothing. When it was all unloaded, Manoli reached in his pocket to tip the porters. Feeling the emptiness, he blushed with embarrassment. In his excitement, he'd forgotten he didn't have a single cent. Hastily he picked up some tins of food and offered them to the boys.

"I'm sorry, lads. I was so overwhelmed by this gift, I completely forgot I came here without money. Please, accept these in payment?"

"Don't worry, *Geta* Manoli," said one of the older boys, speaking for his ragged companions. "This is for your family, yes? We cannot take food from your children. Your supplies will be coming regularly, yes? Like before? When you have work, we have money in our pockets. We can wait. See you next week."

* * *

Two months had passed since the family had moved into Father Irothion's room. Manoli felt it was time to make a move. He had seen a small *tukul* behind the church which appeared to be empty. He took Evangelia to inspect it. It was small but clean so they decided to move in.

The couple had no furniture, but Evangelia was quick to use her ingenuity. The packing cases from Djibouti were converted into tables, chairs and shelves, even a partition to screen off her small charcoal stove. A brightly-coloured orange and yellow bedsheet was cut and sewn into curtains and covers, including a tiny draw curtain for the precious icon which was placed in a position of prominence in the centre of the circular, one-roomed house.

When she'd finished arranging everything to her liking, Evangelia sat on one of the covered cases, leaned back against the white-washed wall and regarded her work with satisfaction. It was strange how life see-sawed; one minute plunging you into the depths of despair, the next raising you from the mire and giving you renewed hope. She shook her head. It must be all part of God's plan, but he did indeed move in mysterious ways. As frequently happened when she was alone, Evangelia's thoughts flew back to the night of the great fire and the death of her darling Sophia. That was the nadir. Yet even then, when nothing seemed to exist but sorrow and pain, a caring, helping hand had reached out. She would never forget that young Abyssinian woman who, with such sympathy and understanding, had offered her shawl as a shroud. It was probably her sole possession to survive the inferno.

Evangelia sat upright. What was she thinking of? She had been so absorbed in her own family affairs, she had never even thanked Askala for her gesture. She owed it to Sophia to find her at once. Removing her apron, she folded it neatly and set out for her old neighbourhood. Charred reminders were still visible, but new *tukuls* had sprung up on the ashes of the old. With dogged persistence, Evangelia enquired at every door, until her determination finally paid off.

Askala was occupying a small corner of a neighbour's house. She showed no sign of surprise when she found Evangelia at the door.

"May I come in?" asked Evangelia hesitantly.

"Of course," said Askala with a smile and nod of recognition. Evangelia squatted on a makeshift stool in the tiny cramped *tukul* while Askala prepared coffee. As they drank and talked, Evangelia learned that Askala, too, had lost everything in the fire. Feeling that here was a way in which she could repay her act of kindness, Evangelia invited her to move in with them. Askala thanked her but shook her head.

"I'll knock on your door when I know that I won't be depriving your children of their bread," she said.

* * *

It would soon be March 25th—Annunciation Day or *Evangelismos* as it was known among the Greek community. A church festival was being organised and, as it was also Evangelia's name day, the Fanouris home was traditionally open house to friends and relatives. This year it would be more difficult in their tiny *tukul* with only a charcoal stove to cook on. Evangelia sighed. She did not feel like tackling all the preparations, but she didn't want to disappoint the boys either. There was little enough for them to look forward to these days. It was almost a year since Sophia's death and the invasion which had totally changed their lives. The Italians had systematically expelled many Indian and other foreign merchants, and for a long while Manoli had been fearful of attracting their attention. But he had gradually built up the business again, sending the boys out to sell newspapers and magazines from door to door. Sometimes, she thought he was a little too hard on them. After all, they were still only eight and eleven. But she never criticised for she knew, although he wouldn't admit it, forcing them to work was the last thing he wanted to do, reminding him of his own father's failure and broken promises of a better future. She sighed again. There was still time. If things went well, maybe they could go back to school next year...

"Evangelia, are you in?" a familiar voice called.

"Father Irothion! Come in. I'm just about to prepare a pot of strong Jimma coffee. I'm sure you haven't even taken breakfast."

"You're quite right, Evangelia. I had early mass and I need nothing more than a cup of your good coffee. Actually I need to talk to you about our Annunciation Day celebrations. We've only a few days to go and I desperately need your help; we shall need at least ten holy breads. I've received messages that despite all the difficulties, many are travelling from the interior, especially from Dembidolo, Jimma and Dessie. Some are even coming from Dire-Dawa. It'll be a great reunion for us Greeks and I want the church to be the first to open its doors wide and welcome everyone."

"I will be delighted to make them for you, Father, if we can get enough flour. I already have sesame seeds washed and cleaned and I know Spyros will bake them in his ovens for us if I stay and supervise his boys."

"It's all set then. I'll get you the flour, and I'm counting on you, Evangelia, to make it a memorable day."

* * *

The peal of church bells invited the 200-strong Greek community to take part in the Annunciation Day celebrations. The smell of freshly-baked bread permeated the church and there, before the altar, lay ten golden, intricately-shaped loaves. Complimentary whispers rippled round the aisles. Evangelia smiled to herself feeling justifiably proud. She had never seen the church so packed. Some were strangers, but others she recognised as neighbours and acquaintances who had fled to the country after their homes were destroyed on that fateful night when Sophia died. When the Italians occupied the capital, they never returned.

The service over, groups began forming in the churchyard, eagerly exchanging news and gossip. A sizeable crowd gathered round a young man who had travelled from Debre Marcos to the north. A latterday Odysseus, he always had a story to tell and a captivating way of telling it.

"...Now I knew that the Nile crossing would be dangerous, what with the crocs attacking my horses and..."

"Nestor, wait,'" Father Irothion interrupted. "Let's first finish the celebrations, then you can tell us about your adventures. I want to hear all about your expedition too."

"You're quite right, Father. First things first. But remind me to tell you about the six-foot mamba I shot," he said as he passed a wide-eyed young girl who had just joined the group.

"Who is that young man?" Manoli asked Dr. Zaphirakis.

"Don't you know Nestor Zissopulos?" said the doctor. "He's the third son of Stellianos and Maria. Came here on his own from Djibouti ten years ago when he was only fourteen. He's a real character, loves to talk but he's as fearless as they come. He rarely comes into Addis Ababa. He travels a lot, trading up and down in skins, musk, coffee, grains, whatever comes to hand. I believe he's also involved in some kind of soap-making business in Debre Marcos. He's made a good name for himself round about and he's said to be honest and hardworking. His elder brother, Thanasakis, is the general manager of the Arabian Trading Company in Djibouti."

"Yes, of course, I know the family," said Manoli. "I met Thanasakis when I was in Djibouti, but he never mentioned he had a brother in Abyssinia."

"Nestor's the outdoor type. He's always going on hunting expeditions. I hear the natives in Debre Marcos have a very high regard for him," said Dr. Zaphirakis.

Their conversation was interrupted by Father Irothion distributing the holy bread and large glasses of wine from the Saris wine cellars. The gathering became noisier and merrier as the wine relaxed stiff manners and shy personalities. Soon young and old were singing and dancing, hands joined, passing the white handkerchief from one to the other.

"Now, let's hear about your adventures, Nestor." Father Irothion joined the group which was still gathered round the personable young man.

"Well, as I was telling these good folk, Father, I was about to set out for Addis with a heavy cargo of soap, hides and musk. I knew of all the dangers that lay ahead: first the *shiftas*, who rove around in bands in the Shoa region and have been known to wipe out whole caravans, and then, of course, the Nile itself, which had to be forded. As you probably know," he winked at a young girl, "there are crocs in there twenty feet long that can swallow a man whole without so much as a belch."

Enjoying his audience, Nestor settled down comfortably to relate his adventures.

"Before I left Debre Marcos, a Catholic priest came to

me and handed me his lifetime's savings. He said he wanted me to deliver it to the Catholic Mission in Addis Ababa and told me I was one of the few people he could trust with such an undertaking. Carrying gold is a great risk with so many marauding bands about and I was a little reluctant, but the priest begged me to take it. He explained that the Mission was in great financial difficulties and that human lives depended upon my getting through with the money. Well, how could I refuse? I tried to keep the contents of the package secret, but of course word got out. When they found I was carrying gold, some of my team refused to accompany me. But I couldn't go back on my promise."

Father Irothion shook his head. "You take some risks, Nestor, but I suppose you were doing God's work."

"Shortly before we reached the Nile, I was joined by another missionary who was travelling alone heading towards Addis," Nestor continued.

"'Can I join you, my son?' he asked. 'I'm a little nervous about crossing the Nile by myself. Only a few months ago a complete caravan of brethren was taken by crocodiles. I was debating whether to attempt the crossing or turn back when I spotted you in the distance.'"

"'You're welcome to join us,' I replied. 'I know a fairly safe crossing point where the waters are shallow and there are few crocs. Don't worry. I've made this trip at least twenty times and I know which places to avoid.'"

"Our horses needed to be rested and fed before we made the crossing and I needed to clean and oil my guns. No croc was going to be given a chance of coming near my caravan. We made camp and some of my men gathered brush and lit fires to cook the evening meal. It was good to stretch our legs after so many hours in the saddle and even better to splash cold water on our burning faces and necks. So far the trip had been uneventful, even monotonous. I picked up a cup of hot coffee and went to join the missionary who was resting under a tree.

"'Don't move,' I whispered. Transferring the coffee to my left hand, I reached for the revolver which I always carried strapped to my waist.

"'Don't kill me, my son,' the missionary pleaded, fingering the cross around his neck. 'I'm a poor man. I'm not carrying anything of value.'"

"'Don't make a sound,' I cautioned. Taking careful aim, I fired. The bullet whistled just inches above his head and a six-foot mamba came toppling down on top of him. I've never seen anyone move so fast; he danced about like a Dervish. As for the look on his face, I think in those few seconds, the pearly gates flashed before him. Sorry, Father," Nestor turned to Father Irothion. "But it's a while since I'd seen anything quite so funny. A few sips of coffee, laced with brandy, brought him back to his senses, then he apologised profusely, asking God's forgiveness for thinking that I was going to kill him."

"To show his gratitude, the missionary stood beside me on the raft the next day, rifle in hand ready to fire at any approaching predators. I knew he'd never held a rifle in his life before, but to give him his due, he did try. I was just shouting some orders to one of the men when I heard a shot and turned to see the missionary staggering backwards from the rifle recoil. 'There,' he yelled. A croc was gliding towards one of the horses, its eyes and snout barely visible on the surface of the water. I aimed straight between its eyes and fired. The water beside us erupted and turned red as the monster splashed and beat the water with its tail, drenching everyone on the raft. The blood began to draw other crocodiles. I fired again and again. Luckily we were nearing the opposite shore. As soon as they found their feet, the horses scrambled to safety."

"The missionary took a handkerchief and wiped his face and neck. 'The Lord be praised,' he said. 'You're very handy with that gun, young man.'

"'You have to be in these parts,' I said, 'but once you have a reputation as a crack shot, the *shiftas* don't fool around with you.'"

"Then the missionary asked if I'd ever killed anyone. I told him, 'No'. I was a God-fearing man and luckily had never had to, but then the *shiftas* in these parts left me alone on the whole because I'd once saved a group of them from a man-eating lion.

"'However,' I told him, 'I'm always on the alert and if it came to killing or being killed, I can't say I would turn the other cheek.'

"The missionary was silent for awhile then he said, 'I don't know what religion you follow, my son, but I'm sure I can convert you to become a good Catholic. What do you say?'

"Well, I didn't want to get involved in any religious debate. I believe everyone's free to follow their own faith, but I respected his suggestion. After all, everyone thinks his own religion is best. So, for the remaining fifteen days of the trip, the missionary indoctrinated me daily with rights and wrongs. He'd set himself a goal of converting me to Catholicism by the time we reached Addis and I just let him talk while I smiled and nodded. Why upset him? He was only doing what he thought was best."

"As we approached Addis, the missionary thanked me for my help and company and said he now had to branch off to go to the Catholic Mission.

"'Well, by a happy coincidence, I'm going there too,' I said. "I have to deliver a package which was entrusted to me, so we can go together.' When we reached our destination and I handed over the gold to the Father in charge of the Mission, the missionary looked at me in disbelief.

"'Here I was trying to convert you to my religion when you already possess good Christian qualities,' he said. 'Maybe, I should convert to your faith.'

"And that, my friends," said Nestor with a hearty laugh, "is all for today."

Chapter Eight

Manoli knew as little Italian as he did French, but Father Irothion had a fair grasp of the language. It became a weekly custom for him to come round after Manoli had collected the latest batch of journals, seat himself at the table with a large glass of *ouzo*, and translate the major items to a growing circle of interested listeners.

The men were anxious to learn more of the developing friendship between Italy and the Germany of Adolf Hitler. Within just a few months, the German ministers Goering, Neurath and Blomberg had paid visits to Rome and now the newspapers were full of Mussolini's impending state visit to Berlin. Earlier in the year, Italy's Foreign Minister Galeazzo Ciano had signed a "gentlemen's agreement" with England that there should be no alteration to the status quo in the Mediterranean, but more recent anti-British press reports signified that the relationship was cooling.

"The B-British should m-make up their m-mind which side of the f-fence they're on," ventured Aleco Moustakis. "One m-minute they're signing p-pacts with M-Mussolini, the next they're demanding s-sanctions, and the Emperor's in the m-middle, g-getting nowhere."

"Well, I suppose the British in their usual muddle-headed way are trying to prevent Mussolini from teaming up with Hitler, but I must admit they're making a hash of it," interposed Logotheti. "The way things are going, I wouldn't be surprised if there isn't a war in Europe before the end of the year—what with Hitler making a song and dance about his people having to have more space to live in. As far as I can see, there's only one direction in which he's headed."

"Let's just hope to God he doesn't turn his eyes in this direction," said Manoli, removing his thumbs from his waistcoat pockets. "He keeps ranting on about getting back the German colonies they lost during the First World War. What was it he said only last week? Something about voicing his demand for living space in the colonies more and more loudly until the world recognized his claim. I don't like the sound of that."

"On the other hand," Logotheti took a sip from his glass, "you could look at it this way, a war in Europe could be to our advantage."

"May God forgive you, Logotheti," said Father Irothion aghast.

"Alright, Father, you tell me who's going to liberate us? The Italians have all but exterminated any opposition here; the Emperor's banging his head against a brick wall in Europe and not even all your prayers will produce an angelic host of deliverance. No, our only hope lies in an all-out European war with a little help from God to ensure right prevails."

"B-but what if m-might prevails? Hitler's m-might, Logotheti? B-Britain has no a-army to s-speak of; F-France isn't m-much b-better. I c-can th-think of only one thing w-worse than living under the I-Italians and that's b-being ordered about by that s-trutting m-maniac."

Evangelia stayed in the background during these sessions, supplying coffee and liquor where required. Europe was a long way away and she had more immediate and tangible worries. She had not been feeling well for some time; her nights were restless and uncomfortable. Since the shock of Sophia's death, her menstrual cycle had ceased, although she was only in her mid-thirties. She often felt depressed and irritable and the talk of doom and gloom made her want to scream. It was no use, she had been putting it off for weeks; she just had to go see the doctor. She unfastened her apron and quietly slipped out of the door.

"Evangelia, when will you stop practising my job and come to see me sooner instead of chaffing on your worries," scolded Dr. Zaphirakis after his examination. "Now, tell me, have you never had similar symptoms before?" The old doctor sat back in his chair, smiling.

"I don't know. Hm, well, perhaps, I can't really say. All I know is I've been feeling so tired and irritable recently. I've been snapping at the children all the time. I just feel as though my nerves are ready to break."

"Well, I can assure you, my dear, you're not headed for a nervous breakdown or any terminal illness—only motherhood. You're pregnant again, my dear child, and what's more, you're four or five months gone already."

"Holy Mother of Christ," cried Evangelia, crossing herself. "Don't joke with me, doctor. I haven't seen my period for the past year and now you're telling me I'm pregnant. How can that be?"

"Well, you've been under a terrible emotional strain for a long time and this has affected your cycle. I presume just as your system began regulating itself, old Manoli performed his miracle again."

They both burst out laughing.

Evangelia hurried home. What a fool she had been. How could she possibly have had four pregnancies and not recognise the signs? She would never live it down.

The rainy season had started again and streams of muddy water were rushing down the steep streets into the river which divided the city in half. The Ras Makonnen bridge was slippery with mud. With her newfound knowledge, Evangelia picked her way carefully across it; nothing was going to happen to this child.

The rain was turning to marble-sized hail as she arrived home. The men had all left and Martha, her next door neighbour, was minding four-year-old Angeliki. She had already lit the fire and had just put some tea with cinnamon and cloves on to boil. The sweet aroma filled the white-washed *tukul*.

"Well, my dear, I'm glad to see you safely back. When the heavens opened, I was worried you might be washed away. I'll get off now. I should get out of those wet clothes before you catch your death."

Evangelia peeled off her soaking garments and with a blanket wrapped round her, sat in front of the fire to warm her numbed feet. She thought of her two boys, scampering round the streets delivering newspapers in the icy rain. She must prepare some hot soup for when they came back. A drop of water landed on her head. Glancing up, she noticed that small damp patches had started to form on the inside of the thatched roof.

"What shall we do if the roof caves in?" she thought out loud.

Angeliki looked alarmed. "Will it crash down and bury us, Mama?" she asked fearfully.

"Of course not. Let's just pray really hard that we don't

get any more hailstorms. It's the hail which makes holes in the roof and we don't want the rain to spoil our cosy little home."

She looked round at the one room which had accommodated them all for the past year. She had grown very fond of it, but it was just too small for five people. The baby would be due in January. If only business would pick up, they might be able to make just enough money to move into something better by Christmas.

Manoli laughed heartily when she told him the news, though she knew beneath the facade he was worried sick about how he was going to provide for the new addition to the family.

A month passed and it was already time for her checkup. Dr. Zaphirakis was out of town on an emergency call, so Evangelia was seen by a young Ethiopian doctor who was standing in. His name was Tilahun and he had just returned from Greece, where he had studied medicine on one of the Emperor's scholarships. He had been abroad during the purge of the country's foreign-trained intelligentsia and was taking something of a risk in returning to his occupied land. He greeted Evangelia with an extended hand, introducing himself rather formally in perfect Greek.

"Dr. Zaphirakis briefed me about your case before he left. I would be honoured to see how the baby is developing if you would allow me to examine you."

Amused by his stiff but friendly manner, Evangelia decided she was going to like this young man. "I am amazed at your perfect Greek," she said shyly. "Tell me, how long were you in Greece?"

"In fact, I have just returned from your beautiful and ancient land after an absence of five years," said the doctor. "I am just sad to be coming back at a time when my country is under Italian rule and my Emperor is in exile. He sent a number of us abroad to train as doctors so we could serve our nation and now he's not even here to see the results of his efforts. When Dr. Zaphirakis offered to take me into his practice, I couldn't believe my luck. Some of my colleagues have been forced to work in army hospitals under the supervision of Italian doctors and that's really no fun at all."

Dr. Tilahun continued to chatter as he gently pressed her stomach, feeling the position of the baby. Evangelia became a little anxious when he kept returning to the same spot.

"Is something wrong, doctor?"

The doctor straightened up. "No, nothing's wrong. It's just that I can feel a head here," he said, pointing to the lower part of her abdomen, "and I think I can also feel a head here beneath your ribs. But, of course, I could be mistaken. Maybe your baby just has a big bottom," he laughed.

Evangelia narrowed her eyes and looked at the young doctor sceptically. He was obviously quite inexperienced, she thought. Maybe she was even his first patient. Fancy mistaking a head for a bottom! She smiled to herself as she adjusted her dress and picked up her bag to leave. It was still quite early. Evangelia walked home in the warm sunshine, feeling at peace with the world. The meskel flower was again in bloom. Feeling the baby stirring in her womb, she felt suddenly optimistic; it was as though nature itself was indicating a change in their fortunes.

She had barely entered the house when Pavlos rushed in, bursting to announce the long-awaited news. "Mother, we can move! The house opposite St. George's Church has finally been repaired and the landlord has told Father that we can move in as soon as we like."

Evangelia was ecstatic. A real house with separate bedrooms, a kitchen and bathroom under the same roof! No more running outside in the middle of the night. And a balcony from where she could wave to a tiny, sparkling star—her beloved Sophia. Best of all, they could move to their new home in time to celebrate Christmas.

"And I, too, have some good news," said Manoli, entering the house on the heels of his son. "I didn't tell you before in case it all fell through, but I bought some furniture from an Italian officer who was ordered back to Rome last week. He sold it to me at a very reasonable price, so now I think we can let these packing cases go. What do you say?" Smiling broadly, he gently lifted Evangelia in the air and swung her round.

"Manoli, careful!" she shrieked.

"I'm always careful with my little island girl." He set her down again.

"Oh, Manoli, I'm so excited. I feel like a young girl again. I know everything's going to be alright from now on."

News spread fast in their compact neighbourhood and a small crowd had soon gathered to hear the details. One old man, who spent most evenings sitting round the fire discussing politics with Manoli, shook his head sadly.

"Don't you like our neighbourhood any more, Manoli?"

"We're only moving up the hill, *Ato* Gabre. We'll still be able to solve the world's problems over a glass of *ouzo*, don't you worry. How can we lose touch with such good friends and neighbours."

The old man shuffled off, still shaking his head.

"Hey, Kostas, come here for a moment," called their next door neighbour, *Woizero* Negatua. "I've just baked some bread and, since you're the fastest runner in your family, I want you to be the first to reach your new house. You know, we Abyssinians have an old custom that when anyone moves to a new dwelling place, a piece of bread must be there to welcome them, then there'll never be a shortage of food while they live in that house. Now take it and run."

Having spent many a night suffering from hunger pangs, Kostas ran as fast as his legs could carry him.

The move to the new house was completed within a few hours and most of that time was taken up with emotional farewells rather than with transporting their few possessions. Early one morning, not long after they had moved in, there was a knock at the door. It was Askala. "I have come," she said, "not seeking your charity, but to ask for work. I heard you had moved and thought, perhaps, your circumstances were now better. There is no one I would rather work for if you feel you are able to employ me."

To Evangelia, who by then was extremely large and heavy, Askala's appearance was a godsend. Overnight, she became one of the family.

As Christmas approached, the children's excitement grew. The business was steadily progressing and the boys had been released from the daily chore of street vending. They had been allowed to return to school, while less fortunate children were employed in their stead. They even began to speculate about whether there might be a gift for each of them this year.

On Christmas Eve, the family gathered around the dinner table and bowed their heads for grace. Manoli reminded them how much they had to be thankful for. The children fidgeted in their seats. They couldn't wait for the meal to be over and to be released from the table, for their eyes were fixed on three packages which had been carefully placed beneath the small tree in the corner.

They had barely begun eating when Evangelia let out a sharp cry. "Oh no! Surely I can't be in labour," she cried, catching her breath. "I still have two more weeks to go."

"Maybe the baby doesn't want to miss all the fun," smiled Manoli. "It's Christmas Eve, after all, and everyone should have fun."

"Well, I can't see me having much fun tonight," said Evangelia, standing up and gripping the table. "Pavlos, you had better hurry and finish your dinner then rush over and fetch Jenny. If she's not there for some reason, go call Dr. Tilahun. He won't be celebrating Christmas until January 6th."

Pavlos gobbled down his food and ran out into the dark. Kostas and Angeliki looked disappointed. Why did this baby have to come now? They would probably have to wait until morning to open their gifts. Manoli crouched down, putting an arm round each of them. "I think it will be fun to sit up and wait for this new arrival. What do you think? Your mother and I will have received our gift from God and you can open your presents."

The children nodded and smiled. They could stay up late and that was a treat in itself. A moment later the midwife bustled in and the house became a hive of activity. An old hand by now, Manoli had everything ready.

"You really do pick your times to deliver, Evangelia," said Jenny as she rolled up her sleeves.

The delivery was easy. Within minutes a small,

shrivelled being made its entrance into the world. Evangelia sank back on the pillows as Jenny slapped the tiny creature into life.

"It's a girl," she said, hurriedly wrapping the baby in a sheet and laying her in the prepared cradle. "Now, Evangelia, you appear to have an oversized placenta, so you must push hard to expel it. Come on, one more effort and your troubles will be over."

Evangelia summoned all her strength and gritting her teeth, she strained herself until she had turned the colour of a beetroot.

"Well, well, now. The Lord bless us and save us," she heard the midwife exclaim softly. "And I never even suspected."

A second cry rang out and Manoli, unable to contain himself a moment longer, flung open the bedroom door.

"What's going on, Jenny? What was that I heard?"

Evangelia raised herself on her elbows and looked from one to the other. The midwife advanced towards the bed, a bundle in each arm.

"Well, you clever, brave little mother, it's not one baby you've brought into this world, but two! Two beautiful, healthy little mites, a boy and girl. They're tiny, but with loving care, they'll survive."

"Two! But you said I had an over-sized placenta, Jenny!" Evangelia nestled a baby in the crook of each arm, scrutinizing each in turn. So Dr. Tilahun was right. He wasn't so inexperienced after all. "Which is which?"

"This is little Sophie. She came first," said Manoli. "And this fine little man is the over-sized placenta. He's obviously going to be a perfect gentleman as he let the lady go first. I think we'll call him Loukianos. What do you think, Evangelia?"

Chapter Nine

On 10 June 1940 Italy entered the war in Europe on Hitler's side. Italy had over a hundred thousand troops in Abyssinia, but it also had four borders to defend with Kenya, Eritrea, British Somaliland and the Sudan. Immediately war was declared, battalions of troops began to move out of Addis Ababa. By late June, it was rumoured that Haile Selassie had arrived in Khartoum and was poised to lead a liberating force. The Abyssinian Patriots, who during the five years of occupation had never ceased to wage a guerilla war from their hideouts in the northern hills, were jubilant. Calling themselves Rastafarians after the Emperor Ras Tafari, they were a wild looking bunch with their great mops of hair which they had vowed never to cut until they had driven the Italians from their land. Now, in their hundreds, they poured over the British Sudanese lines, demanding weapons and ammunition to continue the fight.

In the capital there was a feeling of apprehension. The troops were jumpy and there was talk of evacuating the Italian civilian population, but otherwise there was little news of what was happening. Families hunched around wireless sets, frantically trying to tune in to a station which would bring some enlightenment, but all the news bulletins were propaganda about the progress of the war in Europe.

Lukas was not quite three when, in October, it was announced that Italy had invaded Greece. The move came as a complete surprise to everyone. It was said that not even Hitler was aware of Mussolini's intentions until they were a fait accompli. Certainly, there had been no hint of the invasion in the Italian press. It meant, of course, internment for all the expatriate Greek men of fighting age. As soon as the invasion was made public, the round-up began. Each day truckloads of soldiers conducted a systematic search, bursting into houses, cafes, even churches, bayonetted rifles at the ready. Some walked with dignity to the trucks; others had to be dragged. Those who spat and gave abuse were rewarded with a rifle butt in the groin.

Watching with terror as yet another truck rumbled past, Evangelia gripped Manoli's arm. "Manoli, what are we going to do without you? How will we survive? I can't cope without you, Manoli!".

"Evangelia, just calm yourself. We're luckier than most. At least Logotheti has an Italian passport. There's an irony for you! The Italian occupation of Karpathos did have it's uses, they won't touch him. He'll take care of you all and keep the business running. Pavlos and Kostas are not children any more; they can work in the bookstore. I've given them good training and I'm sure they'll manage very well. Besides, I really don't think they'll keep us in the camp very long. I'm sure the war will be over soon."

"But how will I know where they've taken you? How will I know if they're feeding you properly?"

"Food, food. Whatever the crisis, Woman, your mind

turns to food."

Tears welled in Evangelia's eyes. "I-I'm just so worried you will come to some harm. I don't want them to take you, Manoli. Can't you hide?" She slid her arms round his broad frame as if to hold onto him.

"Am I not a man, Evangelia? Do you think I could hide when my friends and neighbours are all being taken? Come, little one," his voice softened. "Be brave. Your family needs you and I tell you, it won't be for long."

Soon the inevitable green truck stopped outside their home and a detail of soldiers marched in to escort Manoli away.

"Please don't take him," pleaded Evangelia as they hustled him out of the door. "I promise you he won't do anything against your people."

"Shut your mouth, *Signora*, or we'll take you too," said the corporal, pushing her to one side. Pavlos gripped his mother's arm.

"Shh, mother," he whispered. "You'll only make things worse."

"I'll follow them and see where they go, Mama," shouted Kostas. Before she could stop them, both Kostas and Lukas had slipped past her and were running down the street, the toddler screaming: "Wait for me. Wait for me." Kostas grabbed his hand and dragged the youngster after him. The truck made several stops. Almost full, it was making its way slowly towards the outskirts of town, when the boys saw two men chasing after it, shouting and waving.

"We're Greeks too. Don't you want to pick us up?" they were yelling. As they ran, one of them fell and twisted his ankle.

"I can't run any more. You'll have to leave me behind,"

he shouted to his companion.

"No way, Brother. Jump on my back. They're not going to leave us behind. Do they think we're traitors? We'll make this truck stop if it's the last thing we do."

Manoli leaned out of the side of the truck and squinted at the two men. "Isn't that Nestor Zissopulos running like crazy carrying someone on his back," he asked.

Spyros, the baker, looked over Manoli's shoulder. "Yes, it's him. It looks as though he's carrying his youngest brother, Evangelos. Bang on the driver's window and make him stop. I tell you, if we have those two with us at the camp, there'll never be a dull moment."

The truck pulled up and Nestor jumped in, dragging his brother up after him.

"Move on down. Move down," shouted the guard, exerting his authority. Once they had settled, everyone began laughing.

"I mean, there we were, standing in the street, as large as life, whistling to get their attention and they just drove straight past us! It's hellishly demeaning when you actually volunteer to be interned and they ignore you. 'We're Greek,' we yelled. 'We're Greek. We want to be with our compatriots,' but still they didn't stop. I can tell you, Evangelos and I took great exception to being ignored."

The truck gathered speed. The two brothers, gasping for breath, finally gave up their chase. Hand in hand, they stood and waved at their father until the truck turned a corner and was lost from view.

"Come," said Kostas, leading Lukas towards the city centre. "I'll fight them my own way."

The Italians had erected a billboard in the middle of the *piazza* pinpointing the progress of their military invasions in Europe and Africa. Italian flags dominated the map. Glancing around to make sure no one was watching, Kostas sneaked up and hastily removed the symbols of Mussolini's dictatorial rule. Tearing them into tiny pieces, he scattered them in the gutter.

"I'm going to do this every day," he told Lukas. And he did.

* * *

Logotheti assumed full responsibility for the family, trying to make the absence of their father less painful. He gave each child a daily chore to keep both their minds and bodies occupied. The elder boys dusted shelves, unpacked books and laid newspapers out in neat rows while three-year-old Lukas was given the task of collecting bits of string from the floor and storing them in a cardboard box. Angeliki helped her mother in the kitchen and kept a watchful eye over Sophie's movements. She was a little terror who couldn't keep out of mischief!

Each day, neighbours would drop in to discuss the latest news from the front. Rumour had it that the Emperor had crossed the Sudanese border at Umm Idla and was advancing steadily with a combined British and Abyssinian force led by a mad Englishman who ate with his fingers and never washed. Another British force was said to have captured Mogadishu in Italian Somaliland and was headed for Harar, not far from Dire-Dawa.

One day towards the end of March 1941, Kostas came running in to the house "They're leaving, Mama. The Italians are leaving."

Evangelia tied a scarf round her head and, taking Lukas and Sophie by the hand, ran to the end of the road.

Kostas was right. In perfect formation, just as they had marched in to the city in what seemed like a lifetime ago, the invaders were marching out. Crowds lined the streets to watch them go. There were no jeers or cheers, just a passive silence. Only when the last soldier was a mere speck on the road north to Dessie, did the jubilation begin. Strangers hugged and kissed each other, as tears ran down their cheeks. Spontaneous singing and dancing erupted in the streets. Evangelia found herself linking arms and singing with all her might a heartfelt rendering of the national anthem. The theme was taken up by others along the street, until the sound swelled and filled the air. Evangelia fought to stem the tears flooding down her cheeks. Where was Manoli?

"Come, kids. Let's go home."

She walked heavily back towards the house. Away from the crowds, the street was quiet and deserted.

"When's Dad coming home, Mother?" asked Kostas.

"I don't know, son. I wish I did." Preoccupied with her thoughts, her eyes rested unconsciously on a figure walking unsteadily towards her at the far end of the street. The man paused occasionally to rest against a wall and then staggered a few more paces. Evangelia stiffened. Then she quickened her pace, finally breaking into a run.

"Manoli. Manoli. Is it you? My darling, is it really you?"

When the order to retreat had come, the Italians at the internment camp at Koram had simply leapt into their vehicles one morning and left, leaving the gates wide open. The camp was 700 kilometres from Addis Ababa. The men had travelled by mule, camel, ox cart and foot to reach home.

No sooner was the family rejoicing Manoli's return

than their hearts were torn over Logotheti's unexpected and pressing departure. Bitten on the leg by a rabid dog, his evacuation was imperative. He barely made it to Cairo before the forty days incubation period was over, by which time his abdomen was covered in marble-sized lumps, induced by the rabies shots he had received. Sick and tired, he yearned for his wife's loving tender care and so, heartbreaking as it was to shake the African dust from his heels, he returned to Karpathos after an absence of thirty one years.

The actual 'liberation' of the capital came several days later on April 6. In anticipation, by general consensus, the traffic had switched from driving on the right to driving on the left. The British arrived, distributing biscuits and packets of custard powder. To the people's disappointment, the liberating force came from the south and was led by General Cunningham. It was nearly a month later before Haile Selassie entered Addis Ababa at the head of the remnants of the Patriot Battalion, escorted by the man who had dedicated himself to the Emperor's restoration, Lieutenant Colonel Orde Wingate.

The Emperor received an ecstatic welcome. It was May 5th, exactly five years to the day after the Italian invasion had driven him into exile. Facing him was the difficult task of reconstructing his country and reasserting his authority. Despite the years of humiliation and frustration, and watching his people suffer, Haile Selassie was determined to demonstrate to the world that he was a modern, humanitarian ruler. His first proclamation was to urge his people not to spoil their name in the eyes of the world by deeds of vengeance, so there were no reprisals against Italian civilians. While in every country in Europe collaborators were executed by their countrymen, the Emperor forgave and forgot so that all could work together to rebuild the nation.

Nestor and Amalia in Nairobi in 1960 with (l to r) Mellina, 15, Laki, 11 and Elektra, 13..

PART TWO

Chapter Ten

Addis Ababa, 15th August 1966

"Welcome to thirteen months of sunshine, Miss Mellina." The immigration officer smiled as he handed back my passport. The greeting was no surprise. The country's calendar still ran on the Julian system; twelve months of 30 days' duration and a thirteenth month, *Pagume*, for the remaining five days. Unfortunately, they were not all sunny. The rainy season with its overcast skies, daily deluges and terrific thunderstorms occupied four months of the year.

Checking in at the Ghion Imperial Hotel, I dumped my suitcases and went out for a stroll, eager to see if my birthplace had changed in the eleven years I had been away. I had a vivid memory of Addis Ababa, but looking around everything seemed to be different. Wide avenues had remodelled the city and modern buildings had replaced the traditional mud *tukuls*. The mules and donkeys which once carried anyone of standing had been ousted by gleaming, chauffeur-driven limousines, out of which stepped high-powered businessmen in western dress. Street stalls overflowed with tourist souvenirs from brass Coptic crosses to cartoon strips painted on leather depicting the marriage of Solomon and Sheba and the Battle of Adoua.

I felt underdressed compared with the local Amhara girls, Europeanised from head to toe in the latest Paris fashions and Italian footwear with long, manicured nails and stylish henna-highlighted coiffures. Yet their appearance was a strange fusion of the old and the new, for although their delicate, almond-shaped features glowed with Elizabeth Arden and Estee Lauder creams, they still traditionally placed a blob of freshly-churned butter on the crown of their heads, allowing it to slowly melt and oil their skins. Even the heaviest, most tantalizing French perfumes could not totally disguise the pervading odor of rancid butter.

There were also those, proud of Ethiopia's traditions, who refused to change. Gliding elegantly past in white, thinly woven gowns with colorful borders, their faces, necks, hands and ankles were tattooed with blue signs of the cross and adorned with a profusion of jewellery.

It was dusk, yet the streets were vibrant with warm, bustling life. Street vendors, operating out of cardboard boxes, selling everything from braziers to toothpicks, ducked between cars while the traffic lights were at red. In Churchill Road, nicknamed "Enjoyment and Retirement Avenue", red lights were already winking above doorways barred by beaded curtains, while girls in skin-tight skirts lounged sensuously nearby.

I breathed deeply, inhaling the crisp, fresh air, blissfully happy to be back.

Although it was like a holiday, I had actually come to Addis on business, recruited by the United Nations Children's Fund to promote UNICEF greeting cards in

Ethiopia. I was eighteen, fresh out of college and this was my first job. Making my way back to the hotel, I began planning how I would tackle my sales pitch the following day.

Early next morning I was outside the modern Minerva Bookstore with some samples. Taking a deep breath, I strode through the doors and introduced myself. "I'm Mellina Zissopulos from UNICEF," I smiled nervously. "I'm here to persuade you to support us by selling some of our cards."

"Well, Mellina, it's a pleasure to meet you," said the manager, Pavlos Fanouris. "Your name's very familiar." He smiled. Pavlos Fanouris was middle-aged and balding with the beginnings of a pot-belly. He was casually dressed in an open-necked white shirt rolled up at the sleeves and had a kindly, genial face.

Feeling more at ease, I relaxed a little. "My family used to live here," I told him, "but we moved to Kenya in 1955."

"You're not Nestor's daughter, are you?" he exclaimed. Two strong hands gripped mine, shaking them firmly. "Why didn't you say so? I knew your father when I was a youngster. What a character! Well, well! Nestor's daughter! Tell me, how is he?"

"He's fine," I found myself saying. Imagine, the first person I spoke to in Ethiopia knew my father! Seizing the opportunity, I returned to the business in hand, telling him how many children would be vaccinated against smallpox and saved from starvation from the proceeds.

"How long have you been doing this job?" he interrupted me with an amused look in his eyes.

My face began to burn. "A few days," I replied defensively.

"Well, you certainly know how to do business, young

lady. I'll take whatever you've got and I'll also donate our commission to your cause. How's that?"

Back at the hotel, I stood on my balcony and looked out over the city. All along I had been excited about this assignment in Ethiopia. Now, I knew I had made the right decision in coming. I loved the Ethiopian people, so naturally courteous and friendly and I viewed the city with the same kind of excitement and fervor I had experienced as a child. I felt I had come home.

* * *

Although I was born in Addis Ababa, I spent the first seven years of my life in Dessie, in Wollo Province about 200 miles north of the capital, where my father was a successful businessman. He owned huge soap and liquor factories and was forever travelling between the two cities, promoting trade.

With thatched *tukuls* nestling among groves of sweet-smelling eucalyptus, Dessie was an attractive town built on the shelf of a spectacular escarpment eight thousand feet above sea level. We occupied one of the few stone villas adjacent to the palace. My mother had brought hundreds of bulbs and seeds with her from Addis and within a few months of settling in, our garden was a mass of colour. Anything would grow and our artichokes, lettuces and carrots provided not only our own family with fresh salad stuffs but also the royal occupants next door.

As a toddler I thought my father was the tallest person in the world. In fact, he was of medium height with a strong, handsome face, mesmerizing eyes and pitch black hair. I was always so proud of my father who, with his kindness, compassion, and optimism, had the ability to find a solution to the most complex problem. He and my mother were well suited. She was slim and attractive, a few inches shorter than he, with black curly hair, a delicate pink complexion and soft, lustrous eyes with long, sweeping lashes. My father was away quite often; in his absence, Mum was the disciplinarian. She could be strict if necessary, but most of the time she was a playful companion, always ready to put her sewing aside to come and taste the mud pies we had prepared.

Supper time was sacred in our home. Invariably business kept Dad away the whole day, but he seldom failed to head the dinner table. The evening meal was always served early in order to permit time for a discussion on the day's happenings, when Dad would become 'our friend' rather than a parental disciplinarian. "Electra and I gave the neighborhood kids a bath and their mothers are threatening to come and talk to you." 'Our friend' would reply: "When you want to bath someone, try your dolls; they don't catch colds!" He would always end with, "Rest assured, your Dad will never find out about this, unless such mischief is repeated."

On one occasion, there was a knock on our door just as we were sitting down to dinner. "*Woizero* Zenebetch would like to see you, Sir," our houseman Yosef announced. My stomach churned. There was something I had forgotten to tell, 'our friend'.

Zenebetch lived in a grass-roofed *tukul* across the street. I always felt guilty that we lived in a comparative mansion while she inhabited a single-roomed hovel, divided into sleeping and cooking sections by a thin piece of material hung over a wire. Although grotesque cement blocks served as her table and chairs, everything was always immaculately clean. Conscious of her desperate need for blankets and clothing, and despite frequent reprimands, I frequently delved into my mother's bottom drawer for anything Zenebetch might find useful.

In return, she would teach me to cook traditional Ethiopian dishes. Squatting inside her dimly-lit, smoke-filled hut, I watched her grind sun-dried red peppers on an oval stone to prepare *berbere*, the sweat standing in beads on her brow.

"We buy everything in packets and tins. Why don't you do the same?" I once asked.

Zenebetch laughed. "Me, I can't afford such things. Besides we have to prepare everything from scratch."

"Can I try?" I asked eagerly.

"No, you just blister your hands. But," she said, seeing my disappointment, "I teach you how to prepare *injera.*"

Made from finely-ground *tef* flour, *injera* was the traditional Ethiopian bread. A sour-tasting rubbery pancake, it was spread out like a tablecloth and various spicey dishes spooned out on top. Ethiopians ate communally with each person tearing off a piece of *injera* with their fingers and soaking it in the fiery *wat* before twirling it into a small cone-shaped morsel and popping it into their mouths.

When she finally finished cooking, Zenebetch moulded a piece of butter and placed it on her crown before wrapping her head in a towel and sitting cross-legged in front of the fire. Reviving the flames with crisp, dry leaves she placed a heavy skillet in the center which, as it heated, began to sizzle and spit liquefying fat. Wiped clean, the pan was ready for roasting a handful of raw coffee beans which bounced and tossed as they changed colour from a dull green to a rich brown. Zenebetch pounded the roasted beans, adding the fresh aromatic grains to the boiling water. Removing the sooty, orb-shaped pot from the fire and nesting it in a straw ring alongside two rinsed handless cups on a stool, the coffee ceremony began.

To ward off evil spirits, smoking frankincense filled the air. Freshly-picked shoots of *tenadam* or Rue, a sweet-smelling herb, were tossed into the goblets, and then with skilful movements she poured out the coffee leaving the muddy sludge in the pot. As I sipped the steaming beverage, blowing the steam away from my face, I felt slightly wicked and intensely happy.

The thick, grey smoke of the fire stung my eyes, making them water. One look at my puffy eyes and charcoal-covered clothes and my mother would know immediately where I had been, but her stern scoldings were short-lived when I produced a round of freshly-baked *injera*.

The announcement that Zenebetch was at the door, made me tremble. It wasn't going to be so simple this time I thought, as I watched Dad coming back with a dish of *doro wat* and *injera*. "A gift from *Woizero* Zenebetch," he announced as he looked at me. "And what did you do to deserve this?" he asked. "Maybe we should have a talk after dinner, eh, Mellina?"

I swallowed hard. It was time to confess. "Can you both please be really good 'friends' tonight?" I whispered. My parents looked at each other in consternation. I stammered on. "You know I want to be a doctor when I grow up? Well, a few days ago, I was passing outside Zenebetch's *tukul* when I heard her groaning, so I rushed in to see if I could help. She told me she was having a baby and everyone had gone to market. I got frightened when the baby started coming out, but she begged me to stay. Well,

Lukas' family (l to r) Angeliki, Evangelia, Pavlos (standing), Sophie (the twin), Manoli holding Lukas, Costas.

Evangelia after the death of Sophie.

Mellina's family in 1930 (l to r)
Standing: Tasia, Stavros, Nestor, Daphne Seated: Grandmother Maria, Grandfather Stellianos
In front: Evangelos.

Mellina's father Nestor in Debre Marcos where he traded in skins and hides.

A typical row of tukuls.

Nestor was attacked by crocodiles when he crossed these falls on the Blue Nile.

Nomadic herdsmen by the Awash River.

St. George's Cathedral in Addis Ababa, built by Lukas' Uncle Logotheti to commemorate Menelik's victory against the Italians in 1896.

Lij Iyasou with young ras Teferi (right) later crowned Emperor Haile Selassie.

The family bookshop in 1930. When it later burned down in 1941, their home on the 2nd floor was also destroyed. Little Sophia stands on the steps, holding hands with her mother Evangelia.

The maids at Aunt Daphne's house (l to r) Gete and Belletech. Belletech looked after Mellina during her stay.

Zelalem the beloved driver.

The Italians march into Abyssinia 1941

The second bookstore and international press agency in the Piazza as it was in 1961.

Street hawker selling magazines for Manoli and later the army officer who searched Evangelia's bedroom.

Lukas (right) behind the counter of the second bookstore in 1955.

Crowded shelves in the Piazza bookstore, 1961.

Lukas presenting the Emperor Haile Selassie with a gift on the Ethiopian Christmas, 6th January 1965.

The Emperor surrounded by his grandchildren, most of whom were later imprisoned by the Dergue.

The Emperor Haile Selassie and Empress Itigue Menan in the Imperial Palace, circa 1960.

The Emperor with his grandson Iskender Desta, the Rear Admiral of the Navy, (on right of Emperor) who was executed by the Dergue.

The Emperor with his favourite son, Prince Makonen, the Duke of Harar who was killed in a car accident.

Lukas and Mellina on their engagement, 1968.

The palace in Asmara where Lukas and Mellina were received by Asrate Kasa and his wife after their honeymoon.

Asrate Kasa (left) with Lieutenant General Abiy Abebe (right), both later executed by the Dergue.

The bookstore in Addis Ababa, taken just before the Revolution in 1972.

Mengistu Haile Mariam taking the salute on the first anniversary of the Revolution, 1974

March past infront of Mengistu on the first anniversary of the Revolution.

Workinesh (on the right) with her baby brother and sister.

I couldn't just leave her, could I?" I appealed. "The baby was tiny and slimy, and I didn't know what to do, but Zenebetch gave me a knife and told me to cut the cord. I closed my eyes and prayed I wouldn't hurt it, then I ran home as fast as I could."

I stared at the floor and swung my legs nervously. Dad took me on his lap as I struggled on. "I went back the next day to make sure everything was alright, and it was. Zenebetch had shaved off Dehu's hair, leaving just a little tuft in the middle. If he dies, the angel who comes to take him will be able to reach out and pull him up by the fluff on his scalp."

Dad gently removed me from his knee and standing me before him, lifted my chin and stared me straight in the eye. "Listen, Mellina, you thought you did the right thing, but you are only seven! You should have run for help! Promise me that you'll wait a few years before you play at being a doctor again!"

Later, snuggling down into my warm bed, my heart lurched when I heard my father say that I was not receiving the education I needed in Dessie and it was time I went to the English school in Addis Ababa. Visions of being torn away from my warm, loving nest to stay with my Dad's sister, Daphne, disturbed my sleep and turned my dreams into nightmares.

All too soon the dreaded time for departure arrived. My mother ceremoniously threw a glass of water over the car. Her action was a symbolic wish that our journey should run as smoothly as water from a mountain spring. No member of our family ever embarked on a journey without this small ritual.

"Wait, *Geta* Nestor. Wait!"

We turned to see Zenebetch, Dehu strapped to her back

in a beaded leather carrier, his shaven head bobbing up and down as she raced to catch us. She extended her offering, an *agelgil*, a round, straw basket covered with goat's skin, lined with layers of *injera* and *wat*. "Please, accept this *sink*," she said, a slight catch in her voice. "No traveller leaves home without it. However long the trip, it never runs out."

I swallowed hard as the car started rolling, and knelt on the back seat, waving to the beloved family I was leaving behind. Our route wound through groves of sweet-smelling eucalyptus as we slowly descended towards the lowlands. I stared glumly through the window at colonies of cheeky, black and white colobus monkeys, as they swung from branch to branch, turning their inquisitive, monk-like features warily towards the car. Fascinated, I watched as they picked tender leaves and berries, stuffing them into their mouths and occasionally offering tit-bits to the babies clinging to their bodies.

Leaving the wooded slopes behind, we passed Kombolcha—our favorite picnic site with its crystal-clear rivers—and Negus Michael, where endless cotton fields concealed a wealth of bird and animal life. By mid afternoon, we were driving through Bate with its fine sand dunes and warm-water springs, breeding ground for hundreds of goats and sheep, which were forever raising dust clouds with their skipping movements.

The smoky blue shadows of evening were enfolding the harsh cliffs and jagged peaks of the mountain as we approached Karakore. The temperature had dropped and a chill wind was blowing. My eyes felt heavy, but I couldn't find a warm corner to curl up in. Suddenly, my father drew the car to a halt and turned to cover me with a blanket.

"Do you want something to eat, little sparrow?" he asked.

"I'm not hungry," I whispered, trying to control my chattering teeth. "Why are we stopping?"

"There's a funny sound in the engine. But I'll soon have it fixed. Meantime, I'll try and find some wood and fix a fire. You go to sleep." He bent down and kissed my forehead, rubbing his hands together to keep them warm.

It must have been the middle of the night when I was woken by a loud hooting followed by spasmodic cackles.

"Daddy! I'm scared! Where are you?" I called.

"I'm here, Poppet," he said, coming to the car. "Its a miracle, there isn't a single twig in sight, but I found two sacks of charcoal! I've got a strong fire going, and what with that and my Mauzer," patting the gun slung over his shoulder, "the hyenas won't come near us."

That calmed me a little, but I was still frightened. I peeped out of the window, was that a movement in the bush? I had often heard stories of roving *shiftas*—bandits—who attacked stranded travellers. What was my father doing? Sitting by the smoldering coals, he was staring dreamily at the brilliant, star-studded sky above the dark, awesome peaks which surrounded us. A pot of coffee was bubbling steadily and the glow of the fire illuminated the serene, fearless expression on his face.

Early morning sunlight was streaming through the car window when the sound of excited chatter awoke me.

"How do we find, in the middle of nowhere, a white man who speaks Amharic with such fire and passion?" Perplexed local tribesmen and shepherd boys were shaking their heads in amused disbelief. The men wore raincapes made from finely woven grass, while the boys

111

were clad in thick blankets and sheepskin overcoats. Many had woollen caps decorated with baboon hair tassels pulled down over their ears.

"You'll never catch my father out," I interjected in Amharic. "He speaks most of the local dialects and a total of twelve languages. He's been in Ethiopia for 34 years."

Wild giggling broke out at this unexpected intervention.

One of the men was so impressed, he opened his *agelgil* and offered me a piece of fresh honeycomb. I joyfully accepted his precious harvest, sucking out the honey from its perfectly-formed wax mould.

Dad had fixed the car, and was now talking to the charcoal owner.

"I am very pleased that my charcoal kept you warm during this very cold night, sir," the man said. "God moves in strange ways. I was so tired yesterday, I couldn't carry it to the top of the hill. I am glad, for you might well have frozen to death."

"Indeed, your charcoal was Heaven sent," my father replied as he pressed a bundle of notes into the man's hand.

"In the name of Jesus Christ, you have given me far too much, Sir. This is enough for twenty sacks."

"Money has no value. It was useless to me last night; I couldn't even burn it to keep warm," Dad replied. "You never know, I might be passing through again some cold night and need your assistance."

"In that case, Sir, I shall always hide a sack for you here."

* * *

At the end of our second day of travel, a distant circle of flickering lights, resembling candles on a birthday cake, indicated that we were approaching Addis. I twiddled my fingers nervously.

"When we get to Aunt Daphne's house, you will stay with me, won't you?" I asked, fresh tears blurring my vision.

"Of course, I will, Poppet. I won't return to Dessie until I have you well settled in." Dad said reassuringly.

Well, perhaps life wouldn't be so bad after all, I thought, as we turned in through the gate. My aunt's house was situated on Wavell Street—a wide tarmac road named after the British General who co-ordinated the allied liberation of Ethiopia in 1941.

It was an impressive villa in the middle of a huge garden full of fruit trees and beautiful, exotic flowers. Purple bougainvillea climbed over the front porch, while a profusion of pink geraniums covered the sides of the staircase. Out back, a rose garden and a vineyard gave the house an aura of distinction.

It was Zelalem, the family chauffeur, and Beletech, the cook, both old family retainers, who lovingly welcomed us and ushered us up the stairs to the front door.

The dining room door had been left ajar and I peered round Beletech to see what was happening. Several people were seated round a large table covered with a crisp, white cloth and gleaming cutlery. I could hear the soft murmur of conversation, broken by an occasional guffaw. A huge crystal chandelier lit up the animated faces of the diners.

Sharo, the houseman, was serving from large silver platters. He glanced up and caught me looking in.

"Madam Daphne, your brother and Mellina have arrived," I saw him whisper to my aunt.

Aunt Daphne rose hurriedly. Excusing herself from the table, she wiped the corners of her mouth on her white, starched napkin and dropped it on her chair.

"I'm so glad you've finally arrived. We were really getting very anxious and worried," she said embracing and kissing us both. "Only yesterday we heard that the bus from Dessie was attacked by *shiftas* just after Debre Sina. She hugged me again. Her body was warm and she was wearing a wonderful perfume. "Now," she turned to my father. "Why don't you get cleaned up and join us for dinner. We're just on the *hors d'oevres*."

"What in heaven's name were *hors d'oevres*?" I wondered. They sounded disgusting.

"What about some soup for you Mellina?" My aunt looked at me with concern.

"I'll try," I said reluctantly, hugging my *agelgil*. It still contained a few slices of cake Mum had baked for us and some pieces of shrivelled *injera*. I wasn't yet willing to relinquish my last immediate links with home.

Equally reluctant, I trailed to a bedroom adjacent to the dining room. It seemed very familiar to me. Perhaps some furniture had been rearranged but it was the same room that I had grown to love in the past.

"Isn't this grandmother's room?" I turned to Dad who was following me with my suitcase. "Didn't she used to sit in that corner in her rocking chair?" I walked over to the far corner, where her little oil lamp had always burned in front of her icons. It was still there. How I had loved my grandmother. How I had cried when Dad told me that I wouldn't be seeing her again. "Where's Snow-White?" I asked, looking around for my granny's adored, long-haired white Angora cat.

"She's right here," said Dad, reaching under the bed

and picking up a ball of white fluff. He placed her in my arms and I nestled my face against the soft fur. She started to purr, nuzzling her face close to mine. Suddenly my fears disappeared. I could feel my grandmother's spiritual presence all around me and my heart glowed with the warmth and affection she bestowed on us when she was alive. I turned to my father, who was staring at me anxiously.

"I'm not scared any more, Daddy. Granny is here with me and I know I'll never sleep alone. She'll always keep me company."

He took me in his arms. "Sweet little Sparrow, you'll never be alone. Follow your grandmother's footsteps. Remember what she always used to say—'Respect other people's feelings and never, ever forget the poor and the hungry.' If you follow her example, you'll always have friends around and you'll never be alone. Before you know it, the school term will be over and you can come home and teach Electra and Laki all that you've learned. How about that?" He hugged me tight and kissed my forehead.

I slid my thin, tired little body between the bedsheets. After two days on the road, it was bliss to relax and stretch out in a proper bed. I was falling asleep when visions of home and my mother serving dinner flashed before me. Hot tears burned my eyes. I began to imagine I was really there, having dinner with them as usual and telling them all about my day's experiences. That felt better: I would play this game every night and maybe the days would roll past quickly. The reassuring sound of my Dad's voice in the next room made me feel warm and secure, at least for that night. I shut my eyes and slid into sleep.

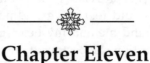

Chapter Eleven

The Sandford School in Addis Ababa, a group of low, single-storey buildings surrounded by exotic, flowering gardens, was run by an elderly English couple and their daughter. There was a friendly, welcoming atmosphere especially important to me as I didn't speak a word of English.

Acting on my father's challenge to turn teacher when I returned home, I began copying everything down twice. One morning, my teacher, Eleanor Sandford, asked me what I was doing.

"It's a game I play, Miss," I answered in Amharic. "I am keeping the second copy so that I can play school with my little sister and brother."

She was touched. "From now on, I will give you two copies of all your worksheets," she said with a smile.

I fought hard with the right words in English to thank her.

"Thank you, Miss Eleanor. You my best friend," I stuttered as my cheeks flushed with embarrassment.

"Well tried!" She patted me encouragingly on the shoulder.

Within a few weeks, I was showing off my newly

acquired expertise. There was no doubt in my mind that I could already speak fluent English. To my Addis aunts and uncles, it was not quite so obvious. The one who suffered most from my unintelligible jabbering was old Zelalem. For him, there was no escape as he drove me to school and back.

"Zelalem, you do understand why I have to learn to speak English so quickly, don't you?" I said one morning. "Those kids at school probably think I'm an orphan with no family. I've got to be able to tell them how things really stand."

Zelalem looked at me with amused, understanding eyes. "Of course, little one, but you must stop being such a worrier. Be patient and before you know it the English language will start flowing from your mouth as easily as water from a spring. You want to accomplish miracles overnight."

Zelalem fumbled in his pocket as he negotiated the school driveway, and a wrinkled hand revealed a bright silver fifty cent coin.

"I saved this for you to buy some sweets. Before your father left, he asked me to offer you *adera*, which means protection and standing in for him if the need arose. It's up to me to make sure you don't feel left out when the other children shop at the kiosk."

I flung my arms round the old man's scrawny neck, squeezing hard. "Zelalem, you're so kind and generous, but I can't accept this, it's a lot of money for you. I can't spend it on sweets!"

"There you go again with your philosophies! You are too young to be talking like an old woman. Now take the money and no more nonsense."

I looked straight into his brown eyes. They looked hurt.

They appeared to be saying, 'Are you too proud to accept a small gift from an old man?' "Alright, Zelalem, I will accept it but only on one condition. It's a loan! The minute my father comes, I shall ask him to give it back to you. Is that a deal?"

By mid afternoon, I was impatient to be picked up. I wanted to show Zelalem what I'd bought from the kiosk. The bubblegum had tempted me, but I'd bought two colorful pencils for Electra and Laki.

Cars came and went. One by one everyone left. I sat glumly on the pavement but the grey Dodge was nowhere in sight. Then my stomach began to flutter; something had happened to Zelalem, I knew it.

"Mellina, over here." It was Evangelos, my father's youngest brother and my godfather, calling from the car park. I ran towards him.

"What's happened, Godfather? Is Zelalem hurt? I have this awful feeling that he's in pain."

"Calm down, darling," he replied. "Zelalem had both his legs broken in an accident, but the doctors say he'll be okay."

"Oh, Godfather, please take me to see him," I pleaded, knowing he would probably be in a hurry to return to work. "He'll never walk again!" I cried dramatically, releasing the tears which I'd been fighting to control.

"Of course, he will walk again, silly. The doctors are going to make him better," he said, handing me a handkerchief as he drove to the Haile Selassie Hospital.

The grey, bare corridors smelled strongly of antiseptic and surgical spirits, immediate reminders of dreaded injections, pain and suffering. A patient awaiting treatment lay groaning on a trolley. Another, his head and leg swathed in bloody bandages sat on a bench nearby.

118

For a second, I was tempted to flee.

"Stay out here while I see if he's awake," my Godfather said gently. I closed my eyes tightly and prayed fervently to God not to take Zelalem away. I reminded Him Zelalem had made a promise to my father and He should not make him break it.

"Mellina, you can come in now, but be very quick," Evangelos interrupted my prayer.

I followed him along the row of iron bedsteads in the dimly-lit ward. Everything was grey—the walls, the bedding, the faces of the patients. Suddenly, there he was, drawn and hollow-eyed, his thin, sinewy arms resting limply on the covers.

"Zelalem!" I cried. "Are you dying?" I took one of his hands in mine.

"I'll be alright, Mellina. I'm an old man and sooner or later I'll have to leave this life, but I won't have some new-fangled automobile choosing the time and place. Besides, *adera* is a promise I must keep, so I'd better get well."

It was an effort for him to talk, so I just squeezed his hand and left him, but I knew his time had not yet come. After two weeks in hospital, he was brought home to convalesce. Each day, with the aid of crutches, he took a few steps more, until gradually his strengthening legs were able to support his emaciated body. Zelalem's favorite spot was beneath the trailing tendrils of a thickly intertwined arch of vines where streaks of sunlight filtered through the bright green leaves, creating dancing patterns on his resting limbs. They were sufficient to gently warm and heal his injuries.

"By the time these grapes are ripe Mellina, I shall be driving you to school again," he said, looking up at the tiny, bitter berries.

"I know you will," I said, putting my arms around him.

"You are nursing me as you would your own father, but there's a difference between us," he said, lowering his eyes, "or I would call you my very own daughter."

"What's that," I asked, concerned that he seemed sad.

"Bring your arm here," he said, placing his alongside mine. "There's the difference. Mine is dark, while yours is light."

"Really, Zelalem, you are foolish," I cried. "Look at those grapes. There are black and white ones, but they grow together and are both delicious when you eat them. We are just like those grapes!"

The old man looked at me and two big tears rolled down his face. "You are right, my child, and may God bless you."

* * *

Such memories coupled with growing up in a home full of warmth and security, created by parents who never believed in discriminating between people of different races or creeds, resulted in us all coming to love the people and country of Ethiopia. It was then, quite devastating for the whole family when, in 1955, my father decided that, for the sake of his children's education, we should move to Kenya. His sister, Daphne, had left Addis in 1954 to buy a coffee plantation outside Nairobi, where she was doing very well. When she invited my father to join her, any doubts he may have had were dispelled.

It was his own lost opportunities that he craved to give to his children. "Wealth comes and goes, but no one can take an education away from you," he used to say. For him, more than any of us, the move was traumatic. He was leaving behind thirty-five years of friendship—Ethiopians he had grown up with like brothers from boyhood to manhood, Ethiopians who had nursed him back to health after severe attacks of malaria in the middle of the bush, on the shores of the Nile; Ethiopian patriots he had fought with shooting down Italian warplanes. He had become one with them in language, in ethnic beliefs and in culture. He never forgot their kindness, which in small ways he tried to repay, making a name for himself as *ye deha abat*—father of the poor. Now, what was in store? He and his family had eaten good, honest, hard-earned bread in Ethiopia. Three times, he had lost all his earthly possessions through fires and floods and three times been able to start again with the aid of those wonderful people who had stood by his side in his time of need. "Nestor, we believe in you. We know you will make it and we're here to help you," they had said. And they had. The memory made the leaving even harder, but he could, at least, go with his head held high.

It was to this country with its gentle, hospitable people that, filled with reawakened memories and emotions, I had returned.

Chapter Twelve

I had been in Addis Ababa a few months when I met the personnel officer at the American Embassy. Overworked and desperate, she asked me half jokingly if I would like to work for her. Knowing that my sister Electra would soon be on the job market, I proposed she should hire her instead.

"It's a deal," said Esther Gray.

A month later, Electra arrived. We now had each other for moral support and managed to overcome some of the initial depressions we experienced being away from home. "It's time for our young birds to fly off and build their own nests," my Dad had said. We decided to hunt for an apartment and within a couple of weeks moved in.

Although both Electra and I were quite extrovert, moving away from our parental home brought on a sudden shyness. We regularly turned down invitations for fear of feeling out of place, or out of embarrassment that we had no chaperon.

"I'm sending Laki to you for a holiday," Dad announced during one of his frequent telephone calls from Nairobi. "Then, the three of you will be able to go out together and enjoy yourselves."

"Dad, that's wonderful, but how did you know we weren't going out?" asked Electra.

"Just because we're hundreds of miles away, do you really think your mother and I aren't picking up the signals about what's going on?" he answered.

It had always been that way. Call it telepathy, extrasensory perception or just being a caring, sensitive parent, Dad could pick up our distress signals and offer a solution.

* * *

When Electra and I arrived in Addis Ababa in 1966, there were between 3,500 to 4,000 Greeks in Ethiopia, concentrated mostly in the capital city as well as in Asmara and Dire-Dawa. A few families lived in the smaller towns of Jimma, Dessie and Dembidollo. A large slice of the economy was in their hands, bringing wealth both to themselves and to their host country. Greek enterprises varied from spinning and weaving factories to oil refineries, flour mills, the curing of skins and hides and the export of coffee, meat and wines. Some ran supermarkets and bookstores. The country was self-sufficient in most basic products, but luxury items had to be imported, the surplus foreign exchange generated by expatriate traders making this possible. Those who could afford it had houses equipped with luxurious, ultra-modern Scandinavian furniture, while there were foodstuffs in abundance to satisfy the varying tastes of the international community.

The Greek community had its own church, primary and secondary schools and a club with sports facilities. The Olympiacos Club was a regular gathering point for old and young. Monday was the club's Bingo night, when the grandmothers sat with their knitting and peered over their spectacles to see who was flirting with whom. Unaware of the gossip being hatched, the younger members would gather around, chatting and playing games. Sunday afternoons, devoted to dancing tea parties, were the highlight of the week for the teenagers where everyone got a chance to demonstrate their gyrating skills.

It was at one of these events that my eyes fell, a little enviously, on a pretty girl full of sparkle and energy as, laughing and joking, she attempted to teach a young boy 'rock and roll'.

Being a total amateur and always shying away from any invitations to take the floor, I was fascinated by her easy, fluid movements and superb timing. She was a little over five feet in height with a well-shaped, flexible body and an attractive round face. Her hair had been freshly styled in a modern cut I had recently seen in a French magazine.

"Who's that girl?" I asked an acquaintance, Chris Poulakis.

"That's Aspa Alexandrou, dancing with her youngest brother, Steve," replied Mrs. Elly, one of the community's oldest settlers and a practiced eavesdropper. "Her family came originally from Alexandria and her father and eldest brother, Yiannis, are one of the finest teams of lawyers in town. Young Aspa is an economist—a very clever girl indeed, with a London degree. She works for the National Bank of Ethiopia."

Little did I know that just a few years later, Aspa and I would become firm friends and this friendship would play a significant part in events which were to be crucial.

* * *

124

It was good to have Laki with us. Together the three of us had no inhibitions. We went on long excursions to the hot springs at Sodere or to the lake region where most of the younger generation gathered at weekends.

Lake Langano was one of our favorite haunts. Magical were the moments when the sun slowly dipped its bright orange rays into the waters of the lake, transforming it into a glowing fire. As the sun disappeared and a star-studded black sky took over, the tents around the shore would suddenly light up like lanterns as fires crackled into life in preparation for the evening barbeque.

Ethiopia was a paradise for both residents and tourists. There were prehistoric sites at Gondar and Axum; churches hewn out of solid rock at Lalibella and areas of breathtaking beauty to survey at Lakes Margarita, Abiata and Awasa.

But what made Ethiopia, and Addis in particular, so cherished were the Ethiopians themselves who went out of their way to make expatriates welcome. They enjoyed entertaining foreigners with their music, locally-fermented drinks and delicious food and were very proud to share their culture and heritage.

* * *

Christmas was approaching. Visions of spending it, for the first time, away from home were making us all rather irritable. We began finding fault with the weather and the food and even with each other. A feeble attempt was made to put up a Christmas tree and buy a few decorations, but it was clear we were all homesick. Everyone else seemed to have their Christmas plans all worked out, but we couldn't decide what to do.

"Look, both the Olympiacos and Juventus Clubs are

holding Christmas balls. If you guys don't make up your minds soon, we shall end up staying at home," Electra announced one evening.

"You're right. We'd better snap out of this apathy and make the best of things," I said. "Let's have a trip round town after dinner and soak up some Christmas spirit. Then, maybe we can go to a movie."

The shops were ablaze with shimmering decorations and flickering lights. Novis, one of the biggest departmental stores in town, had a glittering display of imported crystal alongside delicately-carved ivory figures worked with filigree silver from Asmara. Opposite, the windows of Al'Honesta were resplendent with posing mannequins in the latest fashions from Europe, set against a backcloth of artificial mistletoe and garlands of holly reminiscent of a northern Christmas.

The beauty salons were packed with women, seeking a new French look for the festive season. Stopping at Chez Lily, we peeped in to see if we could make an appointment for the following day. Lily, as her name implied, looked and moved like a dainty flower. She was a fair-skinned petite beauty with green eyes, lustrous auburn hair and a complexion like porcelain. Coming to attend to us, she told us there might be a slim chance she could fit us in the next day. Our spirits lifted. Having our hair done always cheered us up and was something of an incentive to join in the festivities.

* * *

"May I have this dance, please?" said a voice beyond the circle of flickering light cast by the candle on our table.

Electra looked at me. "He's speaking to you, Mellina.

Stop gawping and give the young man an answer!"

My heart sank. I hated dancing in public and especially with a stranger. "I'm sorry," I said, candidly, "but I really am a lousy dancer and I'll just tread all over your toes." I blushed.

"Why are you so sure it won't be me who'll be doing the treading." He leaned forward into the light. A pair of amused, dark eyes with sweeping, long lashes fixed me with their gaze.

I was cornered. Slowly, I rose to my feet. "Alright," I said, "but you have been warned."

He was smaller than me and beneath the ballroom lights, I could see that he was thinning on top although he had disguised it well by sweeping his hair to one side, but he had an attractive, baby face which became animated when he spoke.

"I'm Lukas Fanouris and I know you're Nestor Zissopulos' daughter," he said taking my hand. My pounding heart calmed down a little. If he knew my family, then that would make him a friend. I relaxed and tried not to contemplate what a fool I was about to make of myself. Suddenly, he leaned close to me and whispered as easily as if he were asking my name, "Will you marry me?"

I was stunned. "Certainly not!" I managed to reply, looking affronted.

"I thought that would shock you," he chuckled. "Now we've broken the ice, shall we get on with the dancing?" He led the way to the center of the floor.

It didn't take me long to discover that he was not much of a dancer either and that rocking rather clumsily from side to side in a tightly-packed dance floor suited us both.

"You must be one of Pavlos' brothers," I ventured,

shouting to make myself heard. "You're so alike."

"Yes, I'm the young, good-looking one. Actually, I'm a twin. We're not identical, of course: my sister got the beauty and the long, thick tresses; I got the brains and the bald head! How's that for variety?"

"You're not too bald—just a little thin on top," I said, peering to see exactly how much hair he had.

"No, I've changed my mind. I can't marry you. You're too tall for me," he quipped, sizing me up.

I stopped and stared hard at him.

He raised his hands. "Okay. I promise, no more jokes. What if I told you the reason for my bald head? It's my mother's fault. She had this habit of spanking me on the head with her slipper. I don't know how many slippers she wore out, but she just wouldn't stop," he chuckled.

I had to laugh.

"Come on, that's better. Really don't take me too seriously. I just enjoy terrifying attractive, young ladies."

I could have kicked him. Instead, I allowed him to lead me back to my seat, thanked him coldly for the dance and turned away. I was furious when Laki stood up and invited him to join our table.

"Well, I'm with a group on the other side of the hall, but I'm sure they can do without my company for a while," he said, shaking hands and introducing himself.

After the initial pleasantries, it wasn't long before Lukas had us all rolling with laughter. I couldn't help joining in, although his air of self-assurance still irritated me. Pushing his chair back and rising to his feet, he glanced at his watch. "My party will think I've deserted them," he said. "But don't let's end the fun here. Why don't you come over and join us at our table?"

Hastily, I made negative noises. Totally ignoring me,

my brother and sister immediately got up and followed Lukas. With clenched teeth, I trailed behind. Lukas' companions were busily tucking into plates piled high with roast lamb, turkey, pork, cheese pies, Greek *moussakas* and a variety of mouth-watering salads. Saris wines were flowing freely.

Lukas handed me a glass of chianti. His eyes held mine.

"Salut. Here's to our future."

He began talking to Laki before I had a chance to retort. Several glasses of wine later, I felt his eyes once more boring into me. The moment I looked up, with a mischievous smile, he leaned across the table and said: "Can I kiss you?" I glared at him but quite unabashed, he plastered his lips with chocolate mousse and tried again. "If you're shy, surely this will make it sweeter."

I collapsed with laughter. Tears ran down my cheeks and my jaws ached. It was obviously infectious, all the girls at the table were giggling.

The music was suddenly interrupted, and the President of the club announced the arrival of the two-time Olympic marathon winner, Abebe Bekilla. Everyone stood up and clapped as the tall, gentle-looking athlete entered the hall. He wore a light blue, Olympic blazer and two gold medallions hung round his neck. Formerly a member of the Emperor's bodyguard, he was a simple man whose prowess had been discovered by chance and encouraged by the Emperor himself. He had brought Ethiopia international recognition and his countrymen loved and revered him for it.

Ethiopian and Greek national dances were to be performed in his honour. The band struck up and the first *iskista* dancers entered: the women in finely-woven white dresses with broad embroidered borders in blue and gold and matching sashes tied round their waists, the men in traditional white jodhpurs tightly fitted at the knees and ankles. The women flipped their sashes alternately from one shoulder to the other, clapping their hands and provocatively inviting the men to join them and together they shook their shoulders to the beat of the music.

"Do you think if we practised together for a long time, we might eventually be able to do that?" It was Lukas. When the lights dimmed, he had slipped into a seat beside me.

"Believe me, with my two left feet, it would take a lifetime for me to learn that dance."

"Well, if that's how long it will take, it's okay by me," he replied.

The dance had finished and the spontaneous clapping almost drowned his words. I pretended not to have heard. Some young Greek girls were taking the floor, clad in long, blue satin skirts and short, velvet boleros worn over white lace blouses. They were accompanied by young boys, dressed as *evzones*—Greek national guards—with pleated skirts and pom-poms on their shoes. Slowly, and then gathering pace they began to dance my favourite, the *sirtaki*.

"You know, I'm Greek. I love all things Greek. But I've never seen my homeland," Lukas volunteered.

"Well, I suppose, neither have I. Does it worry you? Do you feel you don't belong here?" I asked, a little surprised by his sudden seriousness.

"No, not at all. My whole life is here. I love this country and, God willing, I shall never have to leave it. But, I have a niggling curiosity to see where my parents were born. Perhaps, we could go together!" The twinkle in his eyes was back. Leaning back, I realized with a sudden tingling sensation in my spine, that his arm was resting on the back of my chair. I sat up abruptly. The dance was drawing to a close, and everyone began flocking onto the floor. "In the meantime," Lukas resumed, "why don't we try another soft-shoe shuffle together."

The dance floor was alive with frenzied activity. The Greek dancers were trying to emulate the shoulder-shaking techniques of their Ethiopian counterparts, while the Ethiopians, holding white handkerchiefs aloft, were attempting to copy the twists and twirls of their Greek partners. The room was in an uproar as people stumbled about, laughing and wiping the tears from their eyes.

Lukas took my hand and led me onto the dance floor. "I think even our feeble efforts will go unnoticed in the middle of this melee. By the way, Merry Christmas." He leaned over and kissed me on the cheek.

Chapter Thirteen

I looked up at the calendar in my office. It was Saturday, 18 May, 1968, and quite a dull morning. Our receptionist, *Ato* Bekele, and I were the only staff on duty.

"Is Miss Zissopulos in please?" I heard someone ask at the UNICEF reception desk.

"The office is closed today," Bekele replied. "If it's official business, then I'm afraid you will have to come back on Monday."

"Actually, it's not for business; it's for pleasure," the self-assured voice responded.

My heart started to beat wildly. What in heaven's name was Lukas Fanouris doing in my office on a Saturday morning? I rushed out into the corridor and waved my hands negatively at Bekele.

"Tell him I'm very busy. I can't see him," I mouthed.

He nodded, but my visitor caught sight of me and strode right in.

"Hi, Mellina. I thought I'd come in and brighten up your day."

It was the first time he had used my Christian name— our community was quite formal about these things. I began to panic, I wasn't ready for this familiarity. I dreaded what might be coming next. I had almost forgotten about him after Christmas until a few weeks ago when we met at the Filwoha traffic lights. It was a difficult junction, extremely steep and could only be negotiated by juggling carefully with the pedals and handbrake. Having not long passed my driving test, I was extremely nervous. Several *seicentos*, the blue and white Fiat 500s used as local taxis, screeched across the junction, the drivers leaning out of their windows to flirt with passing girls or turning completely in their seats to chat to a passenger behind.

I was revving the accelerator when a light blue car drew up within a couple of centimetres from my side door. In a fury, I blasted my horn and turned to give the driver a piece of my mind. The words froze on my lips, as I stared straight into a pair of amused, dark eyes.

"Really!" I yelled at Lukas Fanouris. "Do you always drive so dangerously? You'll ruin my car!"

"I'll buy you a Mercedes," he called as he put his car into gear and shot off. I could feel my cheeks burning with anger and frustration. More was in store.

A few days later, Electra and I were at the airport waiting to pick up our parents, when a familiar voice behind me asked: "Are you meeting anyone I know?"

Again I turned and was met by a pair of innocent eyes, apparently in a serious mood. "Our parents are flying in from Nairobi," I explained.

"Mine too," he replied with a straight face.

"Here they are!" shouted Electra, who had finally spotted our parents coming through the customs.

"Yes. They're finally here!" Lukas grinned looking straight at my Mum and Dad.

"What?" I asked, anger rising in my voice. "You've been waiting for my parents?"

"Well, with two unmarried daughters, that's quite probable, wouldn't you say?" he laughed.

My face flushed with rage. Instantly my father spotted my agitation. "What's the matter, Sweetie? Someone been pulling your leg?"

"One certain young man is really getting to be too much." I looked in Lukas' direction.

"Him! Don't be too hard. After all, you're at that beautiful age now where teasing from young men should be flattering. Or are you still set on becoming a career woman?" Dad asked.

My father had barely finished speaking when a hand was extended and Lukas introduced himself: "Welcome back to Ethiopia, Mr. Zissopulos. Perhaps you don't remember me. I'm Lukas Fanouris. Can I help you with your luggage?"

I breathed a sigh of relief when we were all finally in the car and it pulled out of Bole Airport. On the way home I briefed my parents on what had taken place during the past couple of months.

"Well, Mellina," Dad hooked my arm into his, "I don't know what you find so intolerable about young Fanouris. I think I like him. He's going out of his way to attract your attention, and I feel he could make you happy." I felt shivers run down my spine— Dad was always right.

Now here I was, alone with him in my office, dreading what he was going to say next. But if I was speechless, I noticed that for the first time since I had known him, Lukas was also at a loss for words. His face was deadly serious.

"Actually, I've brought you a present," he said, awkwardly, placing a large, glossy gift-wrapped package on the desk.

"Thanks very much, but I really don't accept gifts

134

from…"

"Strangers?" he finished my sentence.

I took a deep breath and wondered why I was trying to find something to say which wouldn't hurt his feelings. But before I could reply, he pleaded: "I really don't feel like a stranger to you. I feel I've known you for years. Please, just open the gift."

Reluctantly, I picked up the package and untied the pink bow. As I pulled the wrapping paper away, the title of a hard-backed book stared boldly up at me. "How to Build a Successful Marriage" I read. My heart lurched. At any other time, it might have been funny, but not now… he was serious.

"Will you help me build a good marriage, Mellina?" he asked, appealingly.

"I… I… I don't know," I stuttered. "I hardly know you. And to be honest, I don't love you. Without love, it would be difficult to build anything," I finished, swallowing hard to moisten my dry throat.

"Mellina, from the first moment I met you I haven't been able to sleep at nights. I know I've annoyed you by turning up when least expected or wanted, but I've stored up enough love in me for both of us. I'll work hard to earn your love. Mellina… please… will you marry me?"

"I don't know what to say," I replied hoarsely, lowering my eyes and burying my chin deep into my chest.

A gentle index finger slowly raised my chin. "Try saying 'Yes'," Lukas whispered.

I felt cornered. This was not how I had planned things. I was bent on a career and now Lukas was proposing to nip it all in the bud. But, when I looked up at his eyes again, a strange but warm feeling of belonging, of being at home pervaded my psyche. Somehow they were not the eyes of a stranger any more, but those of the man who loved me. But, what about me? This was such a wild idea. Maybe love would eventually grow and blossom like a rare flower, but could I nourish the seed with sufficient patience and understanding? Only a few days ago Dad had been telling me that luck would soon be knocking on my door. "Please, don't shut it out," he had said. How uncannily perceptive he was! I took a deep breath in an effort to control the choking feeling that had engulfed my heart. Then, a thought streaked across my mind: this was my destiny. I had to follow this man who, sometime in the future, would be needing me by his side. Why was a force, beyond my control, pushing me to say 'yes'?

I shook myself free from a momentary trance and tried to concentrate on the reply I was going to give Lukas. On those rare occasions when the thought of marriage had crossed my mind, I always fantasized a tall, blue-eyed prince charming sweeping me off my feet. This was someone who didn't quite fit the picture! Nervously, I chewed my finger nails. The seconds ticked by.

"I don't want to rush you for a reply," said Lukas, breaking what must have been a long silence, "but I do want to go and talk to your Father. Would he have any objections?"

"I'm sure he wouldn't," I blurted out, remembering our conversation at the airport. "He likes you."

"He does? Well, that's great! I must admit he scared the daylights out of me the day I met him at the airport. I'd heard he was a crack shot, and I was convinced I'd be the next trophy on his wall if he suspected I was after one of his daughters!" he laughed. "But, come Mellina, couldn't you find a small corner of your heart that could learn to love me?"

Maybe my father was right about Lukas, but I had to be entirely honest. I took a deep breath. "Marriage is a life-long commitment and I'll accept—but only on one condition," I started. "I'd like a long engagement, and if by the end of that time I don't love you enough to take the church vows, then I won't go through with it."

Lukas looked up, his eyes far away in deep thought. Then, shaking himself out of his reverie, he plunged his hand into his pocket, withdrawing a small, leather box. Snapping it open, he studied the sapphire set in a ring of glittering diamonds. Gently taking my hand, he slipped it onto my finger. Then for a fleeting moment, his lips touched mine.

"I'll take that chance," he whispered.

Chapter Fourteen

During the next nine months, Lukas and I were perpetually in each other's company. Before my parents returned to Nairobi, they organized an outing with the Fanouris family to Sodere, a beautiful spot bordering the Awash river about 100 kilometers south of Addis Ababa, where natural hot springs bubbled up through cracks in the earth's crust. It was a great reunion for Manoli and my father, who spent the whole day reminiscing about the old days, the war, internment and how their lives had progressed.

For Lukas and me, it was the beginning of our learning to know and truly love each other. Having secured what he wanted, Lukas was no longer irritatingly pushy, whilst I was beginning to look at him with new eyes. As the weeks went by, my feelings slowly correlated. He was so patiently loving and yet undemanding, never ceasing to remind me that loving was not possessing. If I could not give myself to him or loved someone else, he wouldn't stand in my way. I was always a romantic, but as our relationship matured, I realized I would be a fool to let Lukas go. My father was right: he was everything I needed. He was steady, sensitive and sensible without being overbearing and he had such a good sense of fun.

When the day fixed for our wedding finally arrived, I no longer had any doubts. It was the eighth of March 1969. By early morning, wedding presents had started to arrive. Many were small but precious gifts bearing heartfelt messages from old and dear acquaintances like Zelalem and Zenebetch. A number had travelled long distances to honour us with their presence. How could one adequately thank those who had sacrificed a good portion of their limited income to crochet a table mat, weave a basket, or present us with family heirlooms they had been saving for a rainy day?

"There's a chauffeur from the Palace outside," Askala called out, hurriedly wiping her hands on her apron and rushing to open the front door. Within a few seconds she was back, looking for Lukas. "He says he's been instructed to deliver the wedding gifts to you personally," she huffed, annoyed that the white-gloved chauffeur had ignored her. Having been with the family for nearly thirty years, ever since the twins were born, Askala was a much-loved mother figure in the household earning herself the respected title of 'Mama'. Being childless, she treated us all like her own, which included doling out sharp reprimands where she felt they were deserved.

Lukas came back, balancing an armful of huge packages from Crown Prince Assfa Wossen, Princess Tenagne Work, the Emperor's daughter, and Princess Sarah Gizaw, widow of the late Prince Makonnen. On opening them, we found a set of beautiful hand-cut crystal wine, champagne and water glasses, a pair of silver candelabra and a magnificent seven-kilo ivory vase with a silver lining.

"These are gorgeous!" I exclaimed. "What on earth did

you do to deserve such beautiful gifts?"

"It's a long story," said Lukas, "which, my Sweetheart, we don't have time for right now. We'd better go down to the church and see how things are shaping up."

The wedding bells were already ringing at St. Frumendios as we entered the courtyard. Bouquets of pink and white carnations and delicately-scented freesias were being delivered to the church and their sweet perfume wafted on the breeze.

"Good morning, my children," called out Father Irothion. "Have you brought the wine, rice and sugar-coated almonds?" The essentials of a Greek Orthodox wedding. The old priest placed a hand on both our shoulders. "I am truly blessing my Redeemer for allowing me to live to see this day when I can join together the children of my two greatest friends. My association with your families goes back many, many years, beyond the Italian occupation and the terror of those terrible days. I've known your parents, Lukas, since 1926 when we all came to Ethiopia. Yes, we've shared many happy and some sad moments, in these quarters," pointing towards the top floor of the stone building next to the church, "after the big fire. A terrible night. Your home was destroyed along with hundreds of others, and young Sophia, your sister, was taken from us. God rest her soul."

"As for your family, Mellina, well, I'm sure your father has told you what we all went through together. Do you know that I was the priest who baptized your mother in Dire-Dawa, that I married her in this very church and baptized you? And now, with God's help, I pray that I will be around to baptize your own children."

He was, indeed, a dear old man, close to our hearts. We both looked with affection at his kindly, wrinkled face and long beard, inwardly praying that God would grant him his wish.

The ceremony was only a matter of hours away. I sped up the road towards Lily's hairdressing salon, my stomach churning. Soon I would be kissing my freedom goodbye. Had I made the right decision?

"Sorry I'm late, Lily," I apologized, hanging up my coat.

"Today iz your day, Mellina. Anyway, it iz traditional for brides to be late, *n'est ce pas*, so zere is no hurry."

Leaning back in the chair, I began to tremble uncontrollably.

Lily tried to calm me down. "Come on, Mellina, I cannot do anyzing wiz all zis shaking going on. Please, try to relax."

"I'm sorry, Lily," I apologized. I'm so nervous about tonight.

"Well, now," called Lily's mother, Madame Mireille. "I 'ave just ze zing for nervous brides. *Voilá*—a mild tranquilizer—tiny, but *très* effective, *ma petite*."

I swallowed the pill. Within minutes it began to take effect. I lost all sense of time. I was so relaxed I didn't care how long it took for my hair to be fixed. I would amble along to the church when I was ready. The sharp ring of the telephone jerked me out of my soporific state. Lily was putting the finishing touches to my eye make-up.

"*Mais oui, Monsieur* Zissopulos, I assure you she will be home wizin a few minutes," I heard Madame Mireille saying down the phone.

"Lily, what time is it?" I asked, suddenly alarmed.

"It is... er... seven-thirty," she replied.

"Oh, my God!" I yelled. I fled home, veil flying, face hot and flushed. Mum and Electra were waiting, wedding

141

dress unzipped ready for me to step into. Then we were flying back down the stairs again.

Dad took my arm: "Come on, sweetheart. You look lovely. But, let's hurry, we're already half an hour late!"

I walked towards the church doorway, clutching my father's arm, glancing shyly at the hundreds of invited guests that were gathered. They were all giving encouraging smiles to help me climb the last few steps to where Lukas was waiting, Evangelia on his right and Manoli on his left.

As my father gave me away, Lukas leant over and whispered in my ear, "I was petrified you had second thoughts…"

I looked into his eyes, hating myself for having put him through so much anxiety. "I love you," I whispered, placing my hand in his and walking slowly down the aisle.

The smiling face of Father Irothion, resplendent in his crimson and gold gown, greeted us with an encouraging wink. We turned and smiled at our two families, grouped on either side of the raised platform where we were to make our vows. A silver tray, bearing a glass of red wine, two white crowns of lemon blossom joined together with a white satin ribbon, the wedding rings, sugar-coated almonds and rice mixed with rose petals, was placed on a table in front of us. They were the symbols of our union.

I looked down at the glittering wedding band as Lukas slipped it firmly onto my finger, sealing our marriage "for better or for worse, until death us do part".

I glanced at my father. He nodded approvingly and blew me a kiss. Mum and Electra were busy drying their eyes.

We were ready to leave the church when I felt Lukas squeeze my hand. "There's something else," he said, delving into his jacket pocket and producing yet another jewel box. I hesitated. "Go ahead, darling. Open it," he insisted, his voice rising with excitement. "It's bigger than you think."

I opened the box, but instead of the jewellery I expected, I found a strangely-shaped key. "A key to what, Lukas?" I asked, puzzled.

"To this," he exclaimed, as we crossed the church gates. There, parked in the road outside, was a brand new Mercedes. "I promised I'd buy you one. Remember?"

Chapter Fifteen

I lay with my eyes closed, letting the soft, white sand sift through my fingers, as the Red Sea surf swished soothingly back and forth. Now that the tension of the wedding was behind us, it was sheer bliss to sprawl on this magnificent, empty beach and do nothing. I sat up and surveyed the unspoiled beauty which surrounded us. Earlier Lukas and I had found a coral reef that led way into the ocean. Outstretched like open fingers, orange and red starfish spread their tendrils, swaying gently with the flow of the waves.

"What a paradise, Lukas. I never imagined it could be so beautiful." I sighed.

Lukas scooped up a handful of sand and allowed it to dribble the length of my bare leg. "Let's enjoy every magical moment as it comes, Mellina," he said.

"The Red Sea is quite different from the Mediterranean. Somehow, it's got a unique beauty of its own. I thought these beaches would be crowded, but there's hardly anyone here."

"Well, we've got plenty of crabs and starfish for company," he joked, quickly drawing up his foot as a large crab emerged from a nearby hole and scurried past. "I'm starved," he groaned touching his stomach. "The sight of these crabs is making me hungry." He stood up, arching his back and stretching his arms. "Don't you feel like eating something?"

"Yes, but I can't spot any eating places around here."

Lukas shaded his eyes and peered up and down the beach. He took a few steps in one direction and then returned. "There's a small, wooden shack in the distance, it might sell snacks," he said hopefully. "Let's go see."

Gurgusum beach was a few kilometers out of Massawa, away from the unbearable heat and congestion of the port. It was a wide, dazzlingly white beach, levelled by the wind to a smooth velvety perfection, spoilt only by the faint traces of scurrying crabs and slithering snails, apparently the sole inhabitants of this remote haven.

"Even if we don't find anything, don't let's go back to the hotel yet," I said, making slow progress as my feet sank into the hot sand. I didn't want to lose that miraculous moment when the sun set the sea aflame and the black night descended to quench it. After what seemed like an eternity, we reached the shade of the shack's small porch.

"*Pronto!*" called Lukas. Everyone in Eritrea spoke Italian.

"*Avanti!*" came a voice and a middle-aged man with a colorful *kitenge* wrapped round his ample stomach and hips, emerged to greet us. "Welcome to my small restaurant," he beamed.

Had he actually said "restaurant"? We looked at each other in disbelief. Waving a hand, the owner ushered us inside. As our eyes adjusted to the shady interior, we detected half a dozen tables neatly bedecked with red and white checkered tablecloths and pristine white napkins.

"Its small," our host said smiling, "but the food is exquisite."

"I wonder if he has *zigini*?," I asked Lukas. At the mention of the local Eritrean spicy dish, similar to the *wot* we ate in Addis, the owner's beaming face suddenly became serious.

"Good people, I can prepare you anything your heart desires; grilled prawns, fried calamari, lobster in garlic sauce…" The choice was overwhelming. Our host pulled out two chairs and fetched us two ice-cold cokes. "Give me half an hour and you will never forget the cooking of Amde Gebreyohannes," he said proudly vanishing into his kitchen. For what seemed like an eternity, we were driven wild by the tantalizing aroma emanating from the kitchen.

Suddenly, the door burst open and Amde emerged with a plate of the largest prawns I had ever seen, bright red and still sizzling from the hot grill. "I have added a little *berbere* for taste. Now squeeze a few drops from a fresh lemon like this," he picked up a prawn to demonstrate, "and then pop it into your mouth, like this." He munched the prawn, rolling his eyes and smacking his lips loudly.

Lukas laughed. "That's an old Ethiopian custom, tasting the food first. It's their way of showing you that it's well cooked and safe to eat with no fear of food poisoning." We had barely finished when Amde returned with two huge platters of calamari and lobster. Lukas raised his hand, "Save some for tomorrow, *Ato* Amde. We shall be back."

Amde shook his head, "Tomorrow, my friends, we shall have parrot fish, red snapper, maybe even a baby shark—all fresh from the morning's catch. I will cook you a meal fit for an emperor!"

Gradually the sun fell behind the clouds and the coconut palms began to bend in the wind. Lukas put his arm around me and looked out to sea. The waves were now getting higher and whitecapped. It was an evening I shall never forget—the food, the sunset, the feeling of utter peace and security. It remained as an indelible cameo in my mind during some of the unhappier, stressful days that lay ahead.

* * *

With sadness we boarded the small DC3 plane which was to fly us to Asmara where we had been invited to spend a couple of days with Prince Asrate Kassa, the Emperor's cousin. I was extremely nervous. My taut nerves were not helped by the aircraft refusing to start. There was some problem with the ignition and when the pilot climbed out and tied a rope round the propeller, instructing the ground staff to pull with all their might, I was ready to walk to Asmara. Lukas just laughed, but only when the pilot reassured me personally that the aircraft was safe, did I finally agree to proceed.

To occupy my mind during the flight, Lukas told me how his relationship with the royal family had developed. As children, they used to pay regular visits to the bookstore in Addis where Lukas would swap marbles and comics. He became particularly friendly with the Emperor's third son, Prince Sahle Selassie, a pleasant, open-hearted boy. At Sahle's insistence, Lukas was frequently invited to the Palace to play games or go horse-riding. As they grew older, their friendship remained firm. When Sahle eventually moved out of the Palace into a residence of his own it happened, by coincidence, to be within walking distance of Lukas' home. It was because of this relationship that Lukas became involved in the events which took place in the early hours of Tuesday, 13th December 1960, when the Imperial Bodyguard attempted to overthrow the Emperor while he was absent on a state visit to Brazil.

At the time, Lukas was working part-time at the Ministry of Information's Printing Office. (Manoli thought it would be beneficial all-round if the bookstore and Ministry worked closely together.) He was reporting for duty at three o'clock in the morning, when an army officer by the name of Colonel Tesfaye, stopped him and, making sure no-one was listening, advised him to go straight back home and keep everyone indoors. A group of anti-royalists had seized the Palace, he said, and there could be bloodshed. Lukas' first thought was for Pavlos, who lived next door to the Army's Fourth Division Headquarters, so he raced to warn him. Hurriedly they woke the children and bundled them in the car to drive over to Evangelia and Manoli's house, which was well-protected and distant from where the action was likely to be. Even as Pavlos pulled out of the driveway, the streets were filling up with armoured cars and tanks. They reached the parental home just seconds before the shooting began. Turning on the radio, they learned that the coup had been engineered by the commander of the Imperial Bodyguard, General Mengistu Neway and his United States-educated brother, Germame. Hearing that they had occupied the Palace and placed the royal family under house arrest, Lukas grew concerned about the safety of Sahle. Undecided, he paced up and down, wondering what to do. Then, the radio crackled as a prelude to an announcement and the voice of the Crown Prince, Asfa Wossen, came over the speaker.

148

Introduced as the new head of a People's Government, he falteringly read a proclamation, saying that he deplored how "a few people, depending on their birth and material wealth, had been exploiting the people for personal benefit." He added: "Today, the will of the Ethiopian people has come to realization".

Lukas didn't wait to hear any more. Ignoring Evangelia's pleas, he raced through the streets, dodging army vehicles, until he reached Sahle's residence. The guards had abandoned their posts, and the place looked completely deserted as Lukas quietly slipped inside. He found his friend fiddling with a wireless set. Sahle was trying to contact someone in Brazil to warn the Emperor about the coup. Together they managed to transmit a message.

In the meantime, fierce fighting broke out around the palace between the rebels and the regular army and air force who had remained loyal. Four days later, it was announced that Germame and Mengistu had fled, but not before shooting eighteen of the ministers they had rounded up.

Lukas picked up Sahle and drove him to Princess Tenagne Work's palace, where all the royal family were gathered. He was invited to accompany them to the airport to welcome the returning Emperor.

It was discovered later that Asrate Kassa had also managed to elude arrest and had got word of the revolt to the Emperor through the British Ambassador, Sir Denis Wright. Prince Asrate Kassa was a kind family man, but a tough ruler. It was because of this that the Emperor had appointed him Governor of Eritrea.

* * *

Asmara was a trim, well-maintained city with modern Italianate buildings and lavishly-decorated stores. Wide avenues, fringed with tall, tropical palms, stretched from one end of the city to the other. Elegant Eritrean women strolled along the boulevards, their hair geometrically segmented and braided but for the ends, which bushed out in a mass of fuzz, gently sweeping their shoulders. Their long, slim necks were embellished with three separate gold medallions passed through thick strands of black silk thread. Those of aristocratic blood wore gold embroidered cloaks over their handwoven cotton dresses, while working women chose to dress in stylish stitched pantaloons and matching overshirts.

The palace was in the center of the city, surrounded by immaculately-kept lawns, exotic flowers and blooming trees. Ascending the marble steps, Lukas and I were shown into the main hall where exquisitely-carved chairs and couches, upholstered in turquoise and gold silk, were grouped at intervals on hand-woven Persian carpets. Before us, a sweeping staircase carpeted with deep red Chino-Turkestan matting, led to a multitude of rooms on the first floor. Dark wood panelling framed hunting trophies of thickly-maned lions and leopards, their gaping jaws exposing fearsome fangs, as they glared down at intruders.

Emerging from a side door, a distinguished figure stepped briskly towards us. "Berhanu, my son," said the Prince, clasping Lukas to his breast. "We are delighted that you were able to accept our invitation."

"The honour is ours, Your Highness," said Lukas, bowing his head. "Allow me to present my bride." He gently guided me forward. I lowered my head and curtsied.

"So you're the girl who won Berhanu's heart?" he said, looking me over. I blushed a deep crimson. "It was unfortunate that we missed your wedding but pressing business kept us here." He looked down, his mind trailing. "Never mind," he perked up, "we'll make up for it now. Come. Ah, here's my wife."

Princess Zouriash Work, accompanied by her son, *Lij* Asfaw Wossen, and daughter, Rebecca, appeared on the stairs. Flanked by a bevy of ladies-in-waiting, she slowly descended, her bearing erect, her head held majestically high. I was transfixed. Her dark, almond-shaped eyes contrasted strikingly with her honey-coloured skin, while gleaming black hair swept back, revealed to advantage a long, slender neck richly adorned with row upon row of sparkling diamonds and pearls. Gliding towards me, she extended a slender, manicured hand.

"Congratulations, Madam, and welcome. We are delighted that you have come to spend some time with us."

Overawed, I managed to murmur, "Thank you for inviting us, your Highness."

Lukas was enjoying a much more relaxed welcome. Having discovered who the visitors were, *Lij* Asfaw Wossen leapt forward to embrace his childhood friend. "Berhanu, you devil. I never thought you had it in you to settle down, leaving your good friends here still bachelors."

"Of course, we're only teasing," Rebecca interposed. "You don't know how happy we are that Berhanu chose you as his bride."

Prince Asrate led us all into the drawing room, summoning some drinks. "Tell me," he asked, "How did you come from Massawa?"

"In a DC3, Your Highness," Lukas replied.

"That must have been quite a bumpy ride. Those small

Dakotas aren't too stable in these skies. You should have informed me and I would have sent my car and personal escort to bring you up."

"Thank you, Your Highness, but it wasn't really all that bad, although we did have a problem starting one of the engines." Lukas related the morning's happenings.

The Prince smiled and nodded in sympathy. "One thing is certain, though, our pilots are highly qualified and well trained; I'm sure he wouldn't have taken off if there had been any danger. But, I shall certainly make sure that plane is overhauled before we have any accidents."

The sound of sliding doors preceded the appearance of a butler wearing a dark blue suit and white gloves. Bowing his head low, he announced that lunch was ready. The long, carved, ebony table was set with gleaming silver platters and sparkling crystal glasses and decanters. As was customary in every Ethiopian home, everyone washed their hands before eating. The butler came round the table with a silver jug containing lukewarm water, which stood in a deep, heavily-engraved dish. Each person extended the hand he or she was going to eat with, while the butler dribbled water gently over the waiting fingers. Another manservant followed carrying individual steamed handtowels dipped in cologne on which each diner could dry his hand.

This formality over, a succession of servants entered, carrying steaming tureens. The first bore pieces of *injera*, which were spread over our plates ready to receive small helpings from each of the mouth-watering dishes. Following one another round the table, the attendants served each person in turn with neat piles of hard-boiled eggs soaked in a peppery chicken sauce, shredded beef in a thick gravy and creamed *gomen*—green vegetables cooked with aniseed, garlic and ginger. Topped with half a dozen mounds of *wat* in varying colours, our plates took on the appearance of artists' palettes. An expert had certainly been at work in the preparation of the food. The fiery *wat* burnt my tongue. The first round was followed by a second and when everyone was satiated, in accordance with tradition, the diner allowed himself to be coaxed to take a little more from the fingers of the host himself. On this occasion, it was Rebecca who did the honours, delicately placing a morsel in each person's mouth.

Our glasses filled with champagne, Prince Asrate rose and lifted his glass: "And now, let us stand for a toast to the newly-weds. To you, Berhanu, our long and trusted friend and…", turning to me, he stopped and thought for a moment, "to a new friend we've made today—to your happiness." As the toast was being drunk, the sliding doors opened once more and two servants came in, carrying a heavy box. They set it down next to Lukas and me. "A small wedding gift in remembrance of this day and to our everlasting friendship," said the Prince.

It was only after we returned to Addis that we opened our "small" gift to discover it was a magnificent, 150-piece canteen of silver cutlery engraved with the Asrate Kassa family's coat of arms.

Chapter Sixteen

Not long after Lukas and I were married, both Electra and Laki left Addis. Laki decided to go to England to study Law and Business Administration and when he returned to Nairobi in 1972, he was offered a job with Olympic Airways as their station manager. Electra, although she liked Addis, preferred Kenya and wanted to be closer to our parents. She was transferred to the American Embassy in Nairobi and within a couple of years had met and married Byron Leondis, the regional manager of Olympic Airways and had given birth to her first child.

The Year of the Cockerel, 1969, witnessed the tying of a number of marital knots in Addis Ababa's Greek community. Among them was the girl whose dancing skills I had so envied, Aspa Alexandrou. She married a successful businessman, Michael Ipsillandis.

Talk at the Olympiacos Club began to revolve, not so much around matchmaking as wedding plans, honeymoons and the setting up of new homes. It was these young wives' chats which initially brought Aspa and me together and cemented our friendship. While our husbands shared the same views on politics and world affairs, we had concentrated our interests more on gardening, flower-arranging and cookery. Inevitably, our conversations began to turn to a subject very much on our minds—starting a family. When Aspa was sent for a pregnancy test, I drove straight to Elda's wool shop and bought all the pastel-coloured yarns I could find. Aspa sat by the phone biting her nails whilst I busily cast on stitches.

The phone rang. "It's positive," she yelled, beside herself with happiness. "It's your turn now, Mellina."

* * *

"Mrs. Fanouris." a nurse called out my name, glancing round the doctor's waiting room. I stood up, replacing the magazine I was pretending to read. "Dr. Roxanov will see you now," she said, opening the door of the surgery and placing my medical history on the doctor's desk. There was the sound of a tap being turned off in the adjoining washroom as a tall, kindly-looking man with grey hair walked through the door, drying his hands.

"What seems to be the problem?" asked the doctor with a heavy Bulgarian accent.

It was the first time I was seeing a gynaecologist and I was nervous. I shyly lowered my eyes. "Well, Doctor, I'm not really sure if there is a problem, but I've been married for nearly two years now and there's still no baby. My husband and I are very keen to start a family," I said fidgeting with the handles of my bag.

"Now, let me see," he said, looking at the medical card. "You're twenty-three years old and your record seems to be pretty straightforward. Tell me something," he raised his eyes and studied me over his glasses, "how long is it since you've been off the pill and who prescribed them?" he asked.

I explained that I was too shy to go to a doctor before I was married, so I obtained some from my chemist. "He assured me that they were very mild, contained the minimum dosage of oestrogen and wouldn't harm me in any way." My voice shook.

Seeing how nervous I was, Dr. Roxanov got up and walked round his desk to pat me gently on the shoulder. "Now, now. Just calm down. There's probably nothing at all to worry about."

Lying on the examination couch, I told myself how stupid I was being frightened of a simple examination when at seven years old I'd helped deliver a baby.

"I can't see any reason for concern," he said. Then he stopped, completely engrossed. I could hear my heart thumping. Could there be something wrong? "No, it won't be long before you will be able to conceive," he smiled. "Some women take longer to fall back into a regular cycle after they stop taking the pill. For the time being, we wait." I could have hugged him.

"I want you," he said, "to take your temperature every morning, before getting out of bed and record it on a chart. We shall review the situation next month."

I drove straight to the bookstore, so preoccupied that I ignored every red traffic light, and ran up the stairs to Lukas' office.

"Hi, Sweetheart," he greeted me. "What's all the excitement about? Your face is glowing."

"Oh, nothing much," I teased. "Just that the miracle of new life might descend at any time."

"Mellina, are you…?" he asked.

"No, silly, not yet, but Dr. Roxanov says I'm fine.

"Well," he said, looking faintly disappointed, "that's good to know." His eyes fell on the order from the Prime Minister's office which hadn't been put through, and turned to me. "Would you mind if we delivered these magazines tonight, before going to Aspa's for dinner?"

The drive to Bole where the Ipsillandises lived was always a refreshing change. It took us out of the congestion of the city into the cool, crisp, clean air of the suburbs. It was a new residential area where foreigners had been encouraged to invest their savings in building luxurious villas with extensive gardens. Most of the residents were Greek, Italian or Armenian, and it was common knowledge that numerous embassies were planning to move there.

"Sorry we're late again," we apologized as Aspa and Michael came out to greet us.

"You're excused this time," Aspa smiled. "I half suspected you would be late, so I deliberately delayed putting the souffle into the oven until you got here." Pregnancy suited her. Her round, attractive face was glowing and her eyes had a twinkle I hadn't noticed before. Her hair and skin glistened and somehow she emanated an air of self-sufficiency and contentment. She turned to me and whispered, "What news from Dr. Roxanov? I can't wait for us to push prams together."

"He's confident but I have this uncomfortable feeling that the pill has messed me up," I explained. After my earlier relief and excitement, the doubts were beginning to creep back. The dinner was delicious and the company fun, but I couldn't dismiss the longing gnawing at my inside.

* * *

"You'll never believe where we've been invited," said Lukas, as he handed me a pile of long-awaited letters from my family in Nairobi.

"To Princess Tsighe-Mariam's wedding," he continued, a little curtly, seeing me engrossed in my mother's letter.

"Oh. Who's she?" I asked without lifting my eyes.

"Well, when you've finished your letter, we'll discuss it," he said, annoyed at my ignorance and cavalier attitude.

"They're all fine and send you their love," I finished the letter, folded it and finally looked up. "Now, what were you saying about a wedding?"

"Only that the Crown Prince's daughter is getting married and an invitation was delivered to us this morning. This is a very special occasion. You'll have to wear your finest gown and your most dazzling jewellery."

"Oh, no, Lukas. You know how I loathe these big, formal affairs where I don't know anyone. Do we really have to go? I've never been to a royal wedding before."

"Well, there's a first time for everything, isn't there?" he teased.

"Come on, there's no need to panic. These occasions are usually incredibly well organized and the atmosphere will be very friendly and relaxed. If you stand close to me, no one will notice you shaking in your shoes," he joked. "La Bergerie has just brought in a completely new stock of evening gowns and shoes from Paris. Go take your pick."

"No chance of you going alone?" I persisted.

"None at all! I've been waiting for a chance to introduce you to the Crown Prince and his family. This is an ideal occasion and there's no way you're going to disappoint me."

The turquoise gown with the plunging neckline fitted perfectly. As I pirouetted from side to side, admiring myself in the mirror, Suzanne, the owner of the boutique, produced a pair of silver shoes embroidered with sequins and glittering stones and a handbag to match.

"'Ow will you be styling your beautiful, long 'air?" she asked in her thick French accent, "and what jewellery will you be wearing?"

"I had thought of putting my hair up with curls falling out at the back, and maybe wear a diamond necklace and earrings. What do you think, Suzanne?"

"Zat would be beautiful. You will look *magnifique!*"

"Thanks, Suzanne. I need every bit of encouragement I can get."

"You must have confidence, *ma cherie*. Hold your head up high," she demonstrated. "*Et voilá!* Pretend you 'ave been zere before."

* * *

The Holy Trinity Cathedral at Arat Kilo, where all royal rituals were observed, was being scrupulously cleaned and polished in readiness for the ceremony. Built in the basilica style, quite unlike the typical hexagonal Ethiopian churches, it was one of the finest examples of architecture in the land. To the left of the altar, behind the painted icons, stood two tombs carved from fine Greek marble. One already contained the body of Empress Itegue Menen, the Emperor's wife and grandmother to the bride; the second awaited the Emperor himself, so that when his time came he could lie alongside his lifelong companion.

Ethiopian weddings usually began at dawn with the arrival of the bride and groom in a limousine decorated with white ribbons and flowers, followed by a long procession of cars, carrying family members and close friends. Royal weddings were no exception. On this occasion, the ceremony was performed by Archbishop Theophilos, head of the Ethiopian Church. The long ritual of chanting, praying and placing two gold crowns on the heads of the matrimonial couple, lasted several hours.

A welcome breakfast was served immediately afterwards at the Imperial Palace, hosted by the bride's grandfather, the Emperor, followed by lunch at the bridegroom's home. The evening reception was given by the bride's father, Crown Prince Asfaw Wossen, and it was to that glittering occasion to which Lukas and I had been invited.

The heavy doors of the Prince's Palace at Sidist Kilo were opened at exactly seven o'clock. Lukas and I arrived a few minutes early and found ourselves surrounded by members of the diplomatic corps, various cabinet ministers and the heads of the respective aristocratic families, all waiting to be announced. A number of tall, well-groomed, young men stood at the entrance, acting as ushers.

"Who are they?" I whispered to Lukas as we joined the queue. He explained that they were the bride's brother and cousins and it was customary for them to honour all the guests. By now, we had passed through the gates and were being approached by one of the young princely ushers.

"Berhanu!" cried Prince Iskinder Desta embracing Lukas. "It's wonderful to have you with us." Turning to me, he extended both hands and cupped mine. "I'm very happy to meet you, Madam. I hope my friend is taking good care of you."

His gaze was quick and penetrating. I returned the greeting with a mumble. The nearest I had ever come to the Rear Admiral and Commander of the Royal Navy was on the television. Now, this distinguished figure was clasping my hand and I was at a loss for words. The Prince escorted us up the stairs and along a wide, red-carpeted corridor. "I hear you are finally one of us, Berhanu. Congratulations!" he said, clapping Lukas on the back.

"Yes, my Ethiopian citizenship came through last month. Thank you," Lukas replied.

The Crown Prince and Princess Medriash Work Abebe stood at the end of the corridor, waiting to greet their guests. Lukas bowed and I curtsied. After a brief exchange of congratulatory messages, we were ushered into the grand ballroom, already thronging with people. Some of the gowns were out of this world and there must have been enough diamonds to ransom a king, flashing in every direction as the light from the myriad crystal chandeliers caught them. Heavy velvet curtains with gold trimmings were draped across the windows at both ends of the enormous hall. At the far end, on a crimson-carpeted platform bedecked with pure white roses and lilies of the valley, stood a white satin couch and chairs for the bride and groom and their entourage of bridesmaids and page boys. The contrast was stunning.

We were shown to a table and seated with three other couples, two of whom turned out to be the French and British Ambassadors and their wives. The room was buzzing with conversation, when suddenly the band began playing the wedding march. A hush fell as slowly the lights began to dim, leaving only a spotlight focussed on the dais. Like actors in a play, the royal couple ascended the platform, Princess Tsighe-Mariam's hand resting lightly on her husband's raised arm. Slim and petite with the delicate features of a Nefertiti, she smiled and bowed shyly as the guests stood and applauded thunderously.

It was then the turn of the bridesmaids and pages to fuss around her like bees, ensuring she was seated in the centre of the settee with her feet comfortably placed on a cushion, while the maid of honor fluffed up her veil. The remaining members of the royal family accompanied by their children came in one by one, taking their places at the high table immediately in front of the platform. Fingers flashed with diamonds and emeralds, and precious stones adorned necks and tiaras.

Princess Tenagne Work, the Emperor's daughter, was swathed in a powder blue hand-embroidered organza offset by a deep blue satin sash draped across her chest from her left shoulder and clipped with a medallion at the waist. Her hair was swept back and held by a brilliant tiara. She was escorted by her son, Prince Iskinder Desta. Princess Sarah Gizaw, widow of the Emperor's deceased second son, Prince Makonnen, Duke of Harrar, was dressed in a stunning lemon chiffon gown, the bodice shimmering with delicately-embroidered flowers. She was followed by Princess Ijigayew, the London-educated eldest daughter of the Crown Prince. They all glided into the room as gracefully as swans on a glassy-surfaced lake.

The buffet dinner, a gourmet's dream, stretched from one end of the room to the other, while in keeping with tradition, white-gloved waiters offered guests their favourite cuts of prime raw beef, which they dipped in a hot chili sauce.

Shortly before 9 p.m., Iskinder Desta approached our table to bid us goodnight. "I hate to leave," he winked, "but duty calls. His Majesty won't go to bed until he has listened to the BBC news and I have to interpret the principal items." Apparently, it was a duty he performed whatever the occasion.

"He's totally dedicated to his grandfather," Lukas told me. "Dinner parties at his own residence are regularly interrupted in order for him to catch news flashes for the Emperor."

The evening drew to a close with the cutting of a fifteen-tier wedding cake, flown in from London. Our glasses bubbling with champagne, we all stood and drank a toast to the health and welfare of the newly-weds. Looking around me, the scene was almost unreal. Dazzlingly draped in diamonds, emeralds and sapphires to match the gorgeous satins and chiffons they were wearing, the entire Ethiopian royal family was gathered before us. It was a sight no one was ever to see again.

PART THREE

Chapter Seventeen

Early in 1972 feelings of uneasiness began creeping into our lives as the country prepared to celebrate the Emperor's 80th birthday. Although Lukas and I had our own apartment, we still dined with Evangelia and Manoli almost every day. When Pavlos' family left for Greece, Manoli persuaded him to come and live with them. Like a broody mother hen, Evangelia enjoyed nothing more than to have her children share the evening meal. Discussions over dinner were invariably lively, often leading to heated arguments.

"With all the prominent buildings outlined in neon lights and the figure '80' displayed everywhere, Addis is going to be lit up like a Christmas tree!" Pavlos remarked one night.

"We've been issued with written instructions not to switch off any lights for the duration of the celebrations," Lukas laughed. "I hate to think what our electricity bill will be that month!"

Pavlos shook his head. "It's not electricity bills that everyone's worried about," Pavlos persisted. "Everyone wants to know why the Emperor hasn't named a successor. It's causing a lot of unrest and all this fuss being made over his 80th birthday isn't helping. A lot of people think he's past it."

"No, he's not," interposed Evangelia, as she served him an outsize helping of spiced meatballs and rice. "Didn't you see him on television—how well he looked at the opening of the Conference on African Unity?"

Everyone fell silent. Evangelia, who remembered the horrors of the Italian occupation, the euphoria of the liberation and the ecstatic welcome accorded by the people to their exiled Emperor, refused to listen to negative comments. There had been peace and stability during Haile Selassie's reign and he had done his utmost to reconstruct the country and bring it into the twentieth century. He had established a state bank, a new currency, a national airline and two universities. He had organized the first general election based on adult universal suffrage and formulated a five-year plan and civil code. Trade had been encouraged and private businesses had thrived without any government obstruction. Among her African neighbours, Ethiopia had gained a stature and influence hitherto unknown. This was demonstrated when in 1958 Addis Ababa was chosen as the headquarters of the United Nations Economic Commission for Africa and the Organization of African Unity in 1963. It was true there had been the abortive coup attempt a decade ago, but with relatively little bloodshed, the rebellion had been crushed. The Emperor had taken no retaliatory action and had overtly accepted the explanation of his son, Crown Prince Asfa Wossen, that he had only read the rebels' proclamation under duress. The students, however, had sided with the rebels and since that time, demonstrated each year with increasing vociferousness against his rule.

Evangelia sighed. She had grown old with the

Emperor. "This country will go to pieces if anything should happen to him," her voice trembled.

Lukas shook his head sadly, torn by his loyalty to the Emperor and the reality of the situation. "The majority feel as you do, Mother, but they are worried. At last week's interview he was very vague about his future plans, especially the fact that he didn't actually name the Crown Prince as his successor."

"Well, nothing's ever been said," Pavlos added, "but the stigma of the 1960 coup attempt is still very much on people's minds, despite the fact that he would have been executed with all the ministers, if he hadn't gone along with them."

"Let's change the subject," Lukas said. "We've been exposed to the same old fears and rumors for years now. It's getting tedious."

Manoli sat quietly listening to his sons argue. Looking up he decided to have the final word. "There has always been tension before every major celebration," he said calmly. "But, after the excitement is over, everyone will settle down. No," he smiled, "there's still a great future in this country. Not only for you," he looked from one son to the other, "but for my grandchildren... and even my great grandchildren!" Manoli looked down at the pocket watch in his hand, remembering the past. "It wasn't easy starting from scratch after the fire..." his voice quivered, "but with sweat and toil, we managed."

Sensing his father's tension, Lukas quickly switched to another topic. "You'll be happy to know, *Papouli*," he said, using the affectionate title of 'grand-daddy' the younger generation had given him, "that the circulations of 'Time' and 'Newsweek' have now reached 3,000 copies a week, an all-time record!"

Manoli's eyebrows rose with delight. "Now, that's what I like to hear!"

As the discussion had ended on a cheerful note, I decided it wasn't the opportune moment to mention what I had witnessed at the Haile Selassie University that morning. The offices of the United Nations were situated within the campus and my office overlooked the students' meeting ground. A large group of scholars had gathered on the lawn attentively listening to the President of their Union. From the sound of his voice, it was obvious that he was highly strung and was losing his voice from the emotional statement he was making. Curiously, I opened my window to a thunderous uproar of cheering and clapping, the students going wild with excitement. I was shocked at what I was hearing. The Emperor was their target. They were making abusive remarks about his age and his state of mind. After what I was witnessing, it was difficult to dismiss the talk of unrest as mere rumors. There was definitely something brewing. Suddenly, half a dozen plainclothes policemen, who had obviously been tipped off and had mingled with the students, pushed their way through the crowd and onto the platform. There was a scuffle as they seized the leader and dragged him away, the students shouting and jeering.

Later, in the privacy of our bedroom, I related the whole incident to Lukas.

"My God!" he exclaimed. "No one abuses the Emperor and gets away with it." He sat on the edge of our bed his mind in turmoil. "Look," he said taking my hand, "I'm sure there's going to be trouble. I don't think you should go to the office tomorrow."

"There's nothing to worry about, Lukas," I comforted him. "The United Nations has nothing to do with the internal policies of the University. Apart from that, I have deadlines to meet."

"Now that we're on the subject," Lukas stood up, "I don't see why you have to continue working. We certainly don't need the money. Why don't you stay home?"

"And do what, Lukas?" I asked, kicking myself for introducing the subject. "Go to coffee parties, or join a card-playing group?" My voice rose in anger. "You know I need to do something more challenging than that. Come on, now. Don't let's go over all that again," I pleaded. Seeing his eyelids droop sadly, I softened my tone. "At least until we have a baby on the way." I was determined and Lukas knew it. He had come to accept that there was no shifting me when I was in one of my unyielding moods. He looked at me helplessly and sighed.

"Come here, you stubborn little mule," he said, beckoning me. He caught my hand and pulled me down onto the bed. "You know I'm only worried about your safety. It could get dangerous..." He kissed the end of my nose. "But why spoil a beautiful evening, arguing. We've got better things to do."

* * *

The following day, Lukas' prediction was rapidly fulfilled. The President of the Student Union was found dead, shot through the head, his body dumped outside the University compound. As I approached the gates of the University at Sidist Kilo, I wished I had listened to Lukas. A crowd of students had already gathered in front of the main block, all wearing black arm bands on their left sleeves. The meeting was peaceful enough. There was no shouting or waving of clenched fists. They were simply walking around waving banners bearing a photograph of the slain student, softly muttering *'lemin mote?'*—'why did he die?'

I pulled up at the main gates and waited for the guards to open them. They waved me back. "*Zig no*—It's closed," they shouted. Seeing my persistence, one of the guards came out from behind the gates and walked up to my car. "The University is closed, Madam. No classes. You'd better reverse and go back," he said politely.

"I'm not a professor," I told him in Amharic. "I work here with the United Nations."

"That's different," he said, taking a step towards the gate. Abruptly he stopped, his gaze shifting to a movement behind me. A row of military trucks, packed with helmeted riot police wielding batons and shields, were parked down the side of the campus, ready to move in if any trouble broke out. No wonder the demonstration was peaceful!

Sensing my anxiety, the guard came up to my window and whispered. "If trouble breaks out, run to the Kennedy Library. I'll help you leave the compound." I thanked him and drove up to the parking lot. As I got out of my car, I looked up at the fluttering face of the young leader who had lost his life. My heart leapt. I recognized him immediately. It was Tilahun Gizaw, youngest brother of Princess Sarah Gizaw, the Emperor's daughter-in-law!

As the day wore on, more students joined the demonstration. Wisely, no individual stood up and spoke. They just sat around, some of them smoking, taking it in turns to hold the banners. I was preparing to leave, when I heard a loud rumbling noise followed by a horrendous splintering crash and screams of fear. Dashing to the window, I saw panic-stricken students running in all

171

directions as half a dozen green army trucks roared into the compound. Their entry was without warning and, as far as I could see, unprovoked. The first had obviously driven straight through the university gates, smashing them to the ground. I watched in horror as the helmeted troopers jumped down from the trucks and chased the fleeing youngsters, thwacking them with their rifle butts and kicking them where they fell. Young girls crouched in foetal positions, trying to shield their heads from the rain of blows. Others, blood trickling from gashes, staggered about blindly, not knowing where to go.

"Mellina," I felt a hand on my arm. It was the girl from the next office. Her face was ashen. "Come," she said softly. "There's nothing we can do. Let's go."

I swallowed hard and nodded. There was nothing any of us could do.

The Emperor lighting the Meskel fire.

View of Addis Ababa just before the Revolution.
The Lion of Judah.

The Red Sea Hotel where Lukas and Mellina spent their honeymoon.

Dannekil tribesmen

Pilgrimage to St. Gabriel: a marker en route.

St. Gabriel's Church at Kulubi

Lalibella: faces of angels painted on the wall of the church.

An Ethiopian priest of the Orthodox Church.

A young priest bearing the brass Coptic cross during the Ethiopian Epiphany, 19th January.

Grinding grain for berbere and shouro.

The Awash River, where Lukas dived into the water to please the children.

An Ethiopian woman fills her water pot on the shores of the Awash River.

Inside St. Gabriel's Church: murals of Emperor Menelik

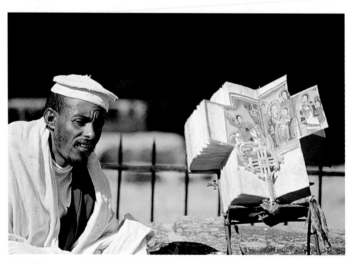

An Ethiopian priest with his bible.

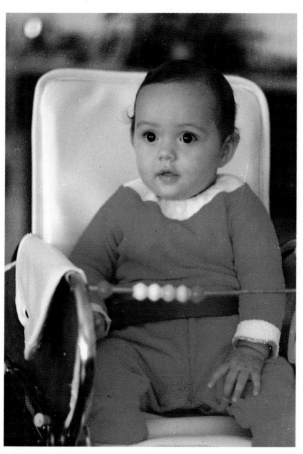

Gabby aged 5 months at Christmas 1977.

Sisters Mellina and Electra with, from left, Nickolas, Stavros, Takis and Gabby. Nairobi, Christmas 1981.

Gabby aged 4 years, hugs her father on Christmas Day in Nairobi 1981

Chapter Eighteen

In the middle of 1973, almost a year after the episode at Haile Selassie University, our office, with Peter Jones as our Chief of Mission, moved to the third floor of the Teacher Training College in Mexico Square. Since the death of Tilahun Gizaw, a number of other students had silently met the same fate and, as the first anniversary of Tilahun's murder approached, student groups throughout the city began staging memorial demonstrations. The Teacher Training College was no exception. Shortly before lunchtime, a few students gathered in the football field facing our office, lounging on the grass waiting to be joined by their class mates. It came as a total surprise when a group of army officers barged into all the classrooms, rounded up all the remaining students and marched them straight to the sports ground.

"Well, I'll be darned!" I heard Peter Jones exclaim. Rushing to his office, I found him looking out of his window. The entire student body was being held at gunpoint while an army officer using a loudhailer was preparing to address them. "Can you make out what he's saying?" Peter turned to me. The scenes from the previous year's university demonstration written indelibly on my brain, I shuddered as I began to translate the menacing message.

"You have been disrupting the peace of this country," the Colonel shouted. "If you," he said pointing from one student to the other, "have the time and energy to engage in demonstrations, then we are going to make damn sure that it is used effectively!" With that, he turned to the officer standing at attention behind him and gave him the signal to begin. Immediately, over a dozen soldiers moved in among the students dividing them into small groups and began enforcing a pre-arranged programme of the most strenuous gymnastics we had ever seen. Those who were slow to start were beaten with batons or kicked, some in the groin, others in the stomach, making them double up with pain.

"This is preposterous!" yelled Peter. "We've got to do something about it. Get me Harvey Williams on the phone immediately."

With trembling fingers, I dialled the number of the Resident Representative of the United Nations Development Programme and the designated official of all UN personnel in Ethiopia.

"Harvey," Peter shouted down the line, "army officers have marched into the college and are torturing our students. The bastards are beating them on the head and kicking them in the privates. Some have already collapsed from exhaustion. Isn't there anything we can do? This is totally inhuman!"

"I'll be right there, Peter," Harvey replied. "I'll see if I can reason with them, but you must understand that as long as UN personnel are not involved, we can't interfere."

"They weren't disrupting the peace," Peter protested. "This is sheer, bloody-minded persecution."

While Peter was talking on the phone, the soldiers had escalated the violence, for when we returned to the window, most of the students were lying on the ground, rolling about in agony with their legs drawn up, clutching themselves. From where we were, it was difficult to make out how severe their injuries were, but even from the third floor, we could clearly hear their groans. Just a few, their endurance reinforced by fear, were still on their feet, but they too looked on the verge of collapse.

"Mulunesh!" I ran to my colleague in the next office. "Quick, let's get some water! Some students are badly hurt."

In disbelief, Mulunesh starred at me. "You must be crazy," she warned me. "This is the army we're dealing with!"

"We can't just sit here and do nothing! I'm going down to plead with the colonel."

In the absence of buckets, we filled plastic wastepaper baskets with water and ran down the three flights of stairs. Outside, it was like a battlefield. Not a single student was standing.

Walking nervously up to the Colonel, I addressed him in Amharic. "Please Sir, would you permit us to offer a drink to the students?" I asked as politely as I could.

His head swivelled and his stern angular face stiffened as he regarded me with piercing eyes. "You think they deserve it?" he shouted, his voice hard and uncompromising. He began to beat his baton rhythmically in the palm of his hand. Alarmed by his attitude, I tried to control the quiver in my voice.

"I don't know what they're being punished for," I said

hesitantly. "Won't you allow us to help—purely on humanitarian grounds?" He studied me for a few seconds; then abruptly, almost dismissively, nodded his head. We rushed from one student to another, giving each one a little water to moisten their throats. Some had suffered serious head injuries. Blood was running into their eyes as they lay dazed and moaning. By the time Harvey Williams arrived, all the college professors and project personnel were following our example, and had come down to join us.

"My God!" I heard Harvey gasp as he walked towards the army colonel.

"Please, Mama, over here!" a weak voice called me from behind. I turned and saw a young man, blood gushing from a gash on his head. I began to feel nauseous and slightly dizzy at the sight, but shook my head vigorously to dispel the feeling. Taking a handkerchief from my pocket, I tried to stem the flow, but it was useless. A vein on his head had been severed. Within seconds my handkerchief was soaked and the blood began spilling into my hands.

"Help," I yelled. "This boy is bleeding to death!"

Leaving the ones with less serious problems, Dr. Lubani, the science lecturer, hurried over. He took one look and turned to Harvey Williams. "This boy needs emergency treatment. We've got to get him to hospital."

At Harvey's insistence, the colonel allowed Dr. Lubani to bring his car round. We lifted the boy into the back and raced off. The Police Hospital was only round the corner from the college—a mere three minutes away. "Hurry, Dr. Lubani," I screamed in a panic. "I think he's fainted."

The doctor from the casualty department rushed out and helped us put the student on a stretcher. Before they had a chance to wheel him to the operating theater, the doctor stopped and sadly shook his head. "I'm sorry," he said, gravely. "There's nothing we can do. He's dead."

* * *

Creeping panic began to grip the civilian population as rumours of unpublicized occurrences involving the army and dissidents became apparent. For the first time, Greek acquaintances began talking openly about running down their businesses and seeking ways of sending money to Greece. Foreigners employed by international firms started packing their belongings and shipping them abroad. The country was in an even greater state of unrest when Crown Prince Asfa Wossen had a stroke and, semi-paralysed, had been flown to London for treatment. The succession question was now an open book.

As September approached, bringing with it long-awaited sunshine and sporadic showers, people began once more to prepare themselves for the celebrations of Meskel—the Finding of the True Cross. As it always happened in the rainy season, the heavy storms of the previous three months had left the tarmac roads in a state of total disrepair, their surfaces pitted with huge potholes and the edges crumbling away. Everywhere repair gangs were disrupting the flow of traffic, as they performed cosmetic surgery on the highways, especially on the route that the Emperor would take from the Jubilee Palace to Meskel Square. On that particular stretch, the repairs continued around the clock in an effort to meet the deadline.

As dawn broke over the city on 27 September, a rough cross, shaped from twigs, could be seen high above the

177

houses outlined against the pink sky. It protruded from the top of the Meskel bonfire. Below, in the square, women were busily scattering freshly-cut meskel daisies. They would eventually carpet the ground where the Emperor would walk to perform the customary task of lighting the holy fire. Offices closed early on the eve of Meskel to allow the public time to assemble. Others were anxious to take advantage of the long weekend and drive down to the lake region.

"Will you be going to Langano?" Mulunesh asked as we hurried to finish the morning's work.

"Not this time," I replied. "Lukas wants to photograph this year's celebrations, so I've decided to play donkey and help him carry his equipment," I laughed. "I'd better hurry though," I said looking at my watch, "he'll be picking me up in a few minutes."

I had barely finished my sentence when Lukas walked in. With no time to lose we drove straight to Meskel Square. The Emperor was scheduled to arrive at four o'clock, and Lukas was in a hurry to find a good spot to position his tripod. We parked our car in Africa Hall, as the headquarters of the United Nations Economic Commission for Africa was popularly known, and took the stairs in front of the main rotunda out to the main road. The splendour of the Jubilee Palace, on the opposite side of the road, momentarily caught our attention and we paused to admire it. The park was at its best. Stands of jacaranda in full bloom, their mauve flowers hanging like grapes, rose among dark green conifers, brilliant red and purple hibiscus and the delicate ash-yellow mimosa. Framing velvet green lawns, a myriad rose bushes threw out splashes of pink, lemon and deep red. Like a jewel in this luxuriant setting, the light, sand-colored walls of the palace dazzled the onlooker. Lounging lazily on the front steps, half a dozen cheetahs, their heads immobile and proud, stared inscrutably into space.

"What a magnificent view of the Palace we have from here," cried Lukas, taking out his camera and focusing the lens. Along the driveway, a row of maroon Mercedes carrying the Emperor's entourage, were parked one behind the other, while in front of the Palace's main entrance a gleaming white Mercedes awaited its Imperial passenger. The Imperial Bodyguards, dressed in olive-green trousers, crimson coats with lion-hair epaulettes and white helmets, their rifles on their shoulders, stood motionless at full attention.

"We'd better hurry," Lukas took my arm and led me down the remaining stairs. We walked towards the main square and looked around for a suitable position. The courtyard around Saint Stephanos Church was already crowded when we arrived. Some, while waiting for the religious procession to start, were literally throwing themselves upon the heavy doors of the church, murmuring their secret prayers. It was a strange and moving sight for anyone unused to seeing people pray with such ardent belief and dedication. Standing beside us was a young Ethiopian woman with a baby strapped firmly to her back in a leather holster. It was decorated with sea shells hanging from tassels, which rattled as she rocked from side to side, keeping the baby quiet. When she saw Lukas take out his camera, she smiled at him shyly.

"Would you like your photograph taken?" I asked, reading the look in her eyes. She lowered her large, brown eyes and feeling a little embarrassed she took the corner of the *shamma* she was wearing and drew it across her mouth. She was ashamed she had betrayed her feelings. Before she had time to answer, the siren of a police car alerted us that the Imperial motorcade was approaching. A few seconds later, the Emperor's Mercedes flying the tricoloured flag and red pennant of Ethiopia glided past, flanked on all sides by protective outriders and followed by the escorting fleet of Mercedes. Everyone stood still, bowing their heads low as the Emperor passed. The motorcade came to a halt and a posse of bodyguards leapt out and rushed to open the door for the Emperor. There to greet him were members of the royal family, a group of ministers and the clergy. Dressed in flowing gold ceremonial robes, *Abuna* Theophilos, head of the Coptic Orthodox Church, stepped forward, holding before him an exquisitely-carved gold cross. The Emperor removed his bejewelled helmet and bowing his head, touched the offered cross three times with his forehead. He then bowed and kissed both the cross and the Patriarch's hand. The church leader stepped back and with slow, measured steps the Emperor, followed by his entourage, walked towards a platform carpeted with crimson Persian rugs. After he had mounted and seated himself in the red leather Imperial chair brought specially from the Palace, his retinue settled themselves behind him.

"His pace has slowed down considerably since last year," we heard someone from behind us comment. The same thought was probably passing through everyone's mind as they witnessed the Emperor's snail-like progress, but few would have dared to voice their thoughts. Many turned their heads, eyebrows raised, to see who had been so audacious. A wiser companion, standing next to him, tried to ease the situation.

"Oh! He's probably got a touch of arthritis—nothing

more. Haile Selassie is a strong man."

"We've got to face it," said another bystander, shaking his head sadly, "he's not getting any younger and he won't live forever."

This exchange was cut short by the cheers and applause which greeted the approaching parade. It was led by youths attired in white national dress holding lighted torches aloft, followed by a band of young women, clapping their hands and swaying rhythmically as they sang hymns rejoicing the discovery of the true cross and the blooming of the Meskel daisy. Their traditional white Ethiopian dresses, overlaid with finely-woven *shammas* embellished with gold embroidery, sparkled in the sunlight. After them came the tribal chieftains, bearded warriors magnificent in dark blue velvet mantles, richly embroidered with silk and gold threads, with leopard skins draped over their shoulders and lion's mane headdresses waving in the wind. They chanted ancient ballads as they passed, while riders galloping alongside accompanied them with high 'looloo' ululations, generating more applause from the excited crowds.

The sun was beginning to sink behind the city's western hills and its fiery rays set the grey clouds ablaze, creating glowing streaks of orange and crimson across the horizon. The dying light cast a warm glow on the faces of both nobility and masses as they waited for the ceremonial lighting of the bonfire.

"Just look at that sunset, Lukas," I cried. "What a wonderful moment. Can't you catch it with your camera?" I breathed deeply, feeling my breast swell with excitement as I gazed at the spectacular scene before us. My euphoria was short-lived.

"The devil's at work," a trembling voice cried from the

181

crowd. I turned to see a frail old man shakily pointing a wrinkled, sun-scorched arm at the flaming sky. His hollow cheeks and dark, sunken eyes were full of sadness. "Evil forces will bleed our sons to death…" His voice trailed off.

I shuddered. "Do Ethiopians believe in such omens?" I said, turning back to Lukas.

"Mm. What?" said Lukas, busy fiddling with his lens.

"That old man. Didn't you hear what he said?" I repeated the old man's words.

"Come on, Mellina. Don't be absurd. There are blood red sunsets every day. So this one is more spectacular than most. Don't start worrying about an old man's superstitions. Look, the Emperor's getting up. He's going to light the fire. Hold my tripod steady for me, will you, Sweetheart?"

The Emperor walked slowly towards the bonfire. Taking a burning torch from the hands of one of the priests, he bent down and ignited some of the dry twigs at the base of the mountainous stack. All eyes were focused on the Emperor and the tiny, dancing flame. He stepped back and within seconds the fire was crackling and spitting like an inferno as flames shot twenty feet into the air, enveloping and consuming the cross. Faces glowing with excitement, many waited anxiously for the heat to recede so that they could light their own torches and carry the holy flame home. Soon, the whole city would be alight with leaping bonfires. Others watched with more deep-rooted concern to see which way the cross-shaped apex of the bonfire would fall, for they believed it was a sign which could govern their future. If it toppled to the right, then the coming year would be fruitful and prosperous, but if it fell to the left, drought and hardship would ensue.

The cross crumbled and slid. From where we stood, there was no doubt about its direction. The crowd gasped.

"I told you the signs weren't good!" shrieked the old man, standing up and supporting himself on a walking stick. "Well, how do you interpret them?" he demanded of other bystanders, who were covering their mouths with their *shammas* and shaking their heads sadly. "I'm warning you," he said, his voice rising, "before this year is ended, we shall face hunger and bloodshed. The days ahead will be hard and full of sorrow. May the Almighty God have pity on us!"

A shiver ran down my spine. Could the old man be right? The rains had already failed in the northern regions of Wollo and Tigre. Another year of drought would be disastrous.

Chapter Nineteen

Christmas had always been a special occasion for the Fanouris family, a great reunion of the entire clan. 1973 marked a break in the ritual with half of the family scattered in different parts of the world. Pavlos' family were on the Island of Rodos, where his wife, Venetia, had decided to stay with her four children while they pursued further studies. Kostas, his wife, Lina, and their two boys had only recently moved to Saudi Arabia to a business opportunity they could not turn down. Sophie, Lukas' twin sister, had also left the country. Married with two children, she was happily settled in Athens, helping her husband with a new career.

It was the first week in December and Evangelia was already preparing her almond and walnut delicacies. Completely absorbed in measuring out her ingredients, sieving her flour and cinnamon, washing and drying her nuts, she tried her best to hide her feelings. A rogue tear trickling down her cheek was quickly wiped away with the corner of her apron as she heard her eldest daughter, Angeliki, come in.

"Morning, mother," Angeliki greeted her, walking up and giving her a kiss. "What's this?" she asked, feeling the dampness on her cheek."

"This will be the first time, since we came to Ethiopia, that the family isn't complete," she sniffed.

"I know," Angeliki patted her mother on the back. "Be thankful we're still around."

"Don't tell me you're also thinking of moving?" Evangelia asked anxiously.

"I know Philip," Angeliki said referring to her husband, "is worried about the future of this country and if trade is curbed, we'll be left with little choice." Quickly she picked up some dough and started rolling it out. Although she dismissed the issue in front of her mother, Angeliki knew she could not brush away her fears lightly. She had a five-year old toddler to think about. Only that morning, her husband had told her of the growing difficulties he was experiencing in trying to export coffee, skins and hides. The Coffee Board itself was having problems. What with the union unrest, the failing rains in the north and rumors of famine, allegations of corruption in the government and the rising food prices, he was seriously thinking of making a life elsewhere. She glanced sadly at her mother as she paused to push back a few wispy grey hairs falling over her face.

* * *

Enticing aromas of freshly-roasted turkey wafted through the room as Evangelia placed the steaming bird in the center of the table. Surrounding it were golden baked potatoes in garlic and oregano, cheese pies with thin strudel leaves and a traditional Greek salad with red tomatoes, green peppers, feta cheese and black olives, tossed together with olive oil. Everyone took their places, the children giggling with excitement as they eyed the mountain of presents under the Christmas tree.

"A toast," Manoli raised his wine glass and looked around the table at the diminishing members of his family. "To absent loved ones," his voice cracked, "health and happiness to us all, and may 1974 bring us peace and tranquility."

We all drank to that.

* * *

"The new year seems to be getting off to a bad start," Manoli looked up from reading his newspaper. "Soldiers at a small garrison in Neghelle Borana have mutinied against their commanding officers. Do you know anything about it?" he asked Lukas, handing him the paper.

Lukas skimmed through the article. "Apparently there's a shortage of drinking water and they claim the food is unfit for human consumption," he replied. "It says here they seized the Emperor's personal envoy—Lt. General Deresse Dubale—and forced him to eat their food and drink their water."

Manoli shook his head. "They'll be severely punished for that. The Emperor will never stand for any trouble in the army. He'll have to take disciplinary measures against the mutineers."

Not only Manoli, but the whole nation was under the same impression. It was, therefore, a shock to everyone when, against the advice of his counsellors, the Emperor decided not to punish the rebel soldiers. The outcome of the Emperor's leniency came a few weeks later, on February 10, when technicians at the Debre Zeit Air Force base revolted, demanding increased pay and better living conditions. This was followed by yet another uprising by the army's Second Division in Asmara, after which a wave of strikes and mutinies broke out all over the country. The government of Aklilu Habte Wold, prime minister since 1961, promptly resigned, and the Emperor appointed a new prime minister, Lij Endalkatchew Makonnen with a mandate to carry out reforms.

Endalkatchew was a youngish man, who, like several of his colleagues, had been educated at Oxford and his government augured well for the future. But, behind the scenes, the Dergue, a committee of young army officers who had instigated the mutinies, were manoeuvreing to seize power. Endalkatchew had barely settled into office when the Dergue arrested him and replaced him with Mikael Imru, the liberal-minded son of the Emperor's kinsman and war hero, Ras Imru.

"What is going on?" I asked Lukas one evening, when I arrived at the bookstore to pick him up.

"It's difficult to say," he replied, locking up the shop. "So far the army is proclaiming unswerving loyalty to the Emperor, but God only knows what's brewing."

I climbed into the car, slamming the door shut. "Don't you think it's time your parents moved to Greece?" I asked. "This uncertainty is bad for them."

"They've got no property or wealth to go to," Lukas said sadly. "This is home. All their worldly possessions are here. Father insists it's just a storm that will blow over."

Lukas was silent during the journey home. He obviously knew more about the situation than he was revealing and I could see that he was worried about how events might affect us all. The guard opened the gate and we drove in. Manoli and Evangelia lived in a modern, five-bedroomed villa with wide, shady verandas and a large kitchen. Each bedroom had its own bathroom and a balcony overlooking the garden, which was always a riot of colour. I stopped to admire some new roses in bloom when Evangelia came out to call us.

"Hurry!" she cried. "Don't miss the news. There's trouble again at the University."

We found Manoli seated in front of the TV set, engrossed in the news item. "I think it's serious this time," he said. "They've got the high school teachers and university professors behind them. They're rejecting the proposed reform of the education system. Who knows what this will trigger off?"

Within a few days, Manoli's query was answered with yet another wave of strikes, demonstrations and violence. Buses and cars were stoned in the streets of the capital. The police opened fire on the students. Teachers went on strike for higher pay and in protest over the proposed reforms. Taxis and *seicentos* were brought to a standstill over an increase of fifty per cent in the price of gasoline. Overnight, the country was in chaos.

* * *

During the weeks that followed, the daily news bulletins were full of the escalating discontent and violence. As the reports became more and more biassed towards the masses and increasingly critical of the Emperor, it became apparent that a creeping coup was taking place. Although the army had openly pledged its loyalty to Haile Selassie, it was obvious that the military was in control of both the radio and television stations.

News of the Emperor was no longer the first item on the bulletins and the people relied increasingly on the BBC's World Service to find out what was happening in their own country. Gradually, most of the Emperor's former ministers were placed under arrest. The Dergue then began to move against leading aristocrats and other significant political figures. During the month of August, a series of stripping operations were carried out, pruning the Imperial institutions one by one, leaving the Emperor powerless and isolated. Finally, mobs began demanding that the Emperor be hanged.

On the night of 11 September 1974, people throughout Addis gathered round television sets in bars and restaurants to watch a widely-advertised film entitled "The Hidden Famine" produced by a British journalist, Jonathan Dimbleby. The film had been shot the previous year in the northern regions of Wollo and Tigre, but had been banned until then. Apart from the reports carried by the Ethiopian press on the failure of the rains and the growing drought in the north, all else was rumour and conjecture. It was only as they watched the film that Ethiopians learned with horror the full extent of the catastrophe which had hit their country.

The effect of the film was devastating. We sat in our living room and cried as we saw children with sunken cheeks and large, protruding eyes staring listlessly into space, their arms lacking the strength to swat the flies swarming over their tear-stained faces. Their matchstick legs wobbled uncontrollably, too weak to support their swollen stomachs as desperate mothers forced them to stand to reveal their disfigured bodies to the cameras. Searching mouths suckled hopelessly at drained, sagging breasts. Dehydration was claiming thousands of lives daily. Corpses, wrapped only in thin *shammas*, were being buried in mass graves, a couple of crossed twigs tied together with a dirty rag the sole signs of a Christian burial.

"It's inconceivable that the Government didn't know about this," cried Evangelia, wiping her bloodshot eyes. I put my arms round her shoulders.

"I don't know what to believe," I said, the tears blurring my vision.

Scenes of the Emperor and members of the royal family eating caviar, drinking champagne and feeding prime beef to their dogs from silver platters peppered the film. Flashing from fathers burying their children in unmarked desert graves, the cameras cut to palace staff pointing out the pre-selected plot in the palace grounds reserved for Lulu, the royal chihuahua.

It was said later that the Emperor had been forced to watch the film as it was televised to the nation. Reportedly he broke down sobbing in anguish. The film left us all confused. Had the old ruler been aware of his people's suffering and ignored it or had his ministers and advisers kept him in the dark? It was so unlike the caring image he had always projected. Until recently, it had been one of his habitual practices to visit poor neighborhoods in the capital and throw money to the destitute. His car was often intercepted by desperate people seeking the Emperor's personal intervention to settle disputes and dispense justice. They were never turned away.

Neither Lukas nor I slept that night, unable to rid ourselves of the nightmare images of those dying children. Drenched in cold sweat, Lukas eventually flung back the covers and swung round to sit on the edge of the bed. He wiped his forehead.

"I just can't get that film out of my mind. I keep seeing hundreds of children, just looking at me with big, mournful eyes, their hands stretched out, begging for food. I feel guilty going to bed with a full stomach, knowing that those kids have probably all died by now from hunger."

I nodded. Yearning for a child of my own, I couldn't bear to think of all those children starving to death a mere hundred miles from our door. Outside, hundreds of dogs yelped and howled. It was a nightly occurrence to which we had become accustomed, but tonight it seemed more intense. It was as if they were echoing the wail of the mothers of Wollo.

It was not yet dawn, but neither of us felt like sleeping. I put on my dressing gown and went to the kitchen to make some coffee. Lukas followed and while the percolator spat and bubbled, we gazed out over Addis from our balcony. Nothing stirred. The city was silent. Even the baying of the dogs had ceased.

"Everything's so quiet, it's almost frightening," I shuddered. Turning away, I went inside to pour the coffee.

"Come and see the sunrise behind the mountains," Lukas called me back. He knew I loved to see the warm spray of colour dispelling the black night. He slipped his arm round my waist and we stood watching the street lights fade as the sun's glowing rays gradually lit up the sky. I was raising the coffee cup to my lips when I heard, from the street below, the crackle of a radio being turned on. My arm froze. I stopped and listened to the dreaded military music we had come to hate and which always preceded a proclamation. Lukas jumped up and rushed to switch on our receiver. We waited with baited breath for the music to stop.

A deep, measured voice began:

"Considering that, although the people of Ethiopia look in good faith upon the Crown, which has persisted for a long period in Ethiopian history as a symbol of unity, Haile Selassie I, who has ruled this country for more than fifty years ever since he assumed power as Crown Prince, has not only left the country in its present crisis by abusing at various times the high and dignified authority conferred on him by the Ethiopian people but also, being over 82 years of age and due to the consequent physical and mental exhaustion, is no more able to shoulder the high responsibilities of leadership. It is hereby proclaimed that Haile Selassie I is hereby deposed as of today, September 12, 1974."

We looked at each other aghast.

"It was inevitable," Lukas muttered. "Let's pray there'll be no bloodshed."

Driving to work, traffic was alarmingly thin with few pedestrians on the road. Surprisingly, no military movement was apparent, not even the expected patrol cars assessing the public's initial reaction to the deposition. Some shops remained closed but bakeries, greengrocers and kiosks, who probably didn't have access to a radio, were rolling up their shutters to commence the day's work.

The staff at the United Nations were stunned by the news. Their compassion was not for the Emperor they had seen the previous night, feeding his pets while his people died, but for a ruler who had once had the respect of the world. I was astounded to learn that while Lukas and I were waiting for the sunrise, nine members of the royal family, including Princess Tenagne Work, the Emperor's eldest daughter, Princess Sarah Gizaw, his daughter-in-

192

law, and Princess Ijigayew, the Crown Prince's eldest daughter, had been arrested and imprisoned. They were apparently put in a dungeon-like cell, their heads shaved and ordered to share two mattresses between them.

When I arrived at Africa Hall for a meeting that morning, I found the seventh floor offices deserted.

"Where is everybody?" I asked a messenger in the corridor.

"They're out on the balconies," he replied. "There's a lot happening at the Palace."

A fleet of green army trucks had replaced the Mercedes which usually parked in front of the Palace. The cheetahs had disappeared; instead a group of soldiers lounged around on the marble steps, while others dashed in and out of the main entrance.

"They're bringing out His Majesty," someone yelled from the far end of the balcony overlooking the entrance to the Palace. Looking frail and exhausted, the Emperor appeared on the Palace steps. Slowly he was guided by two officers towards a small, blue Volkswagen. He paused, looking up for the last time at the Imperial flag, fluttering above the Palace. Then, dragging his feet, he climbed with difficulty into the cramped back seat of the Beetle. There were no guns or salutes. The gates opened and the car drove out. It was later reported that as he left his Palace, Haile Selassie turned to one of the officers and said, "If this revolution is for the good of the country, then I am in favour of the revolution."

The vehicle slowly moved in the direction of the Fourth Division Army Headquarters. A crowd of students who had lined the road began shouting 'leba, leba'. It was disclosed later that the Emperor stooped forward and asked the driver what were the people saying?

"They're shouting 'thief' Your Majesty," the chauffeur recounted.

Without hesitating, the Emperor replied, "What do you expect them to call you, when you have robbed them of a King!"

Already the meticulously dressed *Kibur Zebenia*—the Imperial Guards—had been replaced by soldiers. Tanks were posted outside the Palace's three main gates and the Imperial flag was lowered and folded.

The Emperor was eventually taken to Menelik's palace, where the Dergue had established its headquarters. There he was accommodated in a small hut. Little was heard of him until, eight months later, he underwent a prostate operation and, with the intention of humiliating him, was placed in a public hospital ward. The result, however, was that crowds of people came to visit him daily. It was possibly this evidence of his popularity which prompted Colonel Mengistu Haile Mariam, who had by then seized power, to go with two soldiers to the hut where he was confined and murder him. It was rumoured that Mengistu personally suffocated the Emperor with a pillow. When his death was announced, it was attributed to heart failure, but no doctor was given a chance to verify this. The Emperor's body was secretly removed and buried in an unknown grave.

It wasn't until years later that people, who were present at the hospital when the Emperor was operated, felt safe enough to relate the events and conversations that had taken place at the time. In one instance it was reported that Colonel Mengistu had asked the Emperor for his views on the changes that had taken place in Ethiopia. The Emperor had replied, "When the people of Ethiopia who have been indoctrinated and deceived by the words

194

of *Hebresebawinet* (Socialism) have fully understood the true meaning—they and only they will give you their views. Not you, not even Mussolini nor his compatriots ever managed to change or damage our history and heritage."

Immediately after the deposition, the Dergue set up a provisional military government which offered the crown to Asfa Wossen, who was still undergoing treatment in London. Concerned about his father's safety and possibly about his own, he refused to become involved. Instead, a popular soldier, Lt.-General Aman Andom became the head of state. For one whole year, law and order prevailed. The Government assured the nation that its main objective was equality. Businesses should continue operating as normal. Investments and capital would be safeguarded. After months of anxiety, people began to believe that things were genuinely turning for the better. Many had been arrested, but it had, without doubt, been a bloodless coup.

For the first time since Manoli opened his bookstore in the 1920s, newspapers could be sold without prior vetting by a government censor. Even the sale of 'Time' and 'Newsweek', which during that period carried some highly critical articles about Ethiopia, was permitted. An article in the 'International Herald Tribune' reported that the Minerva Bookstore in Addis Ababa, could, for the first time, put uncensored papers and magazines on their stand.

Unfortunately, freedom of the press was short lived as rumours began to grow of an internal power struggle within the Dergue. In early November of 1973 we heard that Mengistu, then just a leading member of the Dergue, had attacked Aman Andom's residence with tanks. In the fighting which followed, Andom had been killed. The nation mourned the loss of a hero, for it was Aman Andom, popularly known as the Lion of the Desert, who had led the Ethiopian troops to victory against the Somalis in the Ogaden war.

On 13 November 1974, the Dergue released the report of its findings on the Wollo famine. Eighty-seven people were indicted, including 26 members of the former cabinet and two former Wollo Province governors. News spread that formal trials were underway, but before any outcome was announced, the nation learned with shock that 57 of those arrested had been summarily shot at the Italian Prison near what is now the headquarters of the Organization of Africa Unity. They included ministers, high-ranking military officials, the Emperor's grandson, Iskinder Desta, who had greeted us so warmly at Princess Tsighe-Mariam's wedding, the former prime minister, Endalkatchew Makonnen, and Lukas' friend and mentor, *Ras* Asrate Kassa. They had all been found guilty of committing injustices against the Ethiopian people and branded as traitors. No one was permitted to claim the bodies and families were instructed to keep away from the execution ground.

Lukas and I deeply mourned the loss of *Ras* Asrate Kassa, a born leader and statesman and a memorable friend. We remembered the sad, faraway look in his eyes, when we were with him in Asmara. Perhaps, even then, he had a premonition of how things would end. Lukas clenched his fists, fighting the tears. "God damn them!" he shouted.

Overnight the city of Addis went into mourning. Women threw off their white dresses and colourful headscarves, replacing them with black funereal garb.

Sorrow was engraved on every face. The euphoria over the bloodless coup was shattered.

A new era of *Keyishibir*, Red Terror, began. Anyone opposing the new Government would be deemed a reactionary and would be executed, it was proclaimed. The enemies of the regime were to be wiped out, destroyed without mercy. Bodies began appearing in the streets—young and old, men, women and children, left sprawling in the gutters where they had been gunned down the previous night for their anti-revolutionary activities. Students were the main target: Amnesty International later estimated five thousand young people were put to death in a three-month period. Torture was commonplace. People were burned in oil; toe and finger nails were ripped out; suspects were beaten and suspended by wires; women and girls were raped. To add insult to injury, bullet money had to be paid to reclaim bodies.

On 20th December, the monarchy was abolished and Ethiopia was declared a socialist state. On 1st January 1975, the first nationalization of banks and insurance companies took place. Within two months more than a hundred private companies had been nationalised or partially taken over. It was proclaimed that owners and shareholders would be compensated, but what would happen to foreign investment? Many foreign nationals who were out of the country on business chose not to return. It was the beginning of the exodus.

With the number of executions increasing daily, freedom of the press didn't last for long. Foreign journals carrying articles describing the summary executions of the 57 officials and the subsequent reign of terror were confiscated and burned. Democracy was at an end. A curfew was imposed from dawn to dusk. Sounds of gunfire filled the dark hours of the night, instilling an all-pervading fear never before experienced.

Urban neighbourhood associations known as *kebeles* were imposed, which asserted Marxist authority over local affairs. They were run by young, inexperienced militia, who were given guns they didn't know how to use. Food was scarce and the *kebeles* tried to organize co-operatives for the distribution of what little grain and sugar was to be found. The curbs on freedom of expression, coupled with the immediate banning of all demonstrations, began to turn the students and other left-wing intellectuals against the increasingly hardline Communist Dergue. Throughout the revolution they had supported the ideals of equality and democracy, but now faced with the increasing authoritarianism of Mengistu's Government, there were rumblings of dissent. The Dergue soon nipped them in the bud. As students prepared to return to university in September 1975, the Dergue announced that the universities and the last two years of high school would not re-open. Instead, students would be sent out into the countryside to work with the peasantry and teach them about Ethiopian socialism. All rural land was nationalized and sixty thousand teachers and students were mobilized for the *Zemecha*— Development through Co-operation—campaign, designed to fight illiteracy, organize peasant associations and determine how land reform should be implemented.

The students' response was hostile, but after it was announced that those who refused to participate would be unable to continue their studies and would be prevented from getting jobs, they had to yield. Anyone who publicly voiced his opposition to the *Zemecha* met the fate of those who had gone before: they were either arrested or shot. Our heart went out to the suffering masses who were being subjected to incomprehensible conditions, but it wasn't until incidents started affecting the lives of people close to us that the full extent of the predicament was perceived.

On one occasion, an anguished cry coming from the street below, made me drop the flowers I was arranging and run outside. I was instantly joined by Askala who had come to visit me.

"*Sile Mariam, Sile Gabriel,*" we heard a young woman screech in desperate supplication. From where we were standing I could not clearly identify who was kneeling at the feet of the army officer begging for mercy.

"It's Almaz, *Ras* Teffera's daughter," Askala nudged me. "It's not enough they've imprisoned her father, turned their home into a *kebele*, confiscated all their property: now they're taking *Ato* Tewolde away, leaving poor Almaz to care for five infants." Her voice shook with anger. "She's got no job to turn to. What is she expected to do to support her children—turn into a *sharmouta*?" She spat out the Amharic for prostitute.

By the time we reached Almaz the truck carrying her husband had already left. We found Almaz crying and beating her fists on the rough tarmac. In her hysteria, she was clawing at her face and hair. We lifted her from the ground, drawing her hands away from her face before she did herself real harm. She looked at us wildly, her eyes glazed. People were looking at her from a distance, indifferent at what they were witnessing. The sight upset me. The Ethiopians I had known had always been warm, compassionate people, eager to help anyone in distress. What was happening to them?

"Do you blame them?" Askala was quick to reply. "There's bound to be a spy among the crowd, ready to report any sympathizers. Everyone fears for their own life these days," she said, helping me lead Almaz away from the street towards the back of the house. "But," she continued, "I'm too old to care and I'll call them cowards to their faces! If anyone dares, let them arrest me for expressing my natural Ethiopian instincts. I'll spit in their faces!"

The main house had been confiscated, but the family of seven had been permitted to occupy the two-roomed servants quarters at the bottom of the garden.

"I'm sure *Ato* Tewolde will be back soon," I tried to comfort her, but I knew in my heart it was stupid to use words that had no meaning.

"Be back?" she echoed my words. "Someone who is unfortunate enough to be the son-in-law of an imprisoned ex-cabinet minister. Not likely!" she said bitterly. The hopeless reality of her situation suddenly began to dawn on her. She had some money hidden away, but no job to turn to and five mouths to feed. "What am I going to do?" she wept.

I thought for a moment, wracking my brains. Then I remembered a vacancy I had seen advertised on the notice board at work and promised to get her the details. I knew she had a degree in Economics from the University of Cambridge and could be well qualified for the job.

"Please," she begged. "I'll do anything—even clean toilets to feed my kids!"

"I do hope you can do something to help her," Askala gripped my hand affectionately as we left Almaz and made our way home.

"Keep your fingers crossed that the position is still

vacant," I replied skeptically.

When Lukas came home that evening, I told him about the arrest. He listened sadly. "We had a similar incident at the bookstore today." Lukas' eyes were filled with pity. "One of our best customers, a highly educated, courteous gentleman, *Ato* Yohannes has been arrested and interrogated by the Dergue about some publications they've found in his possession. Unless proof is produced of where he purchased them from, he's in deep trouble."

In a desperate effort to help him, his brother, *Ato* Gebre, had appealed to Lukas to search for copies of receipts issued.

"When were the books purchased?" I asked.

"That's my biggest problem," Lukas looked crushed. "It could be as far back as ten to twelve years! "But," he perked up a little, "knowing Father and his obsession with keeping even the most insignificant piece of paper, there might be a chance of finding them."

The following afternoon both Lukas and I were successful in what we had promised to do. I came home with an application form for Almaz. She had an appointment for an interview the next day. They had not been lucky in finding any suitable candidates and were looking for someone with Almaz' qualifications. Within a week she was already feeling comfortable in her new job, but the fate of her husband remained in the balance.

Lukas had, miraculously, managed to find the 12-year-old receipts which would save *Ato* Johannes' life. His brother, *Ato* Gebre was overwhelmed with gratitude and promised to let him know the outcome of the trial, but no one knew how long that would take. Even under Haile Selassie, prosecutions normally ran into years. It was not unknown for them to run from one generation to the next, while the detainees rotted in dank prison cells. There was little reason to believe that military tribunals would be any different, if—in fact—they took place at all.

* * *

Tightening of press censorship began to undermine the bookstore. As more and more newspapers and periodicals were banned, its income started to decline at an alarming rate.

"The Government can't afford to keep everyone in the dark for ever," Pavlos tried to reassure Manoli. "Sooner or later they'll realize it's not worth burning every publication that mentions Ethiopia in a three-line caption. People will simply start looking around for different ways of being kept informed with what's happening in the country. There are enough foreign correspondents around to do that."

Manoli frowned. He had devoted his whole life to building up his business. He had worked hard, struggled and suffered hardships and deprivations in a strange land, and now it was all crumbling round his ears. He sat down, his shoulders hunched.

"You mustn't worry," Lukas patted his father on the back, "until the situation stabilizes, I shall help you meet the bookstore's expenses from my Zwai project."

Manoli looked up. "Now that you mention it, how are you getting along with that venture of yours?"

After Lukas had opted for Ethiopian citizenship in 1971, he had, together with *Dedjazmach* Beyene's son, Merid, bought several thousand acres of undeveloped, but fertile, land next to the Zwai river. When tractors and sophisticated machinery were brought to the land, there was great excitement among the farmers in the area. For generations, they had used oxen to till the soil and depended on rainfall to guarantee them a decent crop. They were fascinated by the machines which churned up the soil and poured hundreds of gallons of water on the land in a matter of minutes.

"The soil is perfect for maize and beans," the old farmers had advised Lukas. Then they struck a bargain with him: they would plant his seeds for him if he, in turn, would till and irrigate their adjoining farms. Both sides gained from the deal. At the end of the first year, the peasants were not only feeding their families but were earning good money from their harvest. After the enormous losses and privations they had suffered in the past due to drought, they were overjoyed.

Lukas, too, had done well. His beans were exported to the United States and the profits were good. Manoli clapped his son on the back. "You know I was against this project, but you appear to have made a remarkable success of it," he said proudly. "Thank you for your offer."

* * *

It was an offer which the founder of the Minerva bookstore had to take up sooner than he thought. At the insistence of the Dergue, only the works of Marx, Lenin and Engels were to be imported for sale. All orders of books and journals from the West were stopped. The business began to flounder.

"I can't see the point of ordering socialist books from Moscow and paying for them in foreign exchange, when the government is distributing exactly the same books free of charge on every street corner," an irate Pavlos shouted one morning.

Lukas sighed. He knew the day was approaching when they would have to close the store. There was enough stock to keep it going for a while longer, but now that supplies from Britain and the United States were terminated, they had no choice.

* * *

"Etiopia Tikdem"—"Ethiopia First"—the proclamation began, preceded by the now most dreaded military signature tune.

I jumped out of the shower, wrapped a towel around myself and, with dripping feet, hurried to the sitting room. I found Lukas, sitting in front of the radio, his eyebrows pinched together, listening intently to the announcement.

"But in September 1974 the Dergue issued statements guaranteeing the safety of foreign economic interests," he shouted, his face turning purple.

"What is it, Sweetheart?" I asked in a whisper, knowing it was bad news.

Jumping up from the chair, he paced up and down the room, waving his arms wildly. "We've lost everything. Fifty years of hard work now belongs to the Government. The bookstore is gone. The land and everything on it in Zwai is gone. Everything's been nationalized!"

He stopped, raising his hand for silence, as the radio announcer continued:

"This declaration on nationalization is the major and immediate economic goal of Ethiopia, and will eliminate poverty and exploitation. This can only be achieved when the Government, as the representative of the people and in the interest of the mass of Ethiopian workers directly owns and controls the natural resources and key industrial, commercial and financial sectors of the country. However, owners and stockholders will be compensated."

"How will you break the news to your father?" I cried cupping my mouth.

Lukas slumped into an armchair. "I'm scared he'll get a heart attack!" he said resting his head in his hands. "I'll have to call Dr. Georgiadis." Straightening up, he walked over and picked up the telephone. "We'd better stop at the bank on the way and draw out as much cash, as we can," he said as he waited for the doctor to answer. "You never know what might happen tomorrow."

The receiver clicked and he began explaining the situation down the telephone. "We'll be able to handle it somehow," Lukas explained, "but it's the old man we're worried about. Thanks very much, Doctor, we'll join you as soon as we can."

The bank was congested. The proclamation had obviously caused a panic. Everyone was trying to get their money out. "I'm sorry, Mr. Fanouris," the cashier announced. "Your accounts were blocked last night. I'm afraid that until further notice we cannot accept your cheques."

"What do you mean?" yelled Lukas, ready to grab the cashier and drag him over the counter. "You nationalize our businesses. You block our accounts. How the hell do you think we're going to live?"

"Please, sir, for your own good," the cashier pleaded with Lukas, looking furtively from left to right for fear he would be overheard. "Keep your voice down. You don't know what these people can do to you. I'm just an employee here carrying out orders. I beg you, keep calm and don't arouse any attention."

I grabbed Lukas' arm and pulled him away. His face had turned a dark red and his eyes were bulging. I was terrified he might get a stroke. "Lukas, you've got to pull yourself together!" I gritted my teeth. "You'll kill yourself. Please calm down." I softened my voice and looked pleadingly into his eyes.

"Keep calm!" he shouted back. "Do you know what this means? We won't even have money for food, let alone anything else!" Nervously, he ran his fingers through his hair.

"They're probably checking everyone's financial statements," I said, trying to introduce a note of reason. "They can't leave people to starve, surely?"

"You might be right," his tone softened a little. "But, what happens if they don't?"

"Now, listen here," I said, fiercely. "You've always showered me with diamonds and gold, now it's my turn to stand by your side."

"But how do you think this makes me feel?" he asked, taking my hand. "Useless, completely and utterly useless!"

"We have other pressing business to attend to," I said gently pulling him up from where he was sitting. "We'll discuss your uselessness later," I forced a weak smile.

"There's little else we can do," he said getting up and walking towards the exit. "We'd better hurry, Dr. Georgiadis must be home by now."

The house was unusually quiet and from the absence of appetizing aromas from the kitchen, we knew immediately that the news had already reached Evangelia and Manoli.

Askala opened the front door, her eyes puffy from

206

crying. "They're in the sitting room," she announced softly, blowing her nose. "The doctor's already been and left. He's given your father an injection."

We hurried through and then paused in the doorway. The two of them were sitting on the sofa, Manoli's big arm cradling Evangelia as she rested her grey head on his chest. Each was wiping away the other's tears.

"What do we say to soften the blow?" Lukas turned and looked at me. Before I had a chance to respond, we overheard them talking.

"We've lost everything before and still managed to survive," Evangelia was saying.

"We're not young any more, Evangelia," we heard him reply.

"But we've got to be strong for our boys," she argued.

Peeping through the door, we saw Manoli press his cheek against the top of Evangelia's head. "You're right, Evangelia. You're always right. What would I have done without you all these years? Yes, we have to pull ourselves together and give them as much encouragement and spiritual guidance as we can. At our age, that's the only thing we can offer."

Silently, we took a few steps back and left the house. We couldn't let them know we had overheard their conversation. They were going to put on a brave show for their children and we couldn't spoil it for them.

Chapter Twenty

Months before Haile Selassie was deposed, the dungeons at Menelik Palace had begun filling up with political prisoners, sometimes as many as fifty or sixty to a cell. They were arrested on a variety of charges, ranging from suspicion of corruption and abusing their position in office to participating in the famine cover-up or simply being a threat to the military Government. Some ministers were seized in their offices without any formal charge. Stripped of any valuables, their heads shaven, they too disappeared into the depths of the Palace to await trials that never came.

Among these was the former Minister of the Interior, Mitiku Mellekot. He was a distinguished looking man, over six feet tall, who had just become a father for the third time. He was in the middle of distributing cigars and glasses of champagne to celebrate the birth of his son when soldiers burst into his office.

Protesting at the intrusion, the officer in charge screamed at him, "You have committed crimes against your country."

"What crimes?" demanded Mitiku.

"Don't be impertinent," yelled the officer, slapping him across the face. "You will be tried in due course and your transgressions will be made known to you."

Mitiku was hustled from the building and thrown into the waiting truck. That was the last his staff saw of him. Mitiku's sole crime was being related to the recently-executed former prime minister, Endalkachew Makonnen.

Abeba, Mitiku's wife worked for the United Nations Development Programme in Addis Ababa. When I was transferred from UNESCO to the UNDP in the early part of 1975, we became close friends. She was a tall, slim, beautiful young woman with distinctive Ethiopian features—large brown eyes, high cheek-bones, a slender neck and long, straight black hair resting on finely-shaped shoulders. Around her throat she always wore a Lalibella cross flanked by symbols of the Holy Spirit. Abeba had a good sense of humor and a warm human quality to her intelligence.

The couple had three children, all under five years of age. The news of her husband's arrest the day after she had given birth was traumatic, but at the end of her maternity leave she was back at work, aware that the burden of being the bread-winner was now hers.

Working in the same office, she used to confide her troubles. Her biggest worry concerned her four-year-old daughter, Workinesh, the little 'black beauty' of the family. She was an intelligent, sensitive child and was teased mercilessly by kids at school. The Government had a policy of indoctrination which began in the kindergarten. Children were persuaded to spy on their parents and report conversations they had overheard to the local *kebele*. If it was discovered that anti-government sentiments had been expressed, it was not unknown for the military to take their protege spies to their homes and shoot them in front of their parents as a warning.

Abeba had tried hard to hide the real reason for Mitiku's sudden disappearance, but Workinesh could not be fooled. Deeply implanted in her mind were the cruel words that she would never see her Daddy again.

"You mustn't take any notice of what children at school say, darling," Abeba would tell her, rocking the child in her arms. But no matter how much she tried to reassure her, Workinesh would not be comforted. She grew more and more melancholy.

I came into the office one morning to find Abeba gazing out of the window in the direction of Menelik Palace and I could see that her eyes were red from crying.

"It's Workinesh," she said. "Her father's absence is torturing her. She won't eat. She tosses and turns all night, screaming for him in her sleep."

"Would it help if you tried to take her to see him?" I suggested.

"The Dergue would never allow it," she said sadly. "No one has seen any of the prisoners." With a look of hopelessness, Abeba glanced once more in the direction of the Palace.

"Appeal to them," I persisted. "All they can say is 'no'. However inhuman the Dergue appears to be, someone's heart will melt when they see Workinesh."

She turned back and stared at me. "I'll give it a try," she said with a slight tinge of hope in her voice.

For once, the miraculous happened. Abeba found a sympathetic ear and she was granted permission for Workinesh to visit her father. The meeting took place through a barbed wire fence. No touching was allowed.

Mitiku was brought out by a guard, who stood a yard away watching every movement. He was haggard and unshaven. Still wearing the same suit he had been arrested in, he had tried to smooth out its creases to look presentable. Abeba looked at him lovingly yearning to touch him, to tell him how much she loved him, but the conditions of her meeting were made very clear to her before she entered. It was forbidden to show any emotion whatsoever.

Mitiku squatted until his face was across from Workinesh behind the wire. "You mustn't worry, Sweetheart," he told her. "I'm fine," he feigned a smile.

"I want you to take me in your arms, Daddy," she pleaded. "Don't you want to kiss me?" The child looked up at the stoney-faced guard.

"I live for the day when I can hold you in my arms...," his voice quivered. "But," he cleared his throat, "I'm saving all the kisses and cuddles till I come home." He stood up, gripping the fence with both hands. Abeba could see there were sores on his wrists. "There are no charges against me," he whispered excitedly to his wife. "There's talk the Dergue will be releasing some of us for the first anniversary of the revolution," he smiled. "Pray I'll be among them."

"That's enough!" The officer stepped up and pulled him away from the fence.

In the seven-line notes that the couple were permitted to exchange when food was delivered each day, Mitiku had purposely refrained from even hinting that a chance for a release existed. The notes were censored by the guards and it was virtually impossible to sneak in a coded message as this would be intercepted and the privilege immediately stopped. He took a big risk in talking to his wife, but this was the first time he had a chance to speak to her since his arrest ten months ago. Any punishment inflicted on him would have been worth it.

Workinesh waved until her father was out of sight. She was happy that he was still alive, but cried all the way home at having to leave him behind. By evening her eyes were so sore and swollen that she screamed every time she tried to open them. The next day they were even worse.

"I'm terribly concerned about Workinesh," Abeba told me when we met at the office. "Her eyes are in a terrible state and they're becoming very sensitive to light."

"You'd better have them checked," I advised.

Abeba took her little girl directly to an eye specialist, but the child's eyesight continued to deteriorate. Even after getting a second opinion, there was a controversy on the diagnosis: while one believed it was trachoma, the other was convinced it was an allergy.

"An allergy to what?" demanded the worried mother.

"It could be dust or pollen or even her own tears. I suggest you ensure the child doesn't cry," said one unsympathetic doctor.

"How do I stop a child from crying for her father?" Abeba sobbed. "Prescribe me something for that!"

"Madam, I am not a member of the Dergue," he shouted, growing angry. "Take your grievances to the right authorities. In the meantime, give the child this antihistamine and come back in a week." With that, he ushered her out of his surgery.

In desperation, Abeba picked up her daughter and went straight to the UN doctor. He took one look at the child's eyes and immediately recommended that she be evacuated to Nairobi for treatment. Due to the political situation, it was unthinkable for Abeba to leave Addis. They needed someone to escort the child. When Abeba put the question to me, I didn't hesitate.

Within a few hours the evacuation request was signed and approved. The next hurdle was getting an exit visa. To speed things up a Note Verbale from the United Nations stressing the urgency of the matter was hand delivered to the Ministry of Interior. Appointments were set up with eye specialists in Nairobi. We were all set to go.

On our way home the following day, Lukas and I dropped in at Abeba's house hoping for news on the exit visa. Elsa, the bouncy three-year-old, was playing with her baby brother, Wondu, in the living room.

"Where's Workinesh?" I asked.

"I'm here."

We found her hiding behind a heavy armchair. "What are you up to, little Chipmunk?" Lukas laughed as he poked his head round the chair to look at her.

"I'm hiding from the sun," she said, getting up and running into Lukas' waiting arms.

Lukas swung her in the air and was about to sit down with her in an armchair, when he felt the child stiffen, her sore eyes getting bloodshot from the tears. "That's my Daddy's chair," she wept.

"I'm so sorry, Sweetheart" Lukas tried to calm her. "No one will ever take your daddy's place, I promise," he said gently putting her down. "I tell you what," he attempted to distract her, "if you put your hand in my pocket, I think you might find there's something there for you."

Her small fingers fumbled and searched until she found the chocolates which Lukas had brought as a treat. Like soap and shampoo, chocolates were considered to be a luxury item and their importation was prohibited. These had come in a long-awaited parcel from my parents, which had arrived only that morning.

While the children were preoccupied with the chocolates, Abeba arrived home. There was no need for any explanations. Her weary, drained face spelled out the cruel decision she had been given. She collapsed on the sofa, her head buried in her hands. "They've refused the exit visa," she sobbed. "She's black listed as the child of a political detainee. Oh, my God," she screamed, hysterically.

Lukas and I were stunned. We stood in front of her motionless not able to utter a single word.

Hearing her mother scream, Workinesh was instantly at her side. She flung her tiny arms round her mother's neck. "Please, Mummy, don't cry," she pleaded. "Look, Mummy, look. I can open my eyes. See, they don't hurt!" The child forced her eyes to open. She turned to us. "I don't want my Mummy to cry."

I picked up that lovable, brave little soul and held her tightly in my arms, feeling my yearning for a child suddenly reawakening.

"Are you crying too, Mellina?" she said, putting her small hand up to feel my cheek and wiping away a tear which had escaped.

"Just a little, Poppet. It's catching, isn't it?"

"Yes," she giggled. "But you're too big to cry."

"I know, I should be ashamed of myself," I replied with a wan smile, "but, I don't have a daughter like you to cheer me up."

"I can be yours too—for a little while," she hastened to added not wanting to hurt her mother's feelings.

Little did we know that the developments of the following days would turn a little girl's moving assertion into reality.

* * *

214

The sun was glinting through the office windows, its rays illuminating the pile of work awaiting attention in my in-tray.

Before I had a chance to attend to any of the correspondence, I heard a heated argument taking place in the corridor. Bill Fielding, our administrative officer, was so loud that he was completely drowning the voices of the visitors.

"This is United Nations property and you have no right to take a single step inside these premises," he shouted. "I don't care what your orders are. We are protected under the Privileges and Immunities signed between your Government and the United Nations."

Before I could leave my seat, Abeba burst through the door and scrambled underneath my desk. "They've come to arrest me!" she screamed. "The Dergue is rounding up all the wives of political prisoners."

Only the previous day, at the height of the first anniversary celebrations, any aspirations she may have had of Mitiku's release were shattered. Not a single political detainee was granted amnesty. Now even her own safety was at stake.

I crouched under the desk, putting my arms around her. "Bill Fielding won't let them take you away," I comforted her. "He'll protect you."

Within a few minutes, our security guards had been positioned at the entrance of the UN offices, keeping at bay the intruding group of army officers. Meantime, Bill marched into the office of Harvey Williams, the Resident Representative.

"This is preposterous!" he shouted, closing the door behind him. "We can't have army personnel invading our premises, Harvey. We'd better make a strong protest right away!"

Harvey strode to the door. "Mellina, get me the Dergue headquarters immediately, will you?"

I quickly dialled the number and asked for General Teferi Benti, the newly-appointed chairman of the Committee. I was told he was out. I put my hand over the mouthpiece. "Would the vice-chairman do?" I asked Harvey, who was bending over my desk. He nodded and moved back to his office to take the call. Anxiously we all stood around, waiting for the verdict. Finally, the door opened and Harvey emerged. He patted Abeba on the shoulder.

"They hadn't realized you were employed by the United Nations. They regret the error," he said grimly.

We all breathed a sigh of relief. Bill Fielding marched off down the corridor to transmit the decision to the waiting officers. They shook their heads in disbelief. They had been given instructions to arrest Abeba and they had no intention of going back without her. One of them peered along the corridor and spotted Abeba hiding behind one of her colleagues. Furious, he shook his finger at her warning her in Amharic that sooner or later they would get her. Reluctantly, they left and walked towards the lift.

"Those ignorant idiots won't give up so easily," Bill turned to Abeba. "You'll be safe as long as you don't leave the premises. Get your family to send you some food and bedding and the couch in Harvey's office should be quite comfortable," he smiled kindly. "Until we have something in writing from the Dergue and this mess is sorted out, I wouldn't trust anyone."

"What about my children?" Abeba panicked. "They're all alone!"

216

"There's no problem," I assured her. "I'll take them home with me."

Abeba sank into a chair. "What would I do without you all?" she cried looking at all her friends around her. "Mellina," she gripped my hand, "make sure Workinesh doesn't worry about me. Elsa likes her juice without sugar. Wondu's milk..." The list of instructions was endless. When I left to pick up the children, I realized how right Bill Fielding had been. Outside the building, soldiers were guarding both the front and rear entrances, waiting for Abeba to make an appearance. I hurriedly drove off in the direction of her house.

Within a few hours our "showroom" apartment was transformed into a chaotic nursery with napkins, feeding bottles, toys and children everywhere. Our miniature brown dachshund, Jeannie, went mad with joy, dashing in circles from one child to the next.

"It's marvelous to see our home in a state of total disarray filled with children's babble and a dog who has gone berserk!" Lukas smiled, with a tinge of sadness.

That same evening our good friend, Mila, a Bulgarian pediatrician, dropped in for a drink and found us giving the children a bath.

"Hey!" she exclaimed in her guttural, east European accent. "Where did you get all these beautiful children?"

"It's a long story," I laughed, up to my elbows in soap suds. "We'll tell you later. But, in the meantime, we would love some expert advice on how to bath a baby."

Mila rolled up her sleeves and with experienced hands slipped her arm under Wondu's back, cradling his head and gripping his little fat arm with her hand. Once she was confident I could manage, Mila went to play with the two girls, tickling them until they screamed with laughter.

217

I noticed, though, that her eye was on Workinesh. "This child has a chronic eye infection," she said looking up at me.

I gave Mila the whole background history and the inconclusive diagnoses.

"I might not be an eye specialist, but I can spot a bad infection when I see one. This could cause serious damage if not treated immediately." Without another word, she ran to her apartment on the floor below and returned with some ointment, eye drops and a syringe.

"Mila!" I gasped when I saw the needle. "You'll have to speak to Abeba first!" I exclaimed.

Mila glared at me. "The child's eyes are in critical condition and we have to start medication right away! If this child had been brought to me earlier, I would have hospitalized her. Don't you see how much she is suffering?" She looked me squarely in the face. "I will take full responsibility. Now, hold her arm."

After the third day of treatment, there was a definite improvement. Workinesh's blood-shot eyes were now less painful and not so sensitive to light. Thanks to Mila, she was on the road to recovery.

Abeba's ordeal lasted five days. On the sixth, the Dergue sent a written notification that due to her status as a UN civil servant, she was exempt from arrest. It was stressed, however, that she should be available at any given time for questioning.

* * *

Barely a week after Abeba's affliction, another incident involving the youngest member of our office, Haleluia, disturbed us all immensely. The question "who's going to be next" was clearly visible in everybody's eyes.

Haleluia, a recent university graduate, had, only the day before, expressed anxiety for her own life and that of her siblings. Mesale, the eldest of her brothers, was a student at Haile Selassie University when in 1975, along with all his fellows, he was dispatched to the interior to participate in the *Zemecha*. The project, however, was not going entirely according to the Government's plans. The students were carrying out health and literacy programmes and had helped establish thousands of peasant associations, but far from indoctrinating the peasants in support of the Dergue, many were actively trying to turn the peasantry against the regime, labelling it as fascist.

Mesale was among those who had publicly criticized the Dergue. Eventually, he had been forced to abandon his assignment and flee the area. Soldiers were waiting to arrest him when he returned home, forcing him to go into hiding. Secretly, he called his sister informing her of his whereabouts and they had made an arrangement, whereby Haleluia would leave packages of food and warm clothing at previously-agreed spots. The plan had worked well for a couple of weeks, but now, death had found Mesale.

The Dergue had outlawed any sizeable funeral gathering. It had also specifically forbidden the mourning of what it termed "traitors" and "anti-revolutionaries". Although many people feared being seen offering sympathy to bereaved relatives, deep-rooted customs and warm-hearted instincts could not be easily destroyed. Despite the consequences, throughout the Red Terror, attendance at funerals never diminished. But people were cautious.

"It's safer to wait a few days before being seen at Haleluia's house," an Ethiopian colleague advised. "There are government spies everywhere and they might suspect that some of us have been sheltering her brother. I must admit I'm scared. My sons are about the same age as Mesale."

Abeba, too, was petrified of being identified. "I'm scared of repercussions on my husband," she voiced her fears.

A few of us made our way to Haleluia's house in a narrow side road near the Guenet Hotel. The small yard was packed with people. The women, their *shammas* pulled over their heads, were softly murmuring and crying. Most had known Mesale since the day he was born nineteen years ago. The deserted house had been stripped of all its decorative trappings and ornaments. Out of a superstitious fear they might reflect the tragedy, framed pictures and mirrors had been removed from the walls, leaving the rooms bare and cold. Black curtains were draped across the windows. The family had moved out into the garage. There, freshly-cut grass had been strewn over the cold stone floor and mattresses imported for everyone to sit and sleep on.

When we arrived, we found everyone clustered together on the floor covered with a heavy blanket. They had all bared their chests, though the women had preserved their modesty with a thin piece of cloth. At the sight of newcomers, the mother, paste-white and vacant-eyed, clambered wearily onto her knees, seeking a helping hand to raise her to her feet. Exhausted as she was, she was obliged to honor her son by expressing her grief to all those who came to mourn. Summoning what strength she had left, she let out a piercing shriek, shattering the still night air. Then, tearing at her hair and beating her bared breasts, she began to wail her son's name. Wavering female voices rose in sympathy. "They murdered my pride and joy!" she screamed. "They threw his naked body in front of my door like a dog!"

Haleluia got up from where she was sitting and took her mother in her arms coaxing her to sit down. Ignoring her daughter, she struggled across the room and before anyone could stop her, rushed to the door. Forcing it open, she screamed uncontrollably into the night, "Why don't you kill me too, you murderous dogs!" Beating her chest with clenched fists, she collapsed onto her knees, shrieking and wailing. A group of neighbors gathered round and wrestled to guide her back into the garage, fearful of who might have overheard her outburst.

"The poor woman! She's gone crazy with grief," cried a friend loudly, for the benefit of any spy in the crowd.

Lukas and I moved round to sit next to Haleluia. I squeezed her hand, unable to find any words.

"I spoke to Mesale yesterday," she whispered between sobs. "Then this morning, when my mother went to open the front door, there he lay with six bullets in his chest! They had pinned a red sticker to him, labelling him an anti-revolutionary and demanding payment for the six bullets they had used to kill him!"

Gruesome deaths like that of Mesale were becoming a daily occurrence in Addis Ababa. While the nights thundered with gunfire, the early mornings brought with them the stench of death. The mutilated bodies of youngsters were thrown into ditches or left sprawled on pavements, their juvenile faces frozen in expressions of terror or contorted with pain. Agonized cries of parents chilled the morning air as they took turns to identify their

221

slain sons and daughters. Sometimes, heaps of corpses were left on street corners until the stench was unbearable. The threat of death hung over anyone who tried to claim a loved one. Later the bodies were shovelled onto an army truck and buried in unmarked, mass graves.

Within a few months of Mesale's death, tragedy struck Haleluia's family again. Her grandfather originally owned several properties in Addis, all of which were confiscated by the Dergue. He had, however, been allowed to retain one for his own use. He chose an attractive, double-storied stone house with wide terraces and spacious rooms. Unfortunately, the local *kebele* decided that the house was perfect for its needs and promptly demanded it be surrendered. The old man was stubbornly unyielding to move out of his dwellings until one night a mysterious fire set the top floor bedroom ablaze, suffocating him to death. The fire brigade was called only after the flames had totally gutted the top of the house.

Members of the *kebele* immediately picked up Mesale's younger brother, Meswaet, accusing him of plotting with his grandfather to destroy the premises. He was beaten, tortured and thrown into a dank cell at the local police station where he was left to rot. There was no light, no lavatory, nowhere to sleep. It was crawling with vermin. His sole privilege was being allowed to receive food from his family. One day, in desperation, he concealed a message in the base of the thermos flask which contained his daily broth. He described the extent of his torment and pleaded with his sister to appeal on his behalf. Haleluia went to the *kebele* and to the Dergue, insisting that her brother was being unjustly and inhumanely tortured and begged for mercy, but her plea fell on deaf ears. The sole result of her persistence was the launching of an investigation into how the information had been leaked out. The entire family was taken into custody. Tight-lipped, they refused to say anything that would incriminate their son, but in those days of terror, having evidence or not having evidence was immaterial. Like his brother, Meswaet's body turned up in the street one day, his skull smashed, his youthful face battered beyond recognition. For him, death had come as a relief, but for those who remained it brought still more sorrow, anger and fear.

Chapter Twenty One

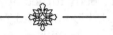

However calm Manoli may have appeared to his family, the loss of his business was more than his old heart could bear. He began to complain of pains in his chest, bringing Dr. Georgiadis to the house almost every day.

"Manoli, you must go down to a lower altitude," his old friend advised during one of his visits. "Greece is beautiful at this time of the year."

"And what's wrong with this one?" Manoli objected. "I have lived here for the past fifty years without ever taking a holiday. Now, all of a sudden, the altitude doesn't suit my system," he said sarcastically.

"Stop being so obstinate, Manoli!" Dr. Georgiadis raised his voice. "Half a century at this high altitude is more than your heart can handle."

"I don't want to leave," Manoli's voice suddenly lost its bluster. "I have nowhere to go and nothing to go to. While others scraped and saved and sent their savings abroad, I invested everything in this country." He looked round the room. "This is all I have. I know I can't offer much in this weary state, but my boys count on me for moral support." Manoli poured the doctor a cup of coffee.

Dr. Georgiadis shook his head. "I respect your views, Manoli, but I must warn you. Your heart is getting weak."

"As long as there's a drop of oxygen in my lungs and I'm still breathing, I will stand by my boys," Manoli said stubbornly.

"Suit yourself," Dr. Georgiadis knew there was no point in arguing. Manoli's mind was made up.

Manoli stood up and walked to the window. For a few seconds he stared at the beautifully kept lawns and the flowering jacaranda, then he looked beyond to the blue outlines of the distant hills. He turned back to Dr. Georgiadis.

"If my time has come, my good friend, at least let me go happy. Do you know something?" He paused. "I want to stay here in this wonderful country that has given me fifty beautiful years." Manoli's voice thickened. "I mustn't forget the one we lost. I want to rest next to my little girl— my Sophia—she's been pretty lonely up in Gulele." A tear rolled slowly down his wrinkled cheek. He wiped it away with the back of his hand. "We didn't even give her a decent burial. I owe it to her…" his voice faded, but he wanted to finish. Clearing his throat, he continued, "…and I must put things right now."

Evangelia's voice broke the silence. "Dr. Georgiadis!" she called. "Someone's here to see you."

As the doctor got up to follow Evangelia, Manoli tugged at his sleeve. Putting his finger to his lips, he whispered, "Not a word about our conversation. Evangelia worries too much and it upsets me to see her sad. Promise me, not a single word."

The doctor patted Manoli gently on the shoulder. "Rest assured, my old friend."

But Evangelia was already aware something was wrong. She ushered him straight into her kitchen. "Is it serious?" she asked, her eyes full of concern.

225

"Not at all, Evangelia! Stop fretting, will you? I find Manoli a little tired. At his age it would be better if he went down to a lower altitude but…"

Evangelia interrupted him, "You're not hiding anything are you, Doctor?" she asked, her voice shaking.

"Come, come, Evangelia. Sit down and take a hold of yourself."

"Oh, Doctor, I don't know what we would do if anything happened to him," she sniffed.

Dr. Georgiadis pulled out a chair and sat down opposite her. "Listen, he's been through a lot, but he's tough. You knew that when you married him. Now, keep him off fatty foods and help him lose a few kilos. His blood pressure is on the high side, so avoid using too much salt in your cooking. I am prescribing a tonic and some vitamin B tablets. Now, will you stop worrying or I'll have another patient on my hands."

As the months passed and grey clouds thickened in the sky heralding the onset of another cold and stormy Ethiopian rainy season, Manoli's health deteriorated. Shooting pains across his chest and back caused him increasing discomfort. "If we make it through August, Evangelia," Manoli told her one cold, dank night, as she rubbed his back vigorously with liniment, "then we'll make it through to the end of the year."

On the morning of the 26 August, having just recovered from a heavy chest cold, Manoli woke up feeling great. When the doctor called, he greeted him with gusto. "We've made it, my old friend! We've made it!"

"Not so loud," said the doctor, who was listening to his chest.

"August is almost over, my cold is cured and I feel so good I could eat a horse and drink a whole bottle of the

226

best wine!" Manoli laughed heartily.

"Why not?" the doctor replied. "You heard him," he said, turning to Evangelia who was hovering around anxiously. "Cook him his favorite meal and let him have just one glass of wine."

Evangelia was delighted. She disappeared into the kitchen to put her talents to the test.

After seeing the doctor to his car, Lukas returned to have a chat with his father. Before he had a chance to sit down, Manoli was up, dressed, freshly-shaven and was splashing Old Spice on his chin.

"How about taking me for a ride, Lukas? I feel mouldy after being cooped up for weeks in this house. I need to blow the cobwebs out of my hair."

"Let's go," said Lukas, delighted at his father's recovery. "It's not raining this afternoon. We could drive up to the Entoto hills."

"I would prefer to visit Saint George's Cathedral, if you don't mind," said Manoli.

The Ethiopian Orthodox cathedral was in the center of town. The octagonal building with its Greek-style cupola was relatively small with wooden stud-embossed doors. Lukas' uncle, Logotheti, had built it for Menelik from local stone in honor of the patron saint who had inspired his army to defeat the Italians at the battle of Adoua in 1896. Now, as Lukas and Manoli approached, they saw that it's walls had been plastered with revolutionary slogans. The doors were locked and it had an air of decay. Passers-by were pausing briefly to mutter furtive supplications before hurrying on.

Manoli stepped out of the car, shaking his head sadly. "I can't bear to witness this change. People are terrified of being caught praying," he said, incredulously. "Even their

Sunday worship has been timed deliberately to clash with struggle meetings and public rallies. To think that at Haile Selassie's coronation in 1930, there were over 100,000 people surrounding these gates, calling on their leader. I remember I was fascinated by the glittering crosses and the turbanned priests; the deacons in their colorful vestments and silver crowns, all chanting and swinging censers, filling the air with the smell of incense."

He paused, lost in the past. "I can see him now—the Emperor, seated on a red velvet throne, with Empress Itigue Menen at his side, being crowned by the Patriarch of Alexandria. What a spectacle! What an honour to be invited! To be included among dignitaries from all over the world to witness his accession."

Manoli fell silent. This neighbourhood held so many memories. It was here that he and Evangelia had started again after the great fire destroyed their first store and all their worldly possessions. It was here they had raised their children and spent their working lives, building a future for the generations to come. Manoli stared at the cathedral's heavy studded doors, remembering how he had never once opened the bookstore without stopping to pray to the great saint.

"Shall we go on, father?" Lukas broke the silence.

Manoli nodded and climbed back into the car. "I'd like to drive past the bookstore, Lukas."

"That's all over now. It will only depress you."

"No, it won't, Lukas. I want to see it, just this once."

Lukas heaved a sigh and put the car into gear. "Alright," he said grimly, "but don't expect too much or you'll only be disappointed."

Lukas pulled up in front of the store. The flashing neon sign had been ripped down leaving jagged metal struts waving and clanging in the breeze. A piece of board had been nailed over a broken glass pane in the door where a stray bullet had entered during a street clash. In the window, the faces of Marx and Lenin, clenched fists raised, stared from the dusty covers of piled-up paperbacks.

Manoli moved to open the door of the car, then hesitated. "I think I've seen enough, son," he said quietly. "Let's go home."

* * *

Evangelia greeted them at the door. "I hope the fresh air has whetted your appetite. The roast will be ready in half an hour."

Manoli sat down at the kitchen table and loosened his waistcoat. "We built a colossal tower, but instead of bricks and stones, we used paper," he said. "Sadly, a catastrophical hurricane has scattered it into a million pieces. How foolish I was to throw all our wealth into the business without ever suspecting that one day things could change," he shook his head sadly. "Our lives flowed along like water finding its own level. We knew there was trouble brewing, but we just didn't want it to infect our lives. The Ethiopia we knew is lost. It has been turned over to a doctrinaire Marxism that fights wars and kills farmers, poisoning the land instead of feeding its people," he lamented. "Well, there's no point now in crying. One thing that has never changed is you, my little one." He put his big arms round Evangelia and gave her a squeeze. Protesting at first, but then allowing her head to rest on his chest, she sighed.

"Oh, Manoli. We have come through some sad and

happy times together and I want to tell you now, I wouldn't have had it any other way. When you first brought me here away from my home, my family and my friends, I thought I would never be happy again. But with you beside me, I don't regret a single moment."

Manoli kissed her on the forehead. "Now, woman, how's dinner coming on? I'm starving!"

The table was set with Rosenthal tableware with its curved blue and gold lines reminiscent of the Baroque era, Beaugency crystal glasses and Christofle silverware placed on top of a pink lace tablecloth. The dinner had been prepared with loving care. Crunchy potatoes, steamed carrots with melted butter and chopped parsley decorated the sizzling roast beef. The whole family, including Angeliki, Philip and their son, was there. Manoli took his usual place at the head of the table.

"This is the best dinner I've had in years," he smiled with satisfaction. "To the good health of the family I was blessed with." He raised his wine glass in a toast. "In memory also of my good friend Saris, whose wine tastes as good as it did fifty years ago," he put his glass down. For a split second he stopped, as if the wine were too strong and had made him a little dizzy. He shook his head and then placed his fingers over his eyes and closed them.

"Father!" yelled Lukas, getting up and rushing to Manoli's side.

"Catch him," Pavlos shouted from the opposite side of the table.

"Oh, no! Mother of Christ!" screamed Evangelia hysterically, clutching Angeliki, who stood motionless.

"He's fainted!" Lukas yelled. "Father, father," he shook the limp body vigorously.

The two men laid Manoli on the floor. While one

massaged his heart, the other tried mouth-to-mouth resuscitation, but their efforts were useless. Their father was gone. He had died peacefully as he wished in the land he loved surrounded by the family he adored.

His desire to be buried with his infant daughter was granted. Sophia's remains were exhumed and placed in her father's arms, ending forty years of loneliness. They were finally together.

* * *

Even before the forty days of mourning were over, tax officials were knocking on the Fanouris door. "Captain Zerefu," the uniformed inspector introduced himself. "I'm looking for Manoli," he said clicking his heels together.

"I'm afraid he's gone," Lukas replied.

"What? He's left the country?" Zerefu shouted his face contorted with rage. "That's a criminal offence! You," he said, pointing a finger at Lukas, "have some explaining to do."

"You'll find him in Gulele," replied Lukas through clenched teeth.

"Gulele?" he repeated with annoyance. "The cemetery? In his absence then, I need a few answers from you," he smirked, handing Lukas a summon.

"I don't believe this!" Lukas exclaimed. "'Having investigated,'" he read out loud, "'… the Bureau finds totally unacceptable tax returns submitted during Haile Selassie's reign. It is hereby estimated that five hundred thousand Birr have been deprived from the suffering people of Ethiopia…' This is preposterous," Lukas hollered. Losing his self control he wildly waved the paper in front of Zerefu. "You've nationalized our business,

231

blocked our accounts—where the hell do you think we're going to find this kind of money?"

Stepping aside, Zerefu swung open the door of his Volkswagen and beckoned Lukas to get in. "We can find a solution in my office," he grinned wickedly. "I can assure you, it won't take long."

"They'll soon realize there was no tax evasion," Lukas assured us getting into the car. "Pick me up in about an hour," he called back at Pavlos.

Distrusting Zerefu's motives, Pavlos and I followed Lukas to police headquarters. We were not permitted to enter, so we sat in the car waiting. Dusk fell and still there was no sign of Lukas. All our enquiries were answered with '*koi*'—wait! Eventually we were referred from one ignorant officer to another, until finally a cleaning woman, glancing furtively about her, whispered that she had seen a '*ferenje*' fitting Lukas' description leaving Comrade Zerefu's office.

We lingered outside the room until almost every light in the building had been switched off and every office door banged shut for the night. It seemed hopeless. We were wandering back towards the duty officer's desk to make a final appeal for information, when Zerefu suddenly appeared and made rapidly for the exit. I pointed him out to Pavlos, who ran to intercept him. Dashing to follow them, I caught the end of their conversation. It sent tingles up my spine.

"Any communication with the prisoner is out of the question," Zerefu was saying.

"What is he charged with?" yelled Pavlos, losing his temper.

"We're not through with the interrogation yet. Until then, we're keeping him in." Evading any further discussion, he brushed us aside and drove off.

Witnessing the incident, the inspector on duty came over to speak to us. "Your husband will be alright, Madam," he assured me. "It's only for one night. Be here in the morning with some hot tea." His was the first civilized, sympathetic voice we had heard that day. We took his advice.

* * *

Lukas, meantime, had been thrust into a crowded, dimly-lit cell in the bowels of the police headquarters. Immediately the door was unlocked, the stench of stale perspiration and musty urine assaulted his nostrils. He had barely managed to squeeze in when, seizing the opportunity, detainees blocked the door, pleading with the guard for a quick run to the toilet. One at a time they were escorted along the corridor, while the rest jostled for position. Lukas watched as one feeble old man attempted to urinate in a tin can, missed and sprayed the floor as well as those surrounding him. Bereft of all dignity, he apologized pitifully to his fellow inmates.

Unsure of his next move, Lukas stood in the middle of the room as his eyes slowly adjusted to the darkness. There were several ill-dressed, uncouth-looking individuals who looked like street robbers, but the majority appeared to be respectable, if dishevelled, citizens. People were wriggling closer to make room for him, but there was still barely room to turn round. Abruptly, a hand reached out and pulled him to one side. "I'll be darned!" said a familiar voice. "What the hell are you doing here?"

"Tamrat!" Lukas shouted, shaking his hand. "Well, it's

233

not exactly the Palace grounds we're meeting in, but under the circumstances, I'm relieved you're alive."

For many years Tamrat had been the Emperor's trusted driver. One of his daily tasks was to call at the bookstore to pick up the periodicals for his master. Always in a rush, the mischievous chauffeur never failed to find time for a joke with his bookseller pal. But now the once mirthful face was lined and drawn. Dark rings circled his eyes, which had lost their lustre and gained a haunted look. Leading Lukas to his corner of the room, he offered to share his meager possessions with him—a thatched mat to sit on, a candle and a piece of mouldy *injera*.

Leaning his aching back against a wall dripping with condensation, Lukas recounted the day's ordeal. "I've been pushed and shoved about like a common criminal. They wouldn't even allow me to call my lawyer," he concluded, still unable to believe it had happened.

"They're insane," Tamrat muttered. "I've spent three years in this snake pit and they're still not convinced I'm innocent. They're obsessed with the misconception that I know where His Majesty's gold is buried." He sniggered. "The only fortune I ever saw was handed out to beggars…" He stopped abruptly, holding his breath and swiftly snuffing the flaming wick. "Someone's outside," he hissed. "We're all supposed to be sleeping now. Play dead or we'll be separated."

Stretching out to sleep was impossible. With sufficient space only for squatting, Lukas gripped his knees and leaning his head on his folded arms, prayed for an early dawn. His lids had barely closed when soft, tickling movements on his skin jerked him awake. A fiery itch covering his whole body made him scratch vigorously. In no time at all, his white shirt was blotched with bloody spots.

Striking a match, Tamrat laughed grimly. *"Ferenje* blood is a real treat for these jail vermin," he said, helping Lukas remove his lice-infested shirt. "Where's that candle?" He fumbled on the floor. "I'm an expert at sizzling these devils without ever burning a hole."

* * *

By six o'clock the next morning, Pavlos and I were outside the high corrugated fence which surrounded the cell block, patiently waiting for some movement. Before long, women carrying thermos flasks and three-decker food containers joined us. Eavesdropping on their conversations, we learned that food deliveries were restricted to once a day and clean clothes could be brought only at the weekends.

"Stop trembling," said Pavlos, seeing my anxiety. "We'll have Lukas out by noon."

Seven days later, I felt sick when I thought of our optimism. Each day we were given one feeble excuse after another. I came to dread the words *'ishi negga'*—'come back tomorrow'. In the end, I began to think they would never release him. Then a little after midnight on the eighth day, the telephone rang. It was Lukas. He was free to leave.

Disregarding the curfew Pavlos and I took a deserted road and raced down to pick him up. When he emerged from the building, I barely recognized him. It was staggering how much weight he had lost. "Are you alright?" I asked, flinging my arms round him.

"I'm fine," he replied. "Let's just get away from this place." Covered in greasy sweat, his crumpled clothes soiled and rancid, he was anxious to get home, soak in a hot bath and drench himself in surgical spirit.

Later, over dinner, he unwound and related his experiences. Finally, he came to his release. "Since they confiscated my watch, I had no concept of time. I was wakened with a torch flashing in my face and ordered to get up and follow the officer. I immediately thought they were moving me away from Tamrat. We'd been cautioned that morning that we were turning the cell into a *buna bet*. That hole was a far cry from a coffee shop, but our sharing food and making the best of some old jokes infuriated them. Anyway," he continued, "I was taken out of the cell and marched upstairs, where I was overwhelmed to see my old friend, Colonel Tesfaye. You remember him, don't you?" Seeing the blank expression on our faces he quickly refreshed our memory. "The guy that warned me of the attempted coup back in 1960. He said he was taking full responsibility for my release." Lukas pushed his plate to one side and leaned back in the chair. "If it hadn't been for Tamrat, I'd have cracked up. I'm amazed he's still sane after three years in that hell hole!"

Accompanied by their solicitor, Pavlos and Lukas returned to the Police Headquarters the following morning. They were escorted to the Tax Bureau, where they were introduced to Comrade Hailu, a severe-looking man with cold, calculating eyes. His fingers interlocked, he regarded them from behind a huge, polished desk without asking them to sit down. Standing by the door was a police sergeant with an automatic rifle slung over his shoulder.

"Your demands are exorbitant," Pavlos began.

"The previous Government was far too lenient," Hailu

replied, unyieldingly. "You made enormous profits in the last fifty years."

"Of course we did. Name me one hard-working, private enterprise that didn't?" Lukas challenged.

"We're not here to play games," Hailu glared at them. "Unless you come up with 500,000 Birr very soon, you'll be in deep trouble. That will be all, gentlemen."

"This is absurd!" yelled Pavlos. "Where do you think we can find a quarter of a million US dollars? Unless, of course," he leaned forward over the desk, "you wish to deduct it from the compensation which we have been promised."

"That's another matter, and don't confuse the issues," he shrieked, banging his hand on the table. "I suggest," he shook his finger at Pavlos, "you return all the money you smuggled out."

Pavlos let out a hard, humourless laugh. "My dear sir, do you think we'd still be here if we'd had the foresight to smuggle funds out of this country. We'd have been gone long ago…"

Lukas tugged gently at his brother's sleeve. "It's no use," he whispered in Greek. "It's pointless to argue. We'll only end up in deeper trouble."

Hailu stood up, motioning to the policeman to show them out. "Until every nickel is paid, not a single member of your family will be allowed to leave this country," he pronounced.

"*Ato* Worku." Pavlos turned to the lawyer, as they walked along the corridor. "Can he do this?"

"His orders come directly from the Dergue. Be thankful they didn't issue you with a deadline."

* * *

While Lukas was in jail he was startled to learn that Tamrat had recent news of the royal family. A loyal manservant, who faithfully took food to the princesses and dropped off the leftovers to Tamrat, knew their whereabouts and also that they were now being allowed visitors. The Sunday following Lukas' release we made plans to visit them. Just as dawn was breaking, Lukas nudged me awake.

"Isn't it too early?" I asked, pulling open the curtains. "It's dark outside."

"Cakes and cigarettes from Enrico's will please them," he said, ignoring my question. "Hurry, or we'll never make it."

Alem Bekagn—'I've had enough of this life'—was the grim nickname of the old Italian fortress in the 21st district. Anyone who had passed through its heavy portals knew why. Built by the invaders to confine a few hundred, its cold, bare, poorly-ventilated cells were now crammed with thousands of alleged political prisoners. Like some medieval anachronism, its crumbling battlements with their narrow slatted windows rose amidst modern villas with meticulously-mowed lawns and multi-storey office complexes.

It was incredible to believe that just a stone's throw away from people sunbathing in their gardens and the headquarters of the Organization for African Unity, a mass of pitiful humanity was struggling in filth and squalor to survive.

By 6.30 a.m. the queue outside the gates was already a mile long. People had begun arriving as soon as the curfew ended. A narrow passage, roofed with eucalyptus branches, sheltered a meager percentage from the heat of the blazing sun. It was furnished with roughly-constructed benches, half-eaten by termites and powdery to the touch. Some were lucky enough to get a seat; the majority flopped down on the tarmac road, forcing traffic to divert into side lanes.

Marking time, knitting needles clicked, crochet hooks flicked and home-made spinning jennys twisted freshly-picked cotton into thread. Men, bored with gossip and accustomed to the interminable wait, sprawled out on the pavements, pulling their *shammas* over their heads, one corner tightly secured between two toes. While they slept, latecomers squeezed into the line ahead of them. Sometimes the queue was there from dawn to dusk.

With only half a dozen prison warders on duty to inspect foodstuffs, we considered ourselves fortunate that it took us only three hours to reach the checkpoint. Every container was being prodded with a special detector and the visitor had to sample the meal before being permitted to proceed.

"Who are these for?" the guard demanded, tearing the wrappings.

"Just friends," said Lukas, avoiding his direct glare. We waited anxiously as each cream-filled eclair was prodded and tested. "Next time, bring one large item. We can't waste time fiddling with these," he said, pushing the tray towards us.

Inside the fortress, there was pandemonium. Two waist-high barbed wire fences with a three-foot no-man's land between them separated the prisoners from the visitors. People were rushing up and down on both sides, trying to spot their loved ones. When contact was made, there were screams of joy and a hubbub of conversation.

We turned away from the bulk of the crowd and headed to our right. An officer stopped us. "Where do think you're going?" he asked.

239

"We're looking for the royal youngsters," Lukas replied. From the way he looked down at Lukas' hands and twisting his lips to form a sickly grin, we knew he wouldn't divulge any information without a bribe. Taking out a five Birr note, Lukas twirled it between his fingers.

"They're all in there," the officer said gruffly pointing towards a row of grim looking prefabricated rooms. "I'll call one for you."

He walked over to one of the shacks, poking his head inside the doorway. It was not long before Rebecca, *Ras* Asrate Kassa's youngest daughter, emerged. Shading her eyes against the bright sunlight, she slowly lifted her head in search of a familiar face. Her skin, which once glowed with vitality, had a sickly jaundiced look and was covered with discoloured blotches. We waved frantically.

"Berhanu!" shouted the teenager, coming towards us. "You came."

"How are you all?" Lukas yelled back.

"Some of us are bearing up, but Princess Tenagne Work's sugar level is dangerously high and Princess Ijigayew's condition is critical."

Lukas' brain whirled. Always high-spirited, jovial and charming, Ijigayew was the one who had coaxed Lukas into conquering his fear of horses. Time and again, she had invited him to the royal stables, patiently instructing him how to handle the prancing, black stallions. He could hear her tinkling laughter now, as she teased him about his timidness. He couldn't bear to think of her lying there, ill and unattended.

With a lump in his throat, Lukas leaned over the barbed wire fence and handed Rebecca the parcel. "Something to sweeten your day," he said, smiling ruefully.

"Thank you so much," she said eyeing the package

rather awkwardly.

"It's your favourite," Lukas was quick to tell her, "eclairs from Enrico's. But, maybe you needed something else?"

"We'd be grateful for a tin of butter," she yelled. "We use it to bribe the guards. A few spoonfuls in exchange for Princess Tenagne Work's diabetes pills," she smiled bitterly.

Visits were restricted to Sundays, so Lukas promised to bring it the following week. As time was getting very short before we would be asked to leave, Rebecca spurted out as many details as she could about their living conditions.

"We're very cramped. Things got better, temporarily, last week when a representative from Amnesty International came to visit us. The day before he arrived we were moved to more spacious quarters, all washed and disinfected. But, unfortunately, as soon as he'd gone, we were moved back again." Rebecca glanced around to make sure there were no guards within earshot. "We were warned to speak only in English, but Princess Ijigayew did manage to whisper a few words in French, even in her weakened state." A guard approached, calling her name. "I have to go. Before you leave…" she hesitated, "We've heard my sister Tsighe has been admitted to Tsehai Hospital." Tears began to stream down her cheeks.

"We'll go straight there to see her," Lukas promised.

"Can you also light a… candle for…" She twisted her fingers, staring at the ground, trying to control the deep-rooted grief. "My father died in agony on the night of Bloody Saturday," she began, the tears welling in her eyes. "He challenged each one of them to fight him openly. Instead, they tied his hands behind his back, covered his

241

head with a filthy sack and riddled his body with bullets."
She paused, swallowing hard. She wiped her eyes.

Lukas stretched out his hand and gripped hers.
"You've got to be strong, things have to get better."

She smiled wanly. "I hope Tsighe's condition isn't
serious. I can't see my mother coping with another loss."

* * *

At the end of a long, gloomy corridor in the third class
section of the Ye Tor Hailoch Hospital, but still popularly
known by its original name, Princess Tsehai, we entered a
small stuffy ward containing six rusty iron beds. Curled
up, facing the wall, covered with a thin, grimy sheet, a
slight figure trembled and shook.

"Tsighe," Lukas called softly.

She turned hesitantly on hearing the call. Huge sores
and lumps rendered her almost unrecognizable.

"Berhanu," she said, extending a hand towards her
childhood playmate "I'm dying!" Hoarsely, trying to clear
her dry throat, Tsighe attempted to explain that the pills
she was given were not helping her and the medical staff
were not bothered with her. "A doctor pops in for a few
minutes during morning rounds and then vanishes for the
rest of the day," she complained.

"What if we asked Mila to see you?" I suggested. "She's
a pediatrician we know."

Lukas left me with Tsighe and hurried to get Mila. In
the meantime, I fed Tsighe segments of orange and
listened as she related the onset of her illness upon hearing
of her father's execution. Her condition had worsened
progressively, resulting in dehydration and shortness of
breath. The authorities at first refused to admit her to

hospital, believing she was shamming and claiming that by using a bed she was depriving a soldier fighting for the motherland of his rights. When she finally collapsed and had to be given oxygen, they agreed to transfer her.

As we talked, I noticed her becoming increasingly uncomfortable. Apologizing for her bad manners, she began scratching her body so vigorously I thought she would tear the flesh. "I can't take this any more," she screamed, rolling and rubbing herself frantically on the rough bedsheets. "Dear God, somebody help me!"

Panicking by her action, I rang for the nurse. The ward door swung open and a furious-looking sister marched in, hands on her hips, her face full of loathing.

"What do you think you're doing?" she asked belligerently. "I've warned you before," she shook a finger at Tsighe. "You and your feudal ways are a thing of the past. Everyone on this floor gets the same treatment!"

"Nurse!" I shouted at her. "It was I who rang the bell."

"Oh," her tone softened a little. "And what can I do for you?"

"Can you let us have some ointment or a cream to ease the itching?

The nurse laughed sarcastically, "Creams are a luxury item, my dear. She will be treated like any other common Ethiopian. Everyone is now equal, thanks to the new regime."

I was about to tell her what I thought of her new regime, when fortunately Lukas and Mila arrived. The nurse turned on her heel and disappeared. Mila quickly took off her jacket and examined Tsighe.

"This is severe allergic reaction which has erupted both internally and externally. You should have been given antihistamine injections," she said. "Who's your doctor?"

Tsighe didn't know. Most of the doctors were Mila's colleagues and she was determined to speak to the one on duty. At the door she motioned me to follow her outside. In the corridor, she explained that Tsighe's condition was critical and if she wasn't treated immediately she would die.

"What if you can't find someone to help you?" I asked.

"I have taken an oath to save lives. I'll give her the injections myself—with or without permission. You forget," she smiled with a wink in her eye, "I'm from a communist country. I know how to handle comrades." I was filled with admiration for her.

"Aha! Dr. Girma!" she called out, spotting a white-coated medic. "Just the man I was looking for!" She shook his hand and patted him on the back. "I need a big favour from you!"

"What can I do for you, Dr. Miroslava?"

From the tone of his voice, I knew he would listen to her. I hurried back to the ward. Before I had finished telling them the good news, the doctor was at Tsighe's bedside, accompanied by the sullen-looking nurse who had obviously been put in her place.

A week later Tsighe was released from the hospital and the city buzzed with news of her audacious escape across the Sudanese border. Dressed as an Arab, she was transported on the back of an unsuspecting camel to freedom.

Princess Ijagayew was not so lucky. Her illness, ignored until it was too late, was finally diagnosed as a malfunction of the liver. She was sent to hospital only to make her last few days more comfortable. She died leaving six young children to an unknown fate.

The rest did live to see better days. In 1988, the

Mengistu government announced the release of all the surviving members of the royal family.

Chapter Twenty Two

The dawn to dusk curfew brought with it an end to evening outings and entertaining friends. The Dergue also imposed restrictions on movement outside the city, which meant that in order to breathe country air, one had to seek permission from the *kebeles* and have a good reason for wanting to leave the capital. Gradually the house which had once been our haven, became a trap averting any free movement. In short, we felt like prisoners in our own home.

Being perpetually in each other's company began to cause tensions. Unused to being idle, Lukas and Pavlos were irritable and short-tempered. Evangelia was missing Manoli and I, more than ever, was despondent over our failure to have a child. Sometimes the longing was unbearable. I would cry myself to sleep at night, swallowing my sobs so as not to wake Lukas and burden him with my problems.

One night, I had gone to bed with a fever and all the symptoms of flu. Drifting into a welcome sleep, I sank deep into a strange, beautiful world where dreams turned yearnings into reality. I found myself on a wide avenue lined on either side with trees, their branches gently brushing my face and even as I watched sprouting buds burst into blooms of pink cherry blossom. I was engulfed by a feeling of freedom and harmony. Suddenly, I heard a faint, distant echo. As the sound grew louder, I heard my name being called out. When I turned to look I saw an elderly woman dressed in black, a scarf twirled around her head framing her gentle features.

"I have something for you," she beckoned me. She was holding an infant in her arms and when I looked down, my eyes fell on a small head covered with blond curls. "She's yours. Take her!" the woman commanded.

I looked into her eyes, wanting so much to put my arms around the child I longed for, but before I could reply both woman and child vanished into thin air. The sense of panic at losing the child sent me into hysterics. The sound of my own scream woke me up. I was drenched in sweat and tears.

"Honey, what is it?" I heard Lukas fumbling with his bedside lamp. He turned towards me and felt my forehead. "Good grief, you're burning! No wonder you've had a nightmare." He got out of bed and started towards the bathroom. "Let me get you an aspirin."

"Forget my fever," I said getting my breath back. "You've got to listen to this extraordinary dream that I've just had."

He came round to my side of the bed and patiently listened. Fresh tears gushed down my burning cheeks as I related the mirage.

"Come on, darling," he comforted me. "It's only a fantasy. You know the saying, 'A hungry man always dreams of food'!"

"I'll tell you something," I yelled angrily. "I've prayed until I'm blue in the face! If He's not able to grant me my wish, then there is no God. There's nothing."

247

Lukas jumped up, shocked at my reaction. "Mellina, I've never seen you like this before. This is blasphemy!"

"I don't care what it is," I shouted back. "If God and his saints have turned a deaf ear, then so be it!"

Lukas tried hard to calm me. "It's the fever. You're delirious. You don't know what you're saying," he said, trying hard to find some excuse for my behaviour.

I was adamant! Only if my wish was granted would I ever believe again!

Shaking his head, Lukas went to fetch the aspirin.

Although my fever gradually subsided, my mental state remained in turmoil. Next morning, I lay with the covers up around my head, staring blankly at the wall. Lukas paced up and down trying his best to make me snap out of it. Then he had an idea.

"I've managed to hoard a few extra litres of petrol. With what I've saved from our own weekly rations, we should have enough to get down to Langano. What do you say?"

"Could we really get away?" I asked, my spirits lifting.

"I'll go down to the *kebele* and get permission."

No sooner had Lukas walked in with the permit, than we started rushing around like two children, cleaning the cobwebs from our camping stove and throwing drinks into a cooler box. It was years since we were down in Langano. I couldn't wait to get out.

By 5 p.m. we were on our way, speeding towards Akaki. Curfew was not until 10 p.m. so we had plenty of time to reach Langano. It suddenly occurred to us that we hadn't made any reservation. "The Bekele Molla Hotel will be fully booked," I exclaimed. "People will take advantage of the long weekend."

"As long as we get out of Addis, who cares where we

sleep," Lukas laughed. Happily he settled back in his seat, his elbow resting on the open window. We had passed the small town of Akaki and were well on our way to Debre-Zeit, when flashing lights in the distance made us slow down and stop at a road block manned by soldiers. Torches were thrust into our faces.

"Where's your pass?" one soldier demanded, as his colleague inspected the car, opening the boot and looking underneath. He took out his notebook and wrote down the registration number then snapped his notebook shut. "You may proceed. But next time, get the *kebele* chief to sign his name in full. His initial is not sufficient." He handed the permit back to Lukas.

"Will do, sir!" Lukas saluted the soldiers, put the car into gear and drove off, letting his breath out in a low whistle. "For a moment there, I was sure he was going to turn us back. He was trying desperately hard to find something wrong with the permit. I wonder what changed his mind?"

"Why the harassment?" I asked.

Lukas shrugged his shoulders. "Gone are the days when we used to drive straight through without any hassle." He let out a nostalgic sigh.

The journey through Debre-Zeit and Modjo was uneventful, but as we approached the beginning of a new stretch of road there was another road block.

"Your permit is not valid," said the grim, unsmiling officer. "You'll have to drive straight back to where you came from."

"But why?" Lukas tried to control his rising anger. "There was no problem at the last check point. If you make us turn back, we'll never make it to Addis in time for curfew."

"This permit has expired. It was for last week."

"We got it today and there's the date, right here." Lukas pointed to the right hand top corner of the permit.

"Oh, that's where they wrote it! They should have put the date down here, at the bottom," said the soldier, prodding the document.

"If there's one more road block, I shall scream," I gritted my teeth.

"Think of the silvery moonlit lake ahead and forget about these frustrations," Lukas was more realistic. "We'll be there in a little while."

The sight of the familiar hills and the lush vegetation which surrounded the lake made us both sigh with relief. We had made it. In the distance we could see the camp fires like tiny stars dotted round the lake shore. As we drove up to the Bekele Molla, it became apparent that very few families had come to Langano. The hotel was almost empty.

"It's difficult to get petrol these days," said the receptionist, as if it were fresh news. "There's not much activity here anymore," he said picking up a key and leading us along a winding path, past thorn trees and flowering hibiscus to a bungalow. It had a small veranda, overlooking the lake, with two chairs and a table. I glanced round at the emptiness that surrounded us.

"It's so sad to see this place deserted," I whispered to Lukas.

"Yes, Madam," said the receptionist, overhearing my remarks. "It's even sadder for us. We were used to wild music and dancing every evening."

I stared at the silent, uninhabited bungalows and nostalgic memories of previous visits came flooding back. Times when we had taken off with carloads of friends, laughing and joking the whole trip. I smiled as I remembered how we had sung and danced around crackling charcoal while we cooked dinner. I could almost hear the light-hearted banter and the bursts of laughter. We had shared such moments with Michael and Aspa but they had recently left with their six-year-old son, Alexander, and were now living in Athens. I felt their absence more strongly here than anywhere else. Somehow, despite the empty darkness, I could still feel an aura of warmth and happiness.

That night I fell asleep, feeling more relaxed and content than I had for months, but my deep-rooted desires were still at work. This time my whirling subconscious took me high on a mountain top overlooking a deep valley, at the foot of which nestled a small town. A man, dressed in armour with a spear in one hand and a shield in the other, stood near me.

"I have been hearing your cries and pleas in the night," he said, "and your agony has reached me." Pointing towards a winding road he said: "Use it to find me." Then the scene in my dream changed and I was in a strange village surrounded by camels and goats.

"Where am I?" I asked a small herdsboy.

"You're at the Denkako crossing between Dire-Dawa and Harrar," the toothless youngster replied.

Suddenly I could hear trees rustling in the wind and the faint melodious chirping of thousands of birds intermingled with the harsh quacking of wild ducks. The sounds gradually grew louder, until waking with a start, I sat up in bed. The dawn chorus was coming from outside. For a moment the dream was still a reality, and I knew what I had to do. I was well aware of the power of Saint Gabriel at Kulubi.

I jumped out of bed and pulled back the curtains, feeling suddenly full of energy. The first glowing rays of dawn were filtering through the trees, refracting obliquely off the glistening dew drops on the flowers and shrubs. The waters of the lake glowed pink as the rising sun cast warm rays over its glassy surface, marked only by the tiny, rippling circles left by fish rising to snap a morning bite.

Lukas stirred in his sleep, flinging back the covers. I jumped on the bed, snuggling close to him. "Come on, lazy bones! It's time to get up." I kissed him on the nose. "You don't know what you're missing. It's simply magical outside. The birds are putting on a show—just for us."

"I'm glad to see you're so happy this morning," he mumbled, not prepared to open his eyes.

"It must be breeding time," I said, going back to the window. "I've never seen so many birds. Mothers are rushing about feeding their young ones and the trees are covered with nests. I can even see some babies with their mouths open waiting to be fed."

"Life is wonderful, sweetheart, but can we eulogize about it later," came a cranky voice from beneath the bed covers, as Lukas pulled the sheet over his head to block out the sunlight.

"You know something, Lukas?" I said, leaping on the bed and yanking the sheet from his face. "I'm sure things are going to change." I rolled him over and began kissing his face and neck.

"What's happened to make you so optimistic this morning?" asked Lukas drowsily, wrapping his arms around me.

"Oh, nothing much!" I said. This time, I was not going to have him demolish my dream! "I'm overwhelmed by the beauty that surrounds us and that we have each other."

"Well, what are we waiting for? Let's make the most of it!" urged Lukas, gently.

* * *

"You've vowed to go where?" Lukas' eyes widened, waiting for my reply.

"To Saint Gabriel's Church in Kulubi," I smiled.

I had made a pledge to the most powerful saint in Ethiopia, to walk the 43 kilometers from the Denkako crossing up to his church, some two thousand feet above the town of Dire-Dawa. St. Gabriel's feast day, celebrated on the 28 December of each year, was only two months away. I had to give my faith one more chance.

"Are you crazy? Walk all the way up that mountain?" asked Lukas perplexed by my sudden announcement. "And how do you think we'll find enough petrol for there and back?"

"I've got to do it," I said stubbornly. "As for the petrol, we'll find a way. Wait!" I said, a thought suddenly striking me. I leapt up from the breakfast table and ran towards the elevator. Mila would help me. Being a doctor she was allowed double rations. I was flushed and excited by my sudden brainwave.

"Mila, I need a big favour," I began excitedly, as she opened her door.

"Let's hear it," she said in her heavy Bulgarian accent. "No more princesses to rescue, I hope."

I shook my head. "Could you spare some of your petrol,?" I asked. "We'll pay for it, of course," I hastened to add. "It's for a very important mission."

She raised her eyebrows and looked at me quizzically.

253

"What are you up to now?" When she heard my explanation, she was more excited than I was. "Of course I can help," she hugged me. "Would there be any space for me? I'd love to go too."

"How could we leave you behind?" I embraced her tightly. "Lukas' classmate, Yiotis will probably be coming with us. You must know him, Mila? The tall, slim guy who looks like James Dean?" Mila had seen him in our home and often wished she had been a few years younger! She was delighted. She confessed that ever since she had arrived in Ethiopia she had wanted to visit the famous church, but the opportunity had never come up.

It was settled. We had exactly six weeks in which to save the petrol and plans were underway to depart from Addis the day after Christmas in time for the Saint's feast day on December 28. During the next couple of weeks, Mila faithfully collected her daily ration of petrol and each night parked her blue Fiat 800 next to our car in the underground garage. When everyone was asleep, Lukas would creep down and siphon out a few liters of petrol at a time, gradually filling up our jerrycans. He always avoided using the lift and was careful not to run into the security guard. It was not uncommon for unfriendly neighbours to report any unusual movements or illegal dealings to the local *kebele*.

By Boxing Day, permit in hand, we were ready to start the long journey to Dire-Dawa. As dawn was breaking, neighbours and friends gathered round to wish us a safe trip and give us their vowed gifts for the saint. We were in the midst of packing these last-minute items, when I heard a breathless voice crying, "Wait!" It was Mama Askala, slowly climbing the steep hill from her home with a cloth bundle under her arm.

"We wouldn't leave without seeing you," I assured her, running to meet her and relieve her of the parcel.

"I have something for you to take to Saint Gabriel," she panted. She handed me her gifts—three bundles of candles and a slightly-worn umbrella. "The candles are for when I nearly died of asthma a year ago, and this umbrella is for finding a job for Almaz," she announced proudly. While Lukas was busy putting the gifts in the boot, Askala pulled at my sleeve and drew me to one side. "This," she said, holding up an old Maria Teresa coin, "is a very special gift." Her eyes filled with tears. "I have saved it for many, many years," she said, hoarsely, "and now it's time to give it away." She wiped her tears with the edge of her *shamma*. "I'm begging him to give you the cries and laughter of a young one."

With a lump in my throat, I hugged the old woman who was so dear to me. "Thank you," I whispered. "I'll never forget this, Mama Askala."

She sniffed. "Be off with you now. The sun is coming up and the trip will be tiring." She was in control again, giving instructions.

Once along the smooth, tarmac road and out of the city limits we all felt as if a heavy blanket had been lifted and we could breathe again. We had flown the coop and for a while—curfews, suppression and terror behind us—could taste the joys of freedom. Even the roadblock inquisitions failed to dampen our spirits. Our minds were far too preoccupied with our pilgrimage.

Dropping from the highlands into a monochromatic desert dotted with grey-green thorn trees, the heat intensified. In the distance, oryx, kudu and gerenuk grazed on patches of dry stubble. The air visibly danced and shimmered as the near vertical sun scorched the earth.

255

Almost obscured by dust and distance, camel-drawn caravans drifted like shadows across the plains.

Close to the road, Danakil youngsters skipped and jumped playfully as they grazed their cattle and goats. Seeing us approach and divert from the main road onto a dirt track, they forgot their chores and ran after us, the billowing powdery dust settling on their silken, dark skins transforming them into grey, ghost-like figures. We were heading for a small oasis of palms, which had beckoned us invitingly from the road. The palms' immense fronds shielded a rejuvenating spring from the excessive heat of the desert and erratic sand storms.

Before we had a chance to change into swimming costumes, a crowd of naked boys jumped into the crystal waters, splashing us until we were soaked to the skin. We decided to join them fully clothed. Timidly, they shied away from us, but furtive glances suggested they were curious to discover if we were the same shape as their own adults beneath our clinging garments. Much to their disappointment Mila and I refused to strip, but Lukas and Yiotis willingly obliged and dived in among the youngsters.

It was difficult to tear ourselves away and back to the sticky heat of the road, but after doling out sweets and biscuits, we finally clambered into the car. Three hundred kilometers of rough, dirt track lay ahead. Not long after passing Awash, we were signalled to stop. It was the final checkpoint. An arrogant sergeant, slapping his hand on the bonnet, demanded to see our suitcases. When he realized where we were going, his attitude totally changed. He apologized for the disturbance and delving into his pocket, took out a crumpled green bank note.

Glancing around quickly, he pressed it into Lukas'

hand, whispering, "It's for Saint Gabriel. Please take it for me."

By nightfall, we had reached Dire-Dawa. We drew up outside the Church of the Holy Trinity in the town centre. We were greeted by Father Proterios, the Greek parish priest who welcomed us with a good meal, a hot bath and camp beds. It was blissful to lie down and stretch out after nine hours of driving.

"Are you asleep?" Lukas turned to ask me as we heard the others snoring. "I've decided to walk from this church up to Saint Gabriel's."

"Are you serious?" I propped myself up on my elbow to look at him.

"I've given it a lot of thought and if both of us walk, we'll present a stronger case."

"Lukas, you're having me on. You don't really mean it, do you?"

"I couldn't be more serious."

"But my vow is to walk from the Denkako crossing. It's another twenty kilometers from here to the crossing and a steep climb at that."

"We'll meet at the crossing," he said his voice gradually fading. He was exhausted and needed to get some sleep.

The following afternoon, Lukas donned an old fedora, picked up a walking stick and set out. We watched him until he disappeared round a curve in the road. Although we had arranged to meet at the Denkako crossing at six o'clock, Yiotis was not so optimistic. Having made this pilgrimage at least four times in the past, he felt Lukas would be slowed down by the steep and winding road and the strong sun and didn't think Lukas could walk more than five kilometers an hour.

"I feel we should be at the crossing by six to wait for

him," I insisted. I wanted to meet up with Lukas before nightfall.

After two hours of sitting around and waiting for the time to pass, I was anxious to be on our way.

"Alright, Mellina. I get the message," Yiotis smiled. Before he could change his mind, we jumped into the car and began to climb the near vertical road.

The sun was still blazing down, creating shimmering mirages on the road ahead. A few kilometers from the crossing, we recognized in the distance Lukas' red striped shirt. Hanging out of the car windows, we shouted and waved until he raised his walking stick and shook it in acknowledgement.

"How's it been so far?" I asked, as we drew alongside.

"Not too bad! I hope you've brought me a change of clothes. I'm soaked through."

"The suitcase is in the boot," I assured him. "Would you like a drink?"

"Yes, please. Anything!"

I was about to hand him a cup of orange squash when Mila came up behind me and popped something in it. "It's a high dose of vitamin C with salt," Mila explained. "I know how fussy he is about taking any kind of medicine, so we won't tell him." she laughed.

Leaving him to catch up, we drove up to the crossing and parked the car in the shade of the only tree of any size in the entire landscape—a small stunted acacia. Fifty yards away a herd of camels were browsing leisurely amongst the dry scrub, their dusty, khaki hides blending perfectly with the surrounding desert and distant brown hills. Occasionally, they raised their heads to give us a rather disdainful look, but on finding us of no particular interest, resumed their steady ruminating.

The children were far more curious. As soon as we stopped, a crowd appeared from nowhere. Of Somali origin, they were light-skinned with beautiful, wide-eyed oval faces. The girls' hair was plaited and the braids elaborately entwined with sea shells and coloured beads. Across their foreheads, they wore a band of brass coins, whilst around their necks a delicate necklace was tattooed. Their bright, almond-shaped eyes, expertly outlined with black kohl, smiled widely as I produced my camera.

"May I take a photograph?" I asked in Amharic. They replied in Arabic, but I knew from their giggles they had no objection. The sun was low in the sky and the light was fading, so I took some quick snaps. At that point Lukas arrived and climbed into the car to change his clothes. He had an instant audience as the children swarmed around the car, pressing their noses to the windows to see the *ferenje* undress.

It was about 7 p.m. when we began our walk. Yiotis drove ahead to find a suitable place to park and wait, while Mila, Lukas and I, munching sandwiches, followed. It was already dark, but as we looked up at the awesome, black mountains before us, a full moon emerged from behind the clouds to light our way.

At first the pace was brisk, but after several kilometers we began to slow down. Each time we reached the parked car, we asked Yiotis the same question. "How many kilometers to go? Each time, we got the same answer. "Just keep walking."

By midnight, Mila couldn't continue. She had a bad cramp in her leg and needed to rest in the car. Lukas and I refrained from stopping even for a few minutes from fear of our muscles stiffening up. The temperature had dropped and our hot breath made steamy clouds in the cold moonlight. "Lukas, did you hear that?" I asked nervously, pricking up my ears.

"What?" he asked, taking off the heavily-lined hood which was keeping his ears from freezing. Suddenly the eerie howling started up again, faint but distinctive.

"There they go again! Don't you hear them? It's a pack of hyenas. They'll tear us to pieces if they spot us."

"They're too far away," Lukas was optimistic. "When we catch up with Yiotis, we'll ask him to keep close to us. The hyenas won't come near the car," he assured me.

The track was deserted. I had somehow expected it to be lined with pilgrims celebrating the saint's feast day, but so far we had met no-one.

"Come to the edge of the road and look down," Lukas suggested. From where we stood, we could see the lights of Dire-Dawa flickering in the valley below. As my eyes moved up the mountainside, I saw it was dotted with tiny moving torches.

"They're all coming to the church, but taking a shortcut up the mountain," said Lukas. That route, he explained, was about fifteen kilometres shorter but quite dangerous. Before one reached the foot of the mountain, a dry riverbed full of soft sand had to be crossed, not to mention an area of thick bush with snakes and leopards.

I shivered, "You do say the right things at the right time, Lukas."

"Mind you, in all the years that people have been coming to fulfil their vows, no dramatic incidents have ever been reported."

"That's good to know," I said looking behind me to make sure nothing on four legs was following us.

The cold was becoming unbearable. We walked with our arms round each other, trying to keep warm. My feet and legs were aching and the stinging sensation on my heels indicated burst blisters. I began to feel a creeping numbness, starting in my fingers and toes.

"Honey, I don't think I can take another step," I whimpered.

"A few more meters and we'll have a cup of strong coffee," Lukas encouraged me on. "I can see the car parked just around the next corner." Gripping me firmly round my waist, Lukas almost carried me to the car. The hot, steaming coffee on my trembling lips was God-sent. With renewed strength, Lukas pulled me up. "Let's go," he urged, "before we seize up for good!"

By 5.30 a.m. we were both dragging our feet, each urging the other to take another step forward. As we approached the end of yet another sweeping curve, I had reached my limit and was ready to collapse. Tears were close and I was about to tell Lukas that this was the end of the road for me, when I felt him hesitate, then stop. Filling his lungs with air, he yelled as loudly as he could.

"Look, Mellina. Look!" His voice bounced from one mountain to another, throwing the echo back to us. "Look!... look!"

Lifting my head, I peered wearily into the distance. There, still several kilometers away, its black shape outlined by what appeared to be a string of glittering pearls, stood the Church of Saint Gabriel. No sinner struggling to find the gates of Heaven could have been more elated.

"We've made it!" we both yelled, hugging and kissing each other. With renewed vigour, we limped the remaining distance, our eyes fixed on that glowing light in the darkness.

After our solitary twelve-hour hike, the sight that met

us at the gates of the church was overwhelming. Hundreds of people were gathered in the yard. Some were singing, some dancing. There were mothers with babies strapped to their backs, crawling about on their knees, giving thanks for the precious gift of life they were carrying. Young deacons, holding richly-embroidered umbrellas, were chanting rhythmically to the accompaniment of drums. As the beat intensified, they performed a slow, traditional dance.

Inside the church itself, turbanned priests in gaudy robes and silver crowns, carried ornate, crudely-wrought bronze crosses. The air was heavy with incense and, after our freezing march, was welcomingly warm. Hundreds more pilgrims, performing all-night vigils, packed the aisles, making it impossible to reach the altar. Seeing us enter, however, people squeezed to one side, creating a passageway to allow us through. The floors were covered with expensive Persian and Ethiopian carpets, the walls were decorated with beautiful hand-painted icons, while sparkling crystal chandeliers hung from the roof.

At the altar, priests held out silver crosses for us to kiss. I placed Askala's gifts next to the Saint's icon and weakly fumbled in my pocket to find the tiny pair of booties I had knitted.

"If You are as powerful as everyone says You are," I prayed, "then prove it to me! Place a pair of healthy little feet in these booties." The icons in front of me started moving from side to side. The walls began to close in on me. I was totally depleted, but I had fulfilled my vow.

* * *

* * *

Little did I know on that night that my prayers had already been answered. Three days before Saint Gabriel's mid-year feast day, on 25 July 1977, my faith in a God was restored. Our wish was granted. A minute, blonde-haired baby girl reached out her tiny hands and found mine. When she was placed in my arms, I clutched her tightly, fearing it was yet another dream and she might disappear. But the warmth generated by that plump little body was no figment of my imagination. She was real and she was ours. I raised my eyes and repented my doubts. We called her Gabby, short for Gabriella.

Three days later, my father died. He had undergone surgery in Nairobi and never came round from the operation. Could it be that this little miracle had been sent in time to ease that overwhelming pain? Never had a day gone by without my father praying that his childless daughter be granted a child. His supplications always ended with "and then I would have fulfilled my earthly deeds".

Was that the bargain? A new life for an old one? He was only sixty-five years old and his death was a mystery to his surgeon and physician. He was a strong man, but was the force of love stronger?

As I held my baby in my arms, I was convinced that my father had relinquished his life to fill my emptiness. Life was eternal and love was immortal and death was only a horizon. He was close to me, sharing my happiness.

PART FOUR

Chapter Twenty Three

Towards the end of 1977, the Vice-Chairman of the Dergue, Lt.-Col. Atnafu Abate, was executed for opposing the revolution, leaving Lt. Col. Mengistu Haile Mariam as the administration's undisputed head.

The war with Eritrea was escalating as the guerrillas steadily captured more and more towns in the north and west, driving back the government forces. Hospital wards in Addis Ababa were overflowing with casualties. The city streets were more treacherous than ever as trigger-happy troops, instructed to stamp out any signs of opposition to the regime, sought out anti-revolutionaries. The crack of wild bullets in the street below awoke me one night and I leapt out of bed, hurrying to Gabby's cot to place my hands over her ears. I didn't want the gunfire to waken or frighten her. She stirred once or twice, but I knew the sound had not penetrated. When the shooting stopped, I covered her with her comforter and returned to bed, snuggling down under the warm bedcovers.

What was all that about? God only knew. I wondered how many mothers would be crying the next morning and shivered. When was all this senseless killing going to end? Suddenly, our front door bell rang. First it was a short buzz, then a more persistent one. My heart leapt. "Lukas!" I nudged my sleeping husband. "There's someone at the door."

Lukas swung himself out of bed, grabbed his dressing gown and stumbled sleepily towards the door. I followed close behind, wondering who it could be at this unearthly hour. It was Pavlos. After Manoli's death, Evangelia and Pavlos had moved into an apartment on the floor below ours.

"What's happened?" asked Lukas.

"It's Mother, she's had a bad fall. She woke up with all the shooting and couldn't go back to sleep, so she decided to go and make herself a cup of tea. Unfortunately, she stumbled over something in the dark and fell. Her legs somehow twisted under her as she went down and the left leg is crushed. She's in a lot of pain and I can't lift her. You'd better come and help."

"I'm coming," said Lukas, hastily. "Mellina, you'd better get the doctor to come as soon as possible. We'll try and pick her up and get her into bed."

The men leapt down the stairs two steps at a time. I rang the doctor, but he was at the hospital so I left a message. Checking that Gabby was sleeping soundly, I ran downstairs to see what was going on. The men hadn't managed to move Evangelia as she was in too much pain. I found her propped against a kitchen cupboard on the cold, stone floor.

"Maybe we shouldn't try to move her. We might do more harm than good. The doctor will be here soon," I said.

"But the floor's so cold. She'll catch pneumonia!" Pavlos exclaimed.

"Let's get a couple of blankets and ease them under

267

her. That should make her more comfortable," I suggested.

We were in the process of manoeuvring the blankets under Evangelia when the door bell rang. It was Dr. Makrinov. "I came as soon as I got your message. Where's your mother?" he asked Pavlos.

"Dr. Makrinov, I've broken something I'm sure," sobbed Evangelia, finally breaking down now that help was at hand. The doctor crouched down to examine her, gently moving the leg which she had fallen. "Is it broken?" she asked, her teeth clenched in pain.

"Your hip bone may have been fractured, but I can't be sure until it's been X-rayed," he replied. Straightening himself up, he thought for a few minutes and then announced his decision. "I don't think we should take any risks. We'd better call an ambulance and I'll admit you to hospital right away. We can do all the X-rays and necessary tests there."

While I rang for an ambulance, the men each picked up a corner of the blanket we had slipped under Evangelia and gently carried her through to her bedroom.

"Ask if there's a private bed available," Dr. Makrinov called to me. "The wards are full of soldiers injured in the Ogaden and Eritrea. In fact, even the corridors are full of beds at the moment, but we might be lucky enough to find a private room. I do know of one that will be vacated this morning."

Evangelia was lying, exhausted, on her bed when I entered with the bad news. "Dr. Makrinov, there's nothing available—no ambulance, no room, nothing. I tried some of the other hospitals and they told me their rooms were reserved for the wounded, fighting for the survival of their country."

"I was afraid of that," he said. "This is disturbing indeed. Even if there is no room available, we should at least get this hip and leg X-rayed. There's absolutely no way we could transport her in a car. There's got to be an ambulance!"

"I have an idea!" I cried, suddenly remembering the ambulance parked outside the United Nations clinic. I rang the UN doctor and as luck would have it, the ambulance was available but we'd have to pick up the keys and drive it ourselves. By mid-day we had managed to transport Evangelia to the X-ray department and back and were anxiously awaiting the results. The news was not good: both the pelvis and hip-bone were fractured and needed pinning. Due to her age, the operation could not be performed in Addis—Evangelia would have to be evacuated.

While she waited for her papers to be processed, Dr. Makrinov fixed a five-kilo weight to her injured leg in order to stretch the muscle and prevent one leg becoming shorter than the other. He said it would also facilitate the operation. Lukas, in the meantime, began an endless marathon from one government office to another, in a fruitless bid to obtain her exit permit. Each office requested more and more paperwork—certificates from the examining doctor, his written findings, his initial diagnosis, certificates from a government-recognized X-ray department, an independent government doctor's recommendation, fresh X-rays as the originals were unclear. The demands were endless.

After eight weeks, with Evangelia still strapped to her bed, the final decision was given. No one from the Fanouris family was allowed to leave the country until all due taxes were paid. There was no argument, no

269

compromise.

Evangelia's fracture was not healing properly. She was confined to a wheelchair, her legs unable to support her weight. As the weeks turned into months, it was pitiful to watch this once energetic woman doomed to a life of immobility.

"Mother, where are you?" I called out one morning, not finding her in her usual place.

"Over here," she called from the kitchen. I found her peeling carrots and potatoes in a bowl on her lap.

"Are you alone?" I asked, looking around for Askala.

"Yes, Askala is not feeling too well. She sent me a message with her neighbour. The weather has changed so suddenly, I just hope she's not getting another asthma attack."

"Why didn't you call me, Mother? It's Saturday today and I won't be going to the office. I could cook lunch for you."

"Please let me feel just a little useful." Her eyes pleaded. "I felt if I didn't get down to doing something, I'd go crazy with boredom. This daily monotony will be the end of me. I wheeled myself into the kitchen and once I was confident I could move around on my own and get to the fridge and the cooker, I knew I could at least prepare a meal for you all."

"You'll never be useless, Mother," I said, putting my arm round her shoulders. "You know that. But it's good to see you back in your kitchen. I can assure you your delicious relishes have been greatly missed."

"I bet Askala will hit the roof when she sees me in here," Evangelia smiled. "She'll calm down though, when she sees what a therapeutic effect it has on me. If my legs refuse to carry me, at least I'm able to exercise my hands."

270

I breathed a sigh of relief. At least she had come to terms with her condition and was finding ways of keeping herself occupied.

"As a matter of fact, Mellina, you could do me a favour," she said.

"Of course, anything."

"I'm cooking Askala's favourite dish. Could you get someone to take down a plateful for her? I know she wouldn't miss coming to work if she wasn't really sick, so she won't be well enough to cook for herself."

"No problem. I'll be back when the food's ready. I'll have put Gabby to bed by then so I'll take it to her myself and I can check what's wrong with her." Just after twelve, the meal was ready and I picked up the four-sectioned container to take to Askala.

"There's sphagetti and meatballs for lunch and some soup and yoghurt for her dinner," said Evangelia. "On second thoughts, tell her to eat it all now and I'll send her chicken soup for dinner."

"Okay," I called. "I'll pass on the message."

The street leading to Askala's quarters was narrow and unpaved. She had been allowed to continue occupying a room on the ground floor of an old double-storey house which had been nationalized. The *kebele* had agreed that, due to her age, it was not fair to throw her out, but the room was cold and damp during the rainy season and not at all the best environment for someone who suffered from asthma.

The boys from the neighbourhood always ran to greet me with outstretched hands, hoping I was bringing them some small treat, which invariably I did. "*Tenaistilin*, Mellina," said one of the boldest, bidding me good day in Amharic. He bowed politely.

"Abebe, how are you today?" I asked him.

"I'm fine, but we're all rather glum," he began, looking down and twisting his fingers.

"And why, may I ask, is that?"

"Well, you know the ball you bought us last week? Well, it got under the wheels of a careless car and was squashed flat. We haven't been able to play football for days." He adopted an exaggeratedly pitiful expression.

"Am I the only one in this neighbourhood who is the supplier of footballs?" I teased.

"But, Mellina, the cause is a genuine one. It was the stupid car's fault. It had to turn into our street just when I was about to shoot a fantastic goal."

"So you scored right between the wheels, eh?" I joked.

"Bull's eye!" he nodded, grinning.

"Okay, here are two birr with which to buy yourselves a stronger ball, but mind it doesn't get squashed or there will be no more balls for a long time."

"But if we buy a ball for two birr, Mellina, there will be nothing left for sweeties," he sighed. He was cheeky but honest and I had to laugh. To these poverty-stricken urchins, who never knew what the next day might bring, candies were the ultimate treat. I delved in my pocket and produced another birr. A delighted Abebe raced ahead of me to Askala's door to announce my arrival. It was his way of thanking me.

"Mama Askala, *ingida metual*," he called, excitedly, knocking on her door.

"You're spoiling these kids rotten," Askala scolded me as she let me in. "I heard them talking outside my window the minute they spotted you walking down the road, conniving how to ask you for money for yet another ball."

"But they're just kids, Mama Askala, and I love

spoiling them, I really do. They're so eager to please in their own little ways and that really touches my heart."

"These are difficult days, Mellina. You should economise instead of throwing your money away on footballs."

"Now, stop scolding me and tell me how you feel," I chided her affectionately, setting down the container on her small, wooden table.

"I have a pain in my chest and I'm coughing a little, but it's nothing too serious. Stop fussing and worrying over me, I'll be up and about tomorrow." She glanced at the container. "And what have you brought here? Food for an army?"

"Well, you know mother! She went into the kitchen for the first time since her accident today and you know how she loves to cook. She's obviously been making up for lost time. Anyway, stop complaining. It's not too much. It's also for your dinner."

"You must be joking! There's enough food here for three days!"

"Now, I'm not going to argue with you, Mama. Just eat as much as you can to get your strength back. Do you need any medicine?" I asked, changing the subject.

"Just some cough mixture will do and don't go buying that expensive stuff from England," she added quickly. "The local one will do just fine."

"I'll go and buy whatever I feel is best for you," I said, tucking the covers round her. "Stop being so concerned about money. Health comes first. Now, take it easy and I'll go straight to the chemist's and send it down to you."

Outside, Abebe was waiting for me to show off his shiny new ball. After admiring it, I asked him to accompany me to the drug store and return with the

273

cough mixture for Askala. When I arrived home from work the following day I found Abebe waiting for me in front of our gate.

"You had better get some stronger medicine for Mama Askala, she can't breathe and she's sent me to get you, you'd better get down there fast," he said all in one breath.

I ran to the pharmacy on the ground floor of our building and explained the situation. The chemist knew Askala and was familiar with her asthma attacks. He gave me an oxygen spray and told me to get it to her quickly. I dashed out of the shop and ran straight into Lukas, who was on his way home. "What's the rush?" he asked. "You look panicky."

"Mama Askala's had an asthma attack and she can't breathe. I'm running down to her with this," I said, waving the spray.

"Let me look in on Gabby and then I'll come down and join you. We might have to take her to hospital if it's serious," he said, getting into the lift.

With Abebe close on my heels, I was just a few yards from Askala's door when a shot whizzed past my ear, followed by shouting and the thunderous sound of heavy boots running. My first reaction was to grab Abebe from behind and pull him to one side, shielding him with my body and covering my ears with my hands as the shots ricocheted around us. Turning my head, I saw a squad of soldiers pounding down the street, rifles raised and blazing, but it was not me they were shooting at. Their target was a well-dressed, sophisticated young man who raced passed us, running for his life.

I closed my eyes. "This is it!" I thought. "One of the bullets is bound to get me straight in the back. I'm going to die!" My legs began to shake involuntarily, giving way beneath me. A terrified growl escaped from my throat. "Oh God, help me!" It was then that two weak, trembling hands, which had gained inhuman strength from hearing the shots, suddenly grasped my shoulders and pulled me to safety. Two tired, sunken eyes scrutinized my face, making sure I had not been harmed. My heart thumped uncontrollably.

"You're safe, my child," whispered Askala, hoarsely. "Mariam, the Virgin Mary, has saved you from certain death. It would have been all my fault. What a waste it would have been for you to have given your life for mine, an old woman who's on the point of death anyway. What a sin." Shaking her head and trembling from her efforts, Mama Askala fell back on her bed, her chest heaving as she tried desperately to suck in air. Her eyes had rolled up revealing only the whites and her lips were blue.

I stood up but immediately ducked as a shot whistled in through the open window. Running to close the shutters, I witnessed the slaughter of the fleeing youth and the mourning of his betrothed. The sound of choking brought me back to Askala's side. With shaking hands, I fumbled for the oxygen spray and began pumping it into her mouth.

"Don't die, Mama Askala. Please, don't give up. Breathe. Don't fight the oxygen. Just relax. Breathe, Mama Askala, breathe." As the old woman's rasping grew easier, I heard an agonized yell from the street outside.

"Mellina, Mellina, where are you? For God's sake, has anyone seen my wife?"

Abebe, who had hidden behind a pile of wood, ran to Lukas and tugged at his leg, trying to explain to him what had happened. But Lukas, his agony so intense, neither felt nor heard the boy. "*Geta* Lukas, listen to me," the boy cried desperately.

Hearing the commotion, I flung open Askala's old wooden door and called out, "Lukas, I'm alright. I'm here. I haven't been hurt."

Lukas rushed over, wrapping me in his arms. "Thank God! Thank God!" he cried. "When I heard the shooting, I..." He put his hand to my face and stroked my cheek. "My God, Mellina..." He shook his head.

Together we went back to Askala. Her cheeks had gained a little colour and her lips were no longer blue. I gave her a few more sprays of oxygen. Her breathing had almost returned to normal. "I'm better. Go home," she said weakly. "Everyone must be worried sick about you. Really I'm feeling much better. Be off with you."

When we were finally convinced she had indeed improved, we made our way home. "Mellina, I can't survive another incident like that!" said Lukas, as soon as we were out on the road. "Next time maybe we won't be so lucky. We'd better start thinking seriously about you leaving Ethiopia. And I want you to take Gabby with you."

The thought of separation after we had waited so many years to be a complete family, to share parenthood and enjoy the laughter and cries of a child in our home, was too much for me. With a lump in my throat and tears ready to flow, I tried to calm things down and put off the inevitable decision. "Let's not discuss it now, Lukas, when we're both so upset. Let's forget about it for now and review the situation later."

"Don't you understand, Mellina," he exploded. "This is the end! When I heard those shots being fired by those ignorant, trigger-happy louts, not caring whether there were women or children on the street, I thought I'd lost you. Can you imagine what it was like when I ran to the balcony and I couldn't see you on the street? All I could think of was that you were lying down there somewhere riddled with bullets. How can anyone justify such mindless, senseless shooting without any consideration for innocent lives? No, the end has come, Mellina. Nothing, nothing is worth losing a loved one. Nothing!" he shouted. I couldn't speak; the lump in my throat was too tight. I squeezed his hand.

"There's nothing more to discuss," he said, his voice flat and resigned. "If you want to save us all, you must take the first step. Gabby needs you more than she needs me. You must both leave."

It was hard for me to face the reality of the situation, but I knew Lukas was right; the revolution was now directly threatening the peace and security of our family and home. But where could we go? There was no foreign account to turn to, no wealth or property. I needed an income to survive and there was not just myself to think of, I had a babe in arms to care for. I decided to enquire at work if it were possible for me to be transferred or reassigned. But where to? If only my father were alive, he would have found a solution for me.

Chapter Twenty Four

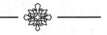

The answer to my prayers came via a telephone call one evening. It was my family in Nairobi.

"Mellina, listen!" It was Electra. "We received your disturbing letter this morning and we've had a family meeting. Mum, Laki, Byron and I all feel you should come here, to Nairobi, and stay with us. There's nothing like family unity at a time like this."

"But can I get a job, Trish?" I asked, using her nickname. "My boss has written to the UNDP headquarters asking if there's any possibility of a transfer, but so far there's been no response. I can't come to Nairobi and be a burden to you all."

"What kind of nonsense is that, Mellina?" her voice came crackling down the line. "Since when can a member of the family become a burden?"

"Well, you know our situation. We're down to nothing and, if I can't get a job, we won't be able to survive."

"With your qualifications and experience in the UN, I'm sure the UNEP headquarters in Nairobi will be able to offer you something. But don't just send an application form, come and see them in person."

"Maybe you're right, but I won't resign from my

present job until I have something definitely fixed up."

"Well, tell us when you can take some leave and Laki will send you the tickets."

"Oh, Trish, we haven't even planned anything definite and you guys are knocking yourselves out already."

"Don't be so proud! It's our turn to stand by you in your time of need. Just let us know when you'll be needing the tickets."

I hung up feeling more lighthearted. Maybe something would turn up. Lukas was delighted with the suggestion. "The sooner you're on your way the better, honey. I'm getting more and more uncomfortable with the situation here."

My boss, Harvey Williams, was sympathetic. He said I could take all the leave I needed and promised to back my efforts to get transferred. My only anxiety, I told him, was procuring an exit visa and I explained how the Fanouris family had been refused permission to leave because of a tax dispute. "My mother-in-law needs to be evacuated for medical reasons, but they won't even let her go. She's been in a wheelchair for the past eight months," I concluded.

"I'm sorry, I didn't know that," said Harvey. "But you've been a United Nations staff member for the past fifteen years, since before you were married. As such, you've never been subjected to any form of tax, so I really don't see anything to worry about. However, to be on the safe side, I'll ask our liaison officer to assist you with all your permits and visas and, eventually, I hope, with the paperwork to export your personal effects."

I could have kissed him! Everything was going smoothly; perhaps too smoothly. I had been secretly hoping for some insurmountable obstacle which would prevent my leaving and breaking up our home. But it was not to be.

On 27 October 1978, after passing safely through customs, Gabby and I boarded the Ethiopian Airlines flight for Nairobi. The blood was still pounding in my ears. I was so nervous I had barely heard what the officer asked me; I simply watched his lips move.

"Do you work for the United Nations?"

"Yes, sir."

"Going on official business?"

"Yes, sir."

"How long will you be away?"

"Just a few weeks."

"If you're going on official business, why are you taking your baby with you?"

I panicked. They were going to find a reason to prevent me from leaving. "My family want to see her. They live in Kenya," I said, trying to control the tremor in my voice.

"How very convenient…," he said sarcastically, "…to have a family at the place of official business." My pulse leapt. He was not going to stamp my passport.

"Yes!" I tried to smile, licking my dry lips.

"Have a good trip," he said, stamping our passports. "See you back in a few weeks."

I don't remember walking away. In a half-swoon, I made it to the departure lounge. I could hardly believe it when the aircraft finally took off and we were on our way to Nairobi. I hugged my fifteen-month-old, suddenly remembering it was her feed time. She must have sensed my tension, for she hadn't uttered a word of complaint, but now she sucked hungrily, grasping the bottle tightly. The flight took an hour and a half. Letting out a long sigh of relief, I put my head back and relaxed.

My father's absence at the airport was painful. Despite

myself, I still looked for his enthusiastic welcome, the waving of his white handkerchief and his loud whistle when he spotted me. It wasn't there! I stifled the tears.

"Hi, Mellina!" came Laki's voice from behind us. I turned, almost falling into his arms. Somehow he had managed to get into the baggage hall. Seeing my eyes water, Laki immediately sensed my pain. "You've got to be strong, Sis," he said. "Dad's loss is hard to accept but life has to go on. No one will ever replace him, but I'm here for you. I'll stand by you like Dad would have done."

"It's such a precious gift to have you as a brother," I whispered, wiping my eyes.

"We began panicking when you didn't come through the barrier," he said, taking hold of my trolley and wheeling it towards the exit.

"Well, with Gabby and all these bags, I decided to sit tight until everyone had disembarked. We were the last off."

"For a while we thought you hadn't made it—that they'd prevented you from leaving."

"I must admit I nearly had a heart attack when we passed through immigration, but, thank the Lord, we're here."

In the high, rather old-fashioned arrival hall, the whole family was congregated to meet us. I had not seen any of them since my father died and when I clasped my mother, the tears flowed on both sides. Gabby saved the day. Strutting up and down in her fluffy white coat and red velvet hat, she instinctively showed off, making everyone laugh.

"She's beautiful!" my mother exclaimed, hugging her. "It's wonderful to have you home."

* * *

281

* * *

After a number of interviews with different United Nations agencies, a few prospects looked promising, but UN wheels ground slowly and time was running out. I had one more appointment with the recruitment officer of UNEP.

As luck would have it, I was interviewed by the Chief of Personnel, *Ato* Getaneh, an Ethiopian national, who used to work with my former Head, Brian Strongman. I met him at the showpiece complex in the Nairobi suburb of Gigiri, surrounded by extensive lawns, trickling streams, exotic flowering shrubs and the fluttering flags of the 159-member nations.

"If you managed to survive working with one of the toughest administrators in the United Nations, I don't think we'll have any problem offering you a job here," he said. "When can you start?"

It was too good to be true. I calculated quickly, "Well, I have to go back to Addis and officially resign from UNDP; then I have to pack up my house and wind up my affairs. I could be back in Nairobi to start work during the first week in January. Would that be alright?"

"I think we can manage it. We'll send an official offer direct to your boss in UNDP and seek an early release date."

"I have no words to thank you, sir," I said, extending my hand gratefully. I floated out of the building, but after the initial euphoria other worries began to weigh me down.

"Have you really got a job?" Electra shrieked with delight at the news.

"The grade isn't too good, but beggars can't be choosers. I'll just have to work hard to prove what I can

282

do."

"You seem a little down. Is something bothering you?"

"Yes, actually, I'm worried what Lukas is going to do in Addis without my salary."

"Come on. He'll be following you shortly. In the meantime, I'm sure he'll find something."

"It's not so easy to get a job in Addis these days," I said. "Most companies are winding up and there's no new investment."

"You're a born worrier, Mellina! Let's tackle one problem at a time and you'll see how everything will work out in the end."

Our conversation was interrupted by the telephone ringing. Electra answered it while my mind whirled round all the plans that needed to be made. "I know this will cheer you up," she smiled, beckoning me over. "Guess who wants to speak to you?" I looked at her blankly, putting the receiver to my ear.

"Give it a try," the caller urged me. "We've been friends for all these years and now you don't even recognise my voice!"

"Oh, my God! Michael! Is it really you?" I shrieked.

After living in Athens for two years, he and Aspa had decided that they were homesick for Africa and were investigating the possibilities of settling in Kenya. Had fate made our paths cross again?

As I was preparing to leave, my mother suggested I left Gabby with them until I returned, thinking it would make packing and moving easier. I hesitated, knowing Lukas would miss her, but it was a more practical arrangement. It was hard to leave behind our little bundle of joy, especially as she was becoming aware that our lives were in for a big change. I bent down and kissed her as she slept, unaware of my departure. Tears sprang to my eyes as I crept silently away.

"Your mission is accomplished?" asked the same customs officer, stamping my passport at Addis Airport.

"Yes," I said, anxious to pick up my papers and move on.

"And where's your child?" he questioned.

"I left her with my mother," I answered, briefly. Realising he needed more elaboration, I continued, "The weather is too chilly here now, so she's enjoying some warmth and sunshine."

"Maybe you're right," he said, looking me straight in the eye. "Our nights at this time of year are very cold."

I hated this chit-chat. One never knew what they were really after. I was glad when he'd finished and I could make for the exit.

Lukas' face fell when he saw I'd left Gabby behind, but he was pleased I had found a job. Matters had deteriorated even since I had left. The killings had increased and every morning there were piles of bodies in the streets with notes stuck on them branding them as dissidents exterminated by the Red Terror.

"It's terrible," said Lukas. "I'm just relieved that you, at least, will be safe in Nairobi. Philip and Angeliki have decided they've had enough; they're planning to leave as soon as they get exit permits."

"But I thought Philip's business was doing well."

"It was until the Government introduced restrictions on exports. His company will soon be working at a loss and it's simply not worth their while to continue."

"Poor Angeliki. She must be devastated."

"She's planning to take Mother with her when she leaves, but I don't know if she'll succeed."

"How have Mother and Pavlos been?"

"Mother's still in a lot of pain, but at least Pavlos has a job at the Olympiacos, caretaking the Club."

I slipped my arm into his. "What about you?"

"I've been for a couple of interviews, but I don't think there's any hope. There's so much unemployment. Jobs are scarce."

"I'm so worried about what will happen to you when I leave. How will you manage?"

"Don't worry about us. We'll manage somehow!"

The uncertainty of it all was terrifying. What Pavlos was earning would barely meet the running costs of the apartment. How would they manage if any crisis arose? They had an elderly mother who needed medical attention. I would leave them all my indemnity money, but how long would that last? And above all, when would I see Lukas again? Unless there was some miraculous change in official policy or another coup, there seemed to be no chance of him being allowed to leave in the foreseeable future. For my sake, Lukas was optimistic.

"I'm sure they'll give us a permit soon. We've been told secretly that they're investigating whether or not we have foreign accounts. When they're satisfied no money was ever smuggled out, they'll undoubtedly deduct the tax they're demanding from our final compensation, when the time comes."

"Do you think they'll compensate you soon?"

"Sure, it won't be long!" I knew from the tone of his voice that in his heart he didn't believe it, but I decided not to pursue the matter further. We had only six weeks left to be together and I wanted to make it as easy as possible for him. His task was going to be difficult enough.

A few days later, a telex arrived from Nairobi offering

285

me a job with the United Nations Environment Programme. "I hate to accept your resignation," Harvey Williams told me when I went in to see him, "but I'm happy for you. I can't say you didn't warn me. You're probably doing the right thing, under the circumstances."

A UN official came to help me itemize all the furniture and household goods which were to be packed. "We have to be careful not to miss anything out. If the customs officer picks up just one item that's not listed, the whole shipment will be in jeopardy," he said. The list then had to be sent to the Central Bank for approval before we could contact a removal firm.

"I think we'll sell everything that's not going," said Lukas, who had already decided to move in with his mother and Pavlos.

"Don't you want to keep anything?" I asked.

"My mother has an apartment bursting with fifty years' worth of antique furniture, carpets and pictures. I doubt very much if there's space for anything else. I'll just keep my collection of books."

I looked round at our comfortable apartment with its panoramic view of the city. "It really breaks my heart to leave. We've been so happy here."

Lukas put his arm round my shoulders. "It isn't of our own choice, Mellina. We're faced with circumstances beyond our control. Come on, we'll have another happy home. You'll see. We won't be apart for long."

Two weeks later, we received Central Bank approval to export our goods, but only after a number of interrogations involving our liaison officer in interminable trips back and forth to supply additional evidence concerning my initial recruitment and subsequent reassignment.

My own departure coincided with that of Angeliki and Philip. Their efforts to secure an exit visa for Evangelia had fallen on deaf ears. We all knew what a great loss it was going to be for Evangelia, who was accustomed to having her daughter around. But she kept faith with Manoli and put on a brave face. "I'll be all right," she assured her daughter. "You must first think of your immediate family. I've got the boys here; they'll look after me until I'm given permission to join you."

As the day for her departure drew near, Angeliki broke down. "I know I'll never see my mother again," she wept.

"Stop being pessimistic!" I tried to console her. "Of course you'll see her again. She'll be coming to join you in Athens soon."

"Even if they let her leave, she'll never be able to travel alone. There'll be no one to help her."

Searching for some words of comfort, I made her a vow which I prayed I would be able to keep. "I swear to you, Angleliki, if Mother is given permission to leave, I'll bring her to you in Athens, myself. I promise I'll do it!"

As my own departure loomed, I couldn't bear the thought of bidding farewell to all the friends and colleagues with whom I had shared so many sentimental moments, both in times of happiness and sorrow.

"Take me with you," begged Askala. "There'll be no one to give me medicine when I'm sick, nor water when I'm thirsty."

"Please, Mama Askala, don't make it hard for me," I pleaded. "I wish to God I could take you all with me. I can't even take my husband; you will take care of him for me, won't you?"

"I'll try; with every breath in my body, I'll try," said the old woman, a tremor in her voice. "Never forget that you're leaving part of you behind. Never forget that, my child!" I stood in front of Evangelia. Her grey hair was pinned back in a neat bun and she was wearing a simple cotton dress with two large pockets. She had worn that same style of dress for as long as I could remember. Pushing herself up onto her elbows, she hooked one hand round my neck, pulling my head down towards her. "May the Virgin Mary guide your steps, my child," she whispered. "Who knows if I'll ever see you again?"

I put my arms around her. "I beg you, don't talk like that. I know something will give soon and they'll let you leave."

"Maybe it might be better if I went to join Manoli and Sophia in Gulele," she said, her lips quivering. "I'm just a nuisance and a burden to my boys in this condition. I can't offer them any help," she said, nodding to herself.

"Don't give up now, Mother. You've always been a tower of strength to your family. I made a promise to Angeliki that I would come back and take you to Athens and I intend to keep that oath. Now, will you give me your word that you'll hold on tight until that time comes?"

"So be it then," she muttered in a barely audible whisper. "I'll be patient till the time comes."

Gebremariam, the UN liaison officer, was at Bole Airport, waiting to see me through customs in case there were any last minute hitches. "The immigration officer is a friend of mine and he knows you're a UN staff member, so there's no problem. Let's go."

My long time friend, May Diamandis, was also at the airport to see me off. We had shared many happy days together and in my most difficult moments she always had an encouraging word to offer. "Take care of yourself and Gabby and don't worry about Lukas," she whispered.

"I'll see to it that he doesn't get too lonely. I'll ask him to join Yerasimos and me for meals. He won't be able to resist my cooking!"

"Thanks, May. I'm going to miss you terribly. You've been such a tower of strength to me. I know Lukas will be well taken care of as long as you're still here." But I knew sooner or later, May and her husband would also be leaving, although the government was making it as difficult as possible for them. Yerasimos Diamandis was a coffee exporter and an invaluable asset to the country's economy.

I kissed Pavlos goodbye and turned to Lukas. We clasped each other briefly, neither of us wanting to break down. "I know God won't keep us apart too long. We'll be waiting for you, sweetheart. Be strong! Don't lose your courage or your good humour."

"I'll try," he whispered.

Our little dog, Jeannie, yelped, wondering when I would give her some attention. "Take care of him, Jeannie," I said, stroking her. She licked my hand vigorously.

"She will. Don't worry," said Lukas. "She'll keep my feet warm at night until we're together again."

Chapter Twenty Five

Driving home from the airport, Lukas felt an empty feeling hit the pit of his stomach. He had tried hard to put on a show for Mellina, making light of the situation, but the reality was that his daily efforts to obtain exit visas were only for Pavlos and his mother. They had Greek passports and the authorities would eventually have to let them go when their investigations proved that no money from the business had ever left Ethiopia. But for him, it was different. As a naturalized Ethiopian, there was no way they would ever consent to his departure, however authentic the reason. He couldn't bring himself to tell Mellina the truth, but he knew he was doomed. He felt sick watching them go, but he wasn't going to allow his wife and daughter to live in fear. They had a right to carry on their lives somewhere safe, where there were no restrictions, even if it was without him. However painful it was, he had to put his own feelings aside; there was no room for selfishness. Loving someone didn't mean possessing them. Caring for his family as much as he did, Lukas knew he had to make sacrifices for them to be happy.

He turned to Pavlos who was sitting in the front

passenger seat, staring at the road, deep in thought. "Penny for your thoughts," he said, breaking the silence.

"Watching Mellina leave has reminded me of the day Venetia left with the children. Three years ago!" He shook his head. "Can you believe it? It's exactly three years since they left."

"I know, Pavlos, I know. In fact, I was thinking the same thing when I saw the plane vanish into the clouds. I wonder how long it'll be before I see Mellina and Gabby again. Maybe, never."

Pavlos sighed. "I get the same feelings. I wonder if I'll ever make it to join my family."

Lukas tried to shake himself out of his depression. "We've got to think positively. Our first concern is to get Mother out. After that, I think they'll allow you to follow her. I've been given some hope, secretly. We'll just have to keep our fingers crossed."

Pavlos brightened a little. "Let's pray it's soon, otherwise it will be impossible to do anything with Mother's hip. She should have had the operation months ago. I just hope it's not too late already." Pavlos asked to be dropped off at the Olympiacos as they approached Revolution Square. "Incidentally," he said, poking his head through the car window, "I heard at the club yesterday that soldiers are conducting house-to-house searches for weapons and ammunition, so you'd better warn Mother. We've nothing to hide, but there's no point in her being frightened."

"I think one of us should be with her the whole time," replied Lukas. "We'll avoid mentioning anything about searches unless we hear they're actually in the neighbourhood."

"Right. See you both at dinner," said Pavlos, walking

291

off in the direction of the club.

Lukas began to feel uneasy. Was the army really searching for arms or was it interested in other things? Over the past fifty years, the family had accumulated all sorts of historical souvenirs, including family gifts, from the Palace. It was probably wise to pack them up and put them out of sight.

As he pulled into the drive, he noticed Dr. Georgiadis' car parked outside the gate. Fearing his mother was ill, he ran up the stairs. Askala opened the door, showing no signs of agitation. "They're just having coffee and a chat," she reported. "Can I get you a cup too?"

"Yes, please, Mama Askala. I haven't had anything since breakfast." Lukas strode into the living room. "Doctor, what a pleasant surprise!" he said, shaking his hand.

"I've been meaning to pay your mother a visit for days now, but my leg has been giving me quite a bit of trouble and I couldn't walk."

"It's old age creeping up on us, Doctor," said Evangelia. "We're not getting any younger."

"My aches might be from old age, but you go and fracture your hip and pelvis. You could have done very well without this inconvenience," scolded the Doctor with a smile.

"I agree it was bad timing, Doctor, but once I'm in the good hands of my nephew in Athens, I know he'll fix me up and make me as good as new. He's a good surgeon."

"Keep up your good spirits now, Evangelia. I'm happy to hear you talk like that." He looked at his watch and decided it was time to take his leave. "I've got to call on another friend who's sick, so I'd better be off," he said, winking at Lukas and motioning him outside.

"Something wrong, Doctor?" asked Lukas, once they were out in the hall.

"Yes," he said, adding hastily, "but it's nothing to do with your mother. She's as well as can be expected. I came to ask you a big favour."

"Anything, Doctor. Just name it."

"Don't be too anxious to agree before you know what I'm going to ask. Actually, I don't like to ask you and if you think there might be any problems, we'll just forget about it." He hesitated.

"Well, go on, Doctor, out with it. I'm burning with curiosity."

Dr. Georgiadis rubbed his chin. "I suppose you've heard that they've started house-to-house searches for arms and ammunition?"

"Actually, Pavlos just mentioned it to me this morning, but only as something he'd heard discussed at the club. Do you know anything more about it?"

The Doctor nodded gravely. "My night watchman alerted me last night that searches were underway at the old airport. Apparently, they've arrested a number of people for possessing antique guns and spears that were nailed to the walls as decorations. I don't know how they missed my house, but I'm almost certain they'll be back tonight."

Lukas noticed the doctor's hands were trembling. He looked at him with concern. "What's making you nervous, Doctor?" he asked.

The old man dived into his coat pocket and produced a brown paper parcel, holding it out to Lukas. "This is a small pistol I've had for self-protection for many years. Could you dispose of it for me, Lukas? Throw it in the river or something? I would do it myself, but I have a

293

driver who accompanies me everywhere and, although he's always been loyal to me, I would hate to think what might happen if anyone suspected me and interrogated him."

"I"ll take care of it for you," said Lukas, taking the package.

The sheer relief of handing over the gun visibly calmed the poor doctor. "Ever since I heard about the searches this morning, I've been frightened out of my wits, wondering what I should do. There are so few people you can trust these days and there's no joking with the Red Terror. Who knows what price one has to pay for something so small? Bless you, Lukas."

Lukas locked the package in the drawer of his bedside table. The minute Pavlos came home, he would drive up to Ras Makonnen Bridge and throw it into the river. Perhaps not, he thought again. What if someone saw him lingering on the bridge? They might report him. No, it was better to wait until dark and drive up towards the Entoto Hills. He could find a spot away from any residential area and avoid getting anyone into trouble. Satisfied with his plan, he picked up a novel and soon became so involved in the plot, he lost all sense of time. A key turning in the front door made him jump. He looked at his watch. It was late, only a few minutes before curfew.

"Pavlos! What happened? You're late tonight!"

Pavlos slumped into a chair, obviously a little shaken. "John Miralis, the guy who was giving me a lift home, got tied up in a card game. I'm lucky to be home at all—a few minutes more and we'd have been spending the night in jail."

"Did someone stop you?"

"Of course they did! One guy pulled us up at gunpoint,

294

insisting his watch was right and ours was wrong by fifteen minutes."

"How did you get out of that?"

"We drove him up to the City Hall to check the time with the town clock. When we finally convinced him his watch was wrong, we had to drive him right back again to where we'd picked him up. By then, we were almost on curfew time. Luckily there wasn't another car on the road—we drove home like maniacs."

"Well, I'm glad you made it. There's some hot soup on the stove for you."

"My stomach's still churning. I don't think I could eat anything right now. I'm dead beat. I think I'm going to turn in."

They had barely switched off the lights, when Lukas heard the squeal of heavy vehicles braking on the road outside the compound. He rushed to the window and between the cracks in the blinds, saw two truckloads of soldiers with guns and walkie-talkies enter the apartment block opposite. Before he had chance to call Pavlos, he was by his side, peering out.

"Do you think they've come to arrest someone or are they searching for guns?" Pavlos mused.

Guns! Lukas broke out in a cold sweat. The doctor's gun! He hadn't had time to get rid of it! "Pavlos, quick!" he yelled, dashing into his bedroom and yanking open the bedside drawer. "We've got to hide this."

"What in heaven's name is that?" exclaimed Pavlos, looking blankly at the brown paper parcel.

"I'll explain later! Now, quick, where do we hide it? If they're in this neighbourhood, we'll be searched next."

Lukas ran into the bathroom, but decided against flushing it away. It was too big. He could feel the sweat trickling from his armpits as he ran back into the sitting room, looking around him wildly.

"Over here!" said Pavlos softly. He had uprooted a plant and, quickly removing the revolver from its wrapping, threw it into the pot. The roots curled themselves round the gun as Pavlos dropped it back into place, pressing the earth down. Sweeping up some spilt soil, he tipped it back into the flower pot. There was no evidence that the plant had been disturbed. The men hurriedly washed their hands and wiped the floor clean.

"If they see as much as a speck of dirt on the floor, they'll suspect we've been up to something," said Pavlos.

"Why then," asked Lukas, his racing heart gradually returning to normal, "don't we move the plant to another corner?"

They had barely finished their rearrangements when angry shouts from the yard below penetrated the apartment. The soldiers were demanding that the night guard open the gates.

"We'd better get back into bed and pretend to be asleep. They'll have to go through seven apartments before they get to us. That'll give us a chance to look sleepy," said Pavlos.

Lukas took a towel and wiped the perspiration from his brow and under his arms before he climbed back into bed. Neither of them had reckoned on the number of soldiers being used to conduct the search. They were obviously well trained, immediately splitting into four or five groups and placing a guard outside each apartment, to ensure that no one left until the search was over. Heavy boots were heard running up and down stairs. Doors opened and shut on the lower floors. Jeannie was getting excited, so Lukas grabbed her, placing his hand over her muzzle to prevent her rushing to the front door and barking to warn that strangers were prowling outside. It was, after all, her job. But Lukas didn't want to attract attention too soon.

It was an hour before the militia began pounding on their door. Jeannie could no longer be controlled and raced to the entrance, barking angrily at the intruders. Lukas and Pavlos deliberately ignored the hammering.

"They must be fast asleep. It's after 2.00 a.m.," Lukas heard one officer say to another. "Their dog will wake them up. It's making enough noise to waken the dead." Jeannie barked and growled with all the strength in her body.

"Watch yourself!" a voice was heard. "That dog sounds vicious."

Lukas made his way slowly to the entrance and, picking up Jeannie, unlocked the door.

"Lock that dog up somewhere," the commanding officer shouted as he pushed his way into the apartment.

"Certainly, sir," said Lukas, going towards the sitting room, where their recent frenzied activity had taken place.

"And don't let her out until we have finished our search. We'll do one room at a time."

Rifles slung over their shoulders, the squad tramped into the kitchen, where they flung open the fridge and stove, tipped out the contents of drawers and even brought out carving knives for their leader's inspection. Some went through cupboards, dragging down suitcases, shaking and throwing towels and freshly-laundered bedsheets on to the floor.

"Tell this woman to get out of bed," ordered the officer, as they moved on to Evangelia's room.

297

"But, Sir, she's an invalid," one soldier argued.

"She could be hiding something under her mattress. Get her off," he shouted.

The young soldier apologised to Evangelia. "I'm sorry, Mama," he said gently. "I'm only following orders."

"I understand," said Evangelia. "And I'm glad that some of you haven't lost your sense of politeness. I'll try and get up for you, but you'll have to help me into my chair."

The youth put down his gun and rushed to bring the wheelchair closer. Hooking his arm under her, he eased Evangelia into a sitting position and helped her climb into the chair. Then with an apologetic smile, he lifted up the mattress and made a brief search of the bed.

"There's nothing here, sir," he reported to his commander. Pushing past him, convinced the search had not been conducted properly, the officer marched up to the bed and poked about with his swagger stick. The boy hung about.

"Get into the next room," he shouted angrily, disappointed his search had been fruitless.

The soldier turned to Evangelia. "I'll fix your bed before I go, Mama," he whispered.

"Over here!" called the commanding officer with satisfaction in his voice. "Just look what they are keeping in their bookshelves—forbidden publications."

Lukas strode over, looking the officer square in the face. "What forbidden publications?" he asked, fighting to control his temper.

"All these books and periodicals: books on Haile Selassie. Why are you keeping them?"

"We have been booksellers for fifty years. These publications were personally autographed for my father before either you or I were born. How can you wipe out history?"

"We managed to wipe out Haile Selassie, didn't we?" he sneered. Suddenly losing interest, he pointed to the sitting room where Jeannie was locked up. Lukas froze. "Have you searched in there?"

"We've searched everywhere. There's nothing, sir," said one of his men.

Truculently the officer flung the books to the ground. Slapping his boot impatiently with his stick, he turned on his heel and headed for the door. "Come on. Come on. Look lively. Let's move to the top floor."

As the last soldier crossed the threshold, he paused and looked at Lukas. "You don't remember me, *Geta* Lukas, do you?" he asked, a thin smile on his face.

"I don't think so..." said Lukas, hesitantly.

"I'm one of the hawkers who used to sell 'Time' and 'Newsweek' in the streets for you. I supported my family for many years on the money I used to earn."

"Ah, yes, now I remember." The uniform had deceived Lukas but, for a nostalgic moment, the face slipped into place. He reached out to shake the soldier's hand, but the boy drew back.

"No, don't show that you know me. Just apologize to Mama for disturbing her."

When the door was shut and bolted, Lukas leaned against the wall breathing a sigh of relief. It could have been worse: they had taken nothing and harmed no one. The Ethiopian soldier, compared with those in neighbouring African countries, was still reasonably civilized he mused. Later he was to learn how wrong he had been.

The penthouse apartment on the floor above was now

occupied by a widow and her three teenage daughters. Tigist, the eldest girl, was a slim beauty of nineteen with dark, sensuous eyes and long, wavy hair which fell in profusion about her shoulders. She always dressed in brightly-coloured clinging tops and flowing skirts, which emphasised the elegant sway of her hips as she walked. After her father's death, the burden of being the family breadwinner had fallen upon her. Her mother was in poor health and her younger sisters had to be put through high school. Feeling her responsibilities, she had turned down a number of marriage proposals. When the soldiers burst into their apartment, Tigist was fast asleep after a hard day's work. Her room, the last on the corridor, faced the back of the building, away from the noise of the street.

One by one, the mother and girls were ordered out of the apartment while the soldiers searched for arms and fugitives. Being Ethiopians, they could have been sympathisers with the underground movement. They were warned to surrender anyone they were hiding before it was too late.

While his men were busy ripping apart the flat, the Major slowly made his way to Tigist's bedroom. The sound of someone entering and locking the door behind him, woke her with a start. Her heart thumping, she fumbled for the bedside lamp. Knocking it over in her haste, all she could see was his silhouette against the window. He wore a green balaclava and she could just make out a thin moustach above his upper lip. As he drew closer, she could feel his eyes fixed on her breasts, as they heaved beneath the thin nightdress. Terrified, she grabbed the bedclothes and pulled them up under her chin. The officer raised his arm and with a sudden movement, ripped the sheets from her.

"Undress and face the wall," he hissed, starting to loosen his belt.

Knowing she could not live with the shame of being raped, Tigist's fear turned to anger. "You'll never have your way with me," she screamed, "not as long as I'm alive. You'll have to kill me first." Then, filling her mouth with saliva, she spat into his face. Furious, the officer grabbed her by the hair and was about to slap her across the face, when the sound of heavy footsteps approaching stayed his hand.

"*Gashe, gashe*," one of his men called. "You're wanted by headquarters."

The officer released his grip, throwing her backwards onto the bed. "My business with you is not finished," he said, wagging his finger at her. "I'll be back." But before he left the room, Tigist had the last word.

"I've taken a good look at your face, Major. Those brass stars have given away your rank. You touch me and I'll personally report to Mengistu what kind of men are running his army."

When Tigist related the incident later, her family were terrified that she would be punished for her audacity. In fact, it saved her. The Major never returned.

* * *

A few weeks after the search, a representative from the Ministry of Housing paid the Fanouris's an unexpected visit. "How many people live in this apartment?" he asked.

"Three of us," Pavlos replied, as the man took out his notebook and began to write down the details.

"How many bedrooms do you occupy?"

"All three. We each have a room to ourselves."

The man scribbled rapidly in his book. "This cannot continue. This is sheer luxury. You can all move into one bedroom and we can rent out the other two."

"Don't be ridiculous," yelled Pavlos, losing his temper. "We have a bedridden mother. We can't all move in with her. We're paying rent for this place, aren't we?"

"You don't seem to understand," said the official, calmly. "We're facing a great shortage of housing. With the nationalizing of urban land, all the landlords have moved into their own houses. We have to take some sort of action."

"That's your problem. You can't impose anyone on us. If you want to rent this apartment out to ten people, then you'd better find us alternative accommodation, or better still, give us permission to leave this God-forsaken country," shouted Pavlos, looking as though he was about to hit the man.

The official shut his notebook nervously. "You'll be hearing from us soon," he said, turning towards the lift.

"Son, don't get them angry, please!" cautioned Evangelia. "We're already in their bad books. You never know what they might do to us."

"More than what they've done already? Give us a break, Mother! They've degraded us, nationalized our business, seized our money, refused us permission to leave and now they want to force us to live with a dozen others. What else is left for them to do?" he shouted angrily.

Lukas went into the kitchen and poured them all a cup of coffee. Handing it round, he put forward a proposition which had been on his mind. "Look, I know this isn't the best time to bring this up, but I was wondering if we

302

shouldn't try to sell some of our stuff. If they do move us to a smaller place, at least we won't have the problem of storage."

"You must be joking, Lukas," Pavlos yelled. "The Housing Ministry has spies all over the city reporting on daily movements. The minute they notice furniture, or even small personal items leaving our apartment, we'll be accused of black-marketing or something similar."

Now it was Lukas' turn to get angry. "Listen! Whether we like it or not, we'll have to start selling some of the family trophies soon, especially the silverware. How else do you think we're going to make ends meet? The sooner we start, the better."

Evangelia sadly surveyed the precious ornaments decorating her showcase—the fine, handcut crystal glasses and the Italian silverware, the beautiful oil paintings on the wall and her cherished carpets. "There's no point in being sentimental at a time like this," she said with a sigh. "If they've got to be sold to help us survive, then they've got to go."

"I don't think we need to take such drastic steps," Pavlos said, lowering his tone. "We've got enough to get by for a few more months."

"But will we be able to sell them when the need arises?" Lukas argued. "Right now, there's a shortage of gold and silver in the market and the goldsmiths will give us a reasonably good price. In a few months time, the economy will have deteriorated so badly there won't be any money floating around."

"Maybe Lukas is right," said Evangelia. "I tend to agree with him. One never knows what could crop up."

Secretly and cautiously, contact was made with a silversmith who agreed to buy a number of pieces of the

303

family silver. He subsequently melted them down to make filigree pendants and rings. It was too risky to sell the items in their original form. Silversmiths could be arrested and forced to testify where they had purchased their silver from.

Lukas' weekly trips to the *piazza* gradually became more frequent. He began to feel like a dealer in stolen goods, slipping the items furtively over the counter. Feeling guilty about selling his own property made him bitter, but he knew if he were stopped, it would be difficult to prove ownership. It was heartbreaking to see the parental home slowly being stripped of its wealth and memories. Nearly all the silverware had disappeared from the showcases and the gaps filled with wooden carvings and seashells. It was not so easy, however, to replace the oil paintings and ceramic plates which had once decorated the now bare walls. One or two calendars and posters were stuck up to cover the odd space, but they gave a drab and melancholy aura to rooms which once vibrated with warmth and life.

Between selling trips, Lukas ran with dogged persistence from one government office to another in a bid to procure his mother's exit visa. Having finally been told that her file was being reviewed, he began to check daily at the Ministry of Interior. He was standing in a queue on one of these daily visits, when a young clerk indicated he wanted to talk to him. Lukas moved out of the line and followed him to a far corner of the room.

"Could you offer me a cigarette?" the youth asked. It was the age-old opening remark when a proposition was forthcoming.

Lukas reached into his pocket and offered him one, striking a match to light it for him. He inhaled deeply, then slowly let out the smoke together with a few mumbled words which Lukas could not catch. "I beg your pardon?" he asked, leaning forward.

"Your mother's file has been lost and your daily visits here are completely useless," muttered the clerk.

"But they told me only this week that they were reviewing her case and that there was hope they would give her permission to leave," exclaimed Lukas.

"I'm telling you, it hasn't yet even been presented to the Permanent Secretary."

"What should I do to ensure that he gets to see it?" Lukas asked, knowing too well that he would demand *goubo* and the price would be high. These youths never worked alone. The messenger probably received the smallest portion. It was the hidden, faceless 'sharks' who would get the lion's share.

"The price is five thousand Birr," he said, without twitching a muscle.

"But you know very well I don't have that sort of money," said Lukas in a choked voice. "I can't even meet half the price you're quoting."

"Fine! I'll report back on our conversation. Come back this afternoon and I'll give you a reply."

Lukas wiped the sweat from his forehead and stepped out into the fresh air. He felt as if he were suffocating. No wonder their case wasn't moving. And if the bribe was not paid, there wasn't a hope in a million of leaving Ethiopia. He decided there was no point in discussing the issue at home until a final figure had been settled upon. But one thing was certain, he would have to sell all the remaining family heirlooms.

Lukas was waiting on the steps of the Ministry when the offices reopened at 3.00 p.m. He walked in and looked around for his contact. He was standing in one corner and, with a slight nod of his head, indicated he had a reply.

"It's three thousand Birr or no deal!" he hissed between clenched teeth.

From his morning sales, Lukas had already collected more than what he was demanding, but previous experience told him that once bargaining had begun, it had to be pursued to the bitter end. He also realised this was only the tip of the iceberg. There would doubtless be more obstructions and more demands.

"I'll offer you one thousand five hundred Birr, but I can't go a single cent higher," he called his bluff.

"But there are three of us," the youth said hastily, biting his tongue.

Lukas knew immediately they must be junior office boys. Five hundred Birr each would be the equivalent to three month's salary. The boy disappeared to consult with his fellow extortioners. When he returned, Lukas knew from the look on his face that they had accepted his offer.

"Get the money here before the office opens tomorrow morning and by 9.00 a.m. your file will be in the right hands."

"How will I be certain that you will have kept your side of the bargain?" demanded Lukas.

"You will call here," he said, scribbling down a telephone number on a scrap of paper. "It's the big boss's secretary and you will ask if your mother's file is with her."

"And what if it isn't?"

"I'm telling you it will be there!"

"No, I can't take that chance," said Lukas, shaking his head. He knew these youngsters only too well. Once they had the cash in their hands, they would renege on the deal and demand more.

"What in hell are you trying to do now?" asked the boy angrily.

"I'll come with the money tomorrow morning, but first I'll call and make sure of your delivery. If everything has gone ahead, you can come down and pick up your envelope."

The youngster hesitated. "Alright, then, but you'd better put the money in a paper bag with some fresh bread on top. It's got to look like a sandwich or something."

"Fine. See you before nine."

Lukas drove home whistling happily. For three months, he had been in and out of those Ministry doors, getting nowhere. At last, there was a glimmer of hope.

True to the office boy's word, Evangelia's file was miraculously found the next day and delivered to the right hands. Lukas asked if they could give him some idea of when Comrade Legesse would review the file. "He is very busy at present. He has too much work. Call us in about a week," said his secretary.

A week meant a month, if not more, but it was something. Lukas handed over the 'bread' and returned home.

"I'm glad you're back early," Askala greeted him at the door. "That man from the Housing Ministry was back again. He wanted to talk to you."

"Did he say anything about us moving?"

"No, he just said he wanted to talk to you or Pavlos."

"Well, did he say where his office was or when he wanted to see us?"

"No, he just said he'd be back."

Lukas pondered. If it was official business, why was he coming to the house? It didn't smell quite right. The sun was just starting to set when the bell rang. It was the Ministry official with an obsequious smile on his face. Before he could open his mouth, Lukas pre-empted him. "Ah, it's you. Come in. Have you managed to find us alternative accommodation? We're ready to move."

"Well, actually…" said the man, following Lukas into the sitting room, "I came to discuss just that with you. I don't think you will actually need to move. After all, you're well settled here and it wouldn't really be fair to move your old, invalid mother. I think we could come to some kind of agreement."

Askala, who had just entered with a tray of coffee, paused for a moment before setting it down. Giving the official one of her most contemptuous looks, she sidled up to Lukas and kicked his foot. "He wants *goubo*," she whispered. "Get rid of him. Let him kick us out. We'll report him to the *kebele*."

Lukas, who had already weighed up the situation, was so amused by Askala's reaction he had to busy himself with pouring the coffee to hide his urge to burst out laughing. "Thank you, Mama Askala," he said, struggling to keep his face straight. "I'll take the appropriate action." Turning to the official, he continued, "Actually, we have been giving the matter some thought and we all think you're quite right. This apartment is far too big for us, when there are so many in need. No, no. We shall await your action in finding us a smaller one."

"But you know it's almost impossible to find any kind of accommodation," the man began to argue against himself, imagining that Lukas had not understood his hint.

"It was your suggestion, Sir, not ours," said Lukas, innocently. "We shall be ready whenever you are."

As the door closed on the bewildered man from the Ministry, Askala grabbed Lukas' hand and shook it hard. "I think we managed that very well," she laughed. "He won't be bothering us again. Incidentally," she said, pointing to the empty corner in the sitting room. "Whatever happened to that lovely potted plant we used to have?"

"Oh, that?" Lukas paused briefly contemplating on a suitable reply. "It went to join its companions on the green hills of Entoto," he chuckled. "Let the army have fun tracking down its owner!"

Chapter Twenty Six

It was six months since Mellina and Gabby had left. Gabby was nearly two and already wearing jeans and T-shirts. Lukas studied the photographs Mellina had sent him, longing to be able to pick her up and swing her round, delighting in her shrieks and giggles. Judging from the weekly missives, they both seemed to have settled well in Nairobi and Mellina was happy in her new job, but it was sheer misery for him trying to find something to write back. He would sit, pen in hand, doodling on pieces of paper while he searched for something positive to say, but what could he write when everything was still in limbo, depending on the whims of corrupt bureaucrats.

He picked up a cup of herbal tea that Askala had put down in front of him and took a sip. "Ugh! Mama Askala!" he called out, screwing his face up. "This tea is as bitter as quinine. I think you forgot to put some sugar in."

"No, I didn't forget. We just don't have any sugar in the house," she replied.

"But I thought we got our ration yesterday," said Lukas, calculating the days on his fingers.

"I went with our card but the *kebele* refused to give me any. They said you had missed going to the parade in

310

honour of Fidel Castro, so our weekly ration had been stopped."

"But I was in bed as sick as a dog!" exclaimed Lukas, pushing his chair back. "I'll go down and tell them."

"It won't do any good," sighed Askala. "I explained to them but they told me they wouldn't accept any excuses."

"Damn!" cried Lukas, beating his hand hard on the door frame. "They're tightening the screws on all sides. One of these days, I'll explode and God knows who'll be around to pick up the pieces."

Askala patted his arm, "Calm down, Lukas, don't get so worked up. We can live without sugar for a week."

"It's not the sugar, Mama Askala, of course we can live without that. It's everything—all these new impositions. Everything's so frustrating and nerve-wracking."

"I see you're writing to Mellina," she said, nodding towards the desk. "Ask her to send us flour and sugar from Nairobi. Oh, and you might also add some soap to the list if you feel like washing," she smiled. "There's none of that in the shops either."

Despite grandiose national development plans, the economy of the country was slowly grinding to a halt. The state farms, established by the Dergue after it nationalized agricultural land, were totally inefficient. Food, followed by just about everything else, had become scarce. Rationing had initially been accepted as just another niggling hardship, but gradually there was becoming very little to ration.

At the same time, the Dergue was running the entire country like an army. The Red Terror had wiped out most of the ideological opposition to the regime and Marxist-Leninist principles were being enforced more and more rigidly. The number of harsh, new regulations and restrictions increased daily, making life intolerable. For weeks in advance of Fidel Castro's state visit to Ethiopia, everyone in Addis was woken up at 5.00 a.m. by loud speakers. All those who were taking part in the parade of honour were expected to congregate, no matter what the conditions, in the newly reconstructed Revolution or Red Square. In rain and hail, people travelled in from the outskirts of the city, some of them walking between five and ten kilometres. The rehearsals were deliberately held in the early hours so that no one need miss work. Everyone was forced to march up and down for hours on end to perfect the forthcoming parade. Those not selected to participate in the parade itself were spared the rehearsals, but were ordered to turn out en masse when the visitor arrived in order to line the entire seven-kilometre route from the airport at Bole to Revolution Square. By nature, the Ethiopian people were hospitable, but this enforced welcome and the severe consequences imposed if they disobeyed, produced a sullen compliance. Lukas had wondered at the time whether his absence would be noticed, but had thought it unlikely. He had been proved wrong; it made him shudder to think how closely their movements were being watched by *kebele* spies.

The reviewing of Evangelia's file by the Ministry of Interior had so far taken sixteen months and still no decision had been reached. By the end of August 1980, Lukas and Pavlos were feeling frantic. Evangelia's health was steadily deteriorating and hopes of moving her were beginning to fade. In desperation, they decided to send a petition to Colonel Mengistu himself to coincide with the sixth anniversary of the Revolution on 12 September. After numerous drafts and redrafts, they finally presented the petition on the eve of the anniversary celebrations. It was addressed to Comrade Mengistu Haile Mariam, Chairman of the Provisional Military Administrative Council and of the Council of Ministers and Commander-in-Chief of the Revolutionary Army of Socialist Ethiopia. It read:

Revolutionary Leader Comrade Mengistu,

May we be allowed to bring to your kind attention the following facts:

1. After exhausting all efforts, going through the proper channels and failing to obtain the requested permission due to avoidance by officials to issue a responsible decision, we are compelled to bring our grievances to your personal attention. Believing that the revolutionary ideals by which you have guided Ethiopia to socialism will once again prevail, we exhort you to give us a just and fair decision to alleviate our suffering.

2. Mrs. Evangelia Fanouris, the 76 year old widow of the late Manoli Fanouris, and her sons Pavlos and Lukas Fanouris, have been refused exit permits to depart for their country because the Inland Revenue administration refuses to issue the necessary release due to outstanding tax claims on the bookshop of which the late Manoli Fanouris was proprietor.

3. In consequence, the organization was nationalized and, as Manoli Fanouris had no other property whatsoever, both mother and sons were left without any means of livelihood and have had to rely on help from relatives and friends.

4. Mrs. Evangelia Fanouris had an accident eighteen months ago and, as per the attached medical certificate issued by the Armed Forces Hospital, she has an untreated fracture of the left femur. Because of her advanced age,

she also suffers from arterial hypertension, chronic myocardiopathy and emphysema of the lungs. She must therefore seek operative treatment abroad as there are no facilities in Ethiopia for such a complicated operation.

5. The issue of our livelihood is becoming more and more acute as we cannot continue to be a burden on our relatives and friends. As we have no income, we ask that you, the Revolutionary Leader, give the necessary orders to the departments concerned to permit us to leave Ethiopia and join our families.

With our grateful thanks, we look forward with confidence to your revolutionary decision.

Evangelia Fanouris

Pavlos Fanouris

Lukas Fanouris

Kebele 24 -308-

Chapter Twenty Seven

Nairobi

"Mellina, quick!" Teresa, my next door neighbour, called. "It's Lukas calling you from Addis."

I had no telephone and could only receive calls via my neighbour. Hurriedly I removed some saucepans from the stove and ran. "Hi, Sweetheart," I called, breathing heavily.

"Did I make you run? You seem to be out of breath."

"No trouble. I never walk when you call, darling. How's everything with you?"

"We live from day to day, but we've sent a petition to the Head of State. I'm sure something will happen soon. We're hoping Mengistu himself will take some positive action." For the first time in months, his voice was full of excitement and optimism.

"That's wonderful, darling. I hope something comes of it. I was planning on coming to spend Christmas with you, what do you think?"

"Maybe I'll be home with you by then," Lukas replied.

"That would be marvellous," I said. Gabby and I hadn't seen Lukas for almost a year.

"How is my little darling. Has she forgotten me?" he

asked wistfully.

"No way! She kisses your photograph every day and says 'That's Daddy'. She speaks quite fluently now. You should hear her speak English and Swahili—both together. She's a scream."

"Are you both happily settled in the maisonette? You will be careful that Gabby doesn't fall down those stairs, won't you?"

"Don't worry. We're fine. We just miss you so much and can't wait for you to come home."

"I don't have to tell you how much I want to be with you all…" his voice faltered for a second. Then he quickly changed the subject. "So, tell me, what's going on in Nairobi?"

I quickly told him all the local gossip, mentioning the fact that the Greek Assistant Minister of Foreign Affairs, Mr. Adrianopoulos, was paying a visit. "The Embassy is giving him a big reception," I said.

"I wonder if you should mention our case to him and what we're going through?"

"Sure, why not? In fact, it might be better if Byron talked to him. He'll be at the reception." We decided that Lukas should post a copy of his petition to Mengistu by express mail so that Byron could hand it personally to the Assistant Minister the following week.

"Any good news?" asked Teresa as I replaced the receiver. Teresa and I had met at UNEP. By coincidence her son and Gabby were born on the same day. We had become close friends and it was due to the efforts of Teresa and her husband, Carl, that I had moved into a maisonette near them. Their friendship had proved invaluable.

"Oh, Teresa! Lukas thinks they might grant him permission to leave. He hopes to be home for Christmas!"

"That would be wonderful. We can all celebrate together as one big family. We'll give him a huge party."

"Let's not count our chickens before they hatch. We've had so many disappointments and there was still a hint of doubt in his voice. Maybe getting a positive decision from Mengistu would be too good to be true."

"Now stop imagining things; you've got to be optimistic, think positively. *Bass-halas!*" she scolded briskly concluding in her native Arabic. Teresa and Carl, better than anyone, knew what we were going through. They had relatives in war-stricken Lebanon and waited anxiously each day for news.

Since I left Ethiopia, Lukas' letters had been brief and not too informative and I realised it was probably wise not to say too much in letters. Most outgoing mail was censored, so it was just as well to limit news to health and weather. When we spoke on the phone, however, I knew immediately from the tone of his voice whether he was happy or depressed. I never asked how he felt. It only invited heartache.

Three days after our conversation, a copy of the petition arrived from Addis. Byron had already spoken to the Greek Ambassador. After the reception for Mr. Adrianopulos, a dinner party would follow at the Ambassador's residence. He and Electra were invited to attend. "The Ambassador is going to seat Electra next to him, so that during dinner she can bring the subject up and give him all the details," Byron informed me.

I relaxed. I knew my sister would make a good job of briefing the Minister. On the night of the dinner, Electra went to great lengths to look her best. She placed the envelope containing the petition in her purse. "I hope I won't lose my nerve," she said as she patted perfume

317

behind her ears. "You don't think I've overdone it, do you?" she asked nervously, turning to Mum and me. "Wearing all these rubies and diamonds?"

"How else do you think he'll notice you?" we laughed. "Don't be silly, you look stunning."

Byron had already started the car. It was a twenty minute drive to the Residence in Muthaiga, one of Nairobi's oldest and wealthiest suburbs. At the turn of the century, the Muthaiga Club was the gathering point for all the white settlers—mostly eccentric British aristocrats and adventurers—who came to farm and shoot game in Kenya. Now, the suburb which had grown up around the club was a veritable colony of embassies and ambassadorial residences.

My mother and I had agreed to babysit Electra's three extremely-active sons. Luckily, Stavros and Takis were already asleep, which left only their eight-year-old Nicholas to entertain. When Byron and Electra returned, they found all three of us sleeping soundly with the television still running, although the station had closed down.

"How did it go?" I asked nervously, after we had carried Nicholas to bed.

"Well, let me tell you, the man was most sympathetic. He wanted to know all the details and wondered why no one had ever brought such a situation to their attention before. He said he would take the petition with him and has promised to take action the minute he returns to Greece."

"That's great! At least there's a chance from two sides now. Maybe things will turn out okay."

Byron looked at me sceptically, he was not a man to mince words. "But what if they don't, Mellina? You realise

318

that, if all these attempts fail, we're going to have to look into different possibilities for getting them out of there."

"What possibilities?" I asked, for a moment confused. All our actions and hopes had been based on the premise that eventually they would all be given legal permits to leave. I tried to imagine alternative plans and couldn't. "It can't be done," I said, shaking my head. "It's impossible."

"What are you saying?" asked Electra, puzzled. "How can they possibly make any plans to leave when they have an invalid mother with them. It's insane. Evangelia can't take a single step by herself. To move her from the bed to her wheelchair is such agony that she has to take a heart tonic after each attempt."

"I know it's difficult to imagine any such move right now," Byron continued, "but I'm beginning to think that if they're ever going to get out of there, it's up to us and we've got to examine other possibilities."

Chapter Twenty Eight

Addis Ababa

Christmas came and went and nothing happened. As the months dragged by, the only thing that relieved Lukas' depression was receiving letters from Nairobi. He loved to read the long, descriptive pages from Mellina, transporting him momentarily to her side, although sometimes he found it hard to grasp how his small daughter was changing in his absence.

Easter was approaching and he was expecting a letter any day. Unlocking their post office box, he plunged his hand inside feeling for the familiar thick envelope. It was there. Ripping it open, he hurriedly scanned the contents. Racing back to his car, he drove home.

"They're coming!" he shouted excitedly to his mother and Pavlos, who were waiting anxiously to hear the news. "I can't believe it! Mellina's managed to get her UN Laissez-Passer renewed with Gabby included on the same travel document. They'll be here next week to spend Easter with us."

"Oh, I can't wait to see them both," cried Evangelia, wiping away a happy tear. "If only I had flour and sugar and spices to bake Easter bread and cookies for them. I don't even have any dyes for the eggs." She shook her head sadly.

"Mellina's bringing everything with her," said Lukas, reading through the letter again more slowly. "She says here that her mother has already prepared a whole lot of almond and cinnamon cookies and she'll bring some with her. She's also going to bring as much as she can carry of all the foodstuffs we can't get here." He paused. "I can't wait to hold them in my arms again. I just hope Gabby remembers me. I don't know what I'll do if she doesn't recognize me, it will kill me."

Evangelia patted his arm. "Don't expect too much, son. She was only a baby when she left and now she's nearly three years old. Give her time."

The week before their arrival felt like the longest in Lukas' life. He washed and polished the car. He bought flowers for the house. He searched the attic for the toys Gabby had left behind. On the day itself, he cut himself trying to shave too closely, had to visit the bathroom half a dozen times and bit his nails almost down to the wick.

"I'd better come to the airport with you to make sure you get there in once piece," laughed Pavlos.

* * *

Seeing the familiar mountainous landscape below me give way to cultivated patches of green dotted with the occasional *tukul*, made my heart swell with happiness. How I loved this country! We were flying low over the outskirts of Addis.

"Look, Mummy," Gabby shrieked with excitement as the plane banked giving a magnificent view of the landscape, "chocolates on a cake."

321

"That's land, sweetheart, and those chocolates are small mud huts. People live in them," I explained, amused by her interpretation.

"But not like our house." She paused. "Will Daddy be waiting for us?" She popped the question that was uppermost in her mind.

"Of course he'll be waiting for us. He's waited a long time to see us."

"Will he have presents for me?"

"Wow! Look at those houses coming towards us." I said, quickly changing the subject. From what I had heard, I doubted very much if there would be anything in the shops to buy. Gabby clasped my hand tightly as we entered the terminal building, her curly, blond ponytail bobbing jauntily.

"Mellina! What are you doing here?" a familiar voice called out. It was Gebremariam, the UNDP colleague who had organized my departure.

"You just had to be the first person I would meet upon arrival!" I exclaimed, embracing and kissing him.

A small hand tugged at my dress. "Is this Daddy?" she asked.

"Dear God," I panicked. "She doesn't remember Lukas."

"Don't tell me this is Gabby?" said Gebremariam. "My, my. How you've grown."

"This is the gentleman who saw us off when we left," I explained.

"Can he take me to Daddy?" she asked plaintively.

"I've seen Lukas. He's outside. Of course I'll take you," replied Gebremariam, extending his hand. She grabbed his finger and allowed him to lead her away. Forgetting about my luggage, I followed close behind to make sure she was alright.

Gebremariam took her to the exit, where Lukas and Pavlos were anxiously craning their necks to see if we were among the arrivals. On spotting Gabby, Lukas pushed through the crowd and crouching down, opened his arms. Without any prompting, she released Gebremariam's hand and ran as fast as her infant legs would carry her straight into her father's arms. As he picked her up, she tightened her hands around his neck.

A lump rose in my throat seeing them both together again. I turned back to claim my baggage. There was a lot, but with Gebremariam's help I managed to clear it. I found Lukas and Gabby still locked together, her head snuggled against his neck. Seeing me, she lifted her head and announced proudly, "Look, Mummy. I found him!"

All four of us hugged one another. Lukas looked tired and thinner than when I left. I knew he needed and missed us. It was good to be back.

The food consignment I had brought caused more excitement that I had ever imagined possible. "I know it's a joke, but we really will keep the whisky for medicinal purposes," said Pavlos. Evangelia's eyes sparkled when she saw the corn oil, sugar and flour. Lukas dived straight for the chocolates. "Just one piece a day, okay, Pavlos?" he laughed. "We'll show real self control. We'd better go slow on the tobacco and cigarettes too; they're going to have to last us a long time."

They were even ecstatic about the soap and toothpaste, making me feel guilty that I took all these basic items for granted in Nairobi. "I had no idea things had deteriorated so badly," I exclaimed. "Lukas, you never told me. How on earth has it happened?"

"Well, no imports are allowed any more and what is

available is distributed to the soldiers fighting in the Ogaden or in the North. They are the first priority, everything else is secondary. The economy is totally paralysed."

I was a little hurt that Lukas had been too proud to tell me of their situation but I realized he just didn't want to upset me. Was the same true of the progress, or lack of it, he was making in procuring exit visas? When I asked him, he said they were still reviewing his mother's case. "I guess we just have to be patient. What else is there to do?"

"I suppose so. But do you know, only last week, I met a group of men in Nairobi who had just crossed over to Kenya through the Bale mountains. Apparently, it was a gruelling experience, but they made it. They just couldn't bear the situation here any longer, so they decided it was worth a gamble."

"They were lucky," said Lukas. "If they'd been caught, they'd have been arrested and probably shot. It was a big risk. Do you know what happened to Theodorakis, who tried to escape through Jigjiga into the Sudan?"

"No, but why should he have wanted to escape?"

"They nationalized his company, left him without a job and refused him permission to sell his house. He nearly went crazy. While he was feeling desperate, someone offered to take him into the Sudan on a camel, at a price. He came to us saying he was in a tight situation and needed money. Well, not knowing what it was for, we all chipped in. The next thing we knew he'd been arrested at the border and brought back in chains. He's spent the last six months in prison."

"Poor old soul. Is he still inside?"

"He was released a few days ago. He looks terrible— under-nourished and sick. We should go and visit him now you're here and take him a few things. The worst part of it was the interrogation itself. It was totally inhuman."

"Did he tell you about it?"

"With great difficulty, yes, he did. Let's not talk about it now. It's terribly disturbing. Some other time, maybe. Let me enjoy your homecoming and leave out the miseries we have to live with, okay?"

Poor Theodorakis, poor Lukas, poor Ethiopia. I slipped my arm round Lukas as we sat together on the settee. Seeing us so close, Gabby ran over and jealously planted herself between us. "I want a cuddle too," she cried.

Lukas folded his arms round both of us, burying his head in my hair. "It's so good to have you here, you've no idea how I've missed you both," he said brokenly. "Dear God, show us a way out of this."

* * *

A few days after our arrival, Theodorakis came round to seek help and I had the opportunity to see for myself what his escape attempt had done to him. He had lost so much weight; the skin hung in folds around his face and neck and his eyes had a haunted look. It was obvious he needed to talk about his ordeal to people who would listen and be sympathetic in order to exorcise his bitterness and sense of injustice. When he spoke, tiny crevices around his mouth quivered with disguised tension. He began by telling us of how he was stripped of his clothes and locked in a dark room for what seemed like three to four days.

"They threw me scraps of food through a hole. It was so dark I had no means of telling the difference between night and day, I just spent my time trying to kill the lice that were making a meal of me. My body was covered with itching lumps." The old man paused, reliving his nightmare. "On the last day, before I was transferred to the prison camp at Carcelli, I heard a door open and heavy footsteps approaching. Without warning, they started firing questions at me in the dark from four different directions. 'Who was the person who arranged your escape?' 'How did you manage to avoid the roadblocks?' On and on. Before I had a chance to answer, someone slapped me hard across the face, another kicked me in the genitals, next I was whipped with something that felt wet and slimey. They're no fools. The pain was excruciating but there wasn't a mark to be seen on my body. I was in agony. What made things worse was that, with the first slap, my false teeth flew out of my mouth. Without them, there was no way I could make any sense. No one could understand what I was saying. The more I mumbled, the more they beat me." He clasped his head, trying to blot out the visions. "Heaven only knows how I survived. I couldn't believe it when they finally left the room. My skin felt raw but I couldn't feel any blood or open wounds."

"My God," I said, totally shocked by the old man's story. "How did you survive all those beatings?"

"You know, Mellina, it was pure will-power. I felt so angry and degraded that I was determined to survive so I could one day revenge myself on those inhuman bastards. Excuse me," the old gentleman apologised, "but that's what kept me going. I kept telling myself I had to survive so that I could send a report to Amnesty International and tell them what's going on in this country and what kind of torture I was subjected to."

"Will you do it, though?" asked Pavlos.

"Once I'm out of this country, yes, I'll do it. I've written everything down, all the details, so that I won't forget them. Then I'll show them!" His eyes gleamed with a feverish determination.

"What are you going to do in the meantime?" asked Lukas.

"I'm going to find another way out. I've heard of several different routes people have taken successfully crossing the border. I'm just so bitter that there's nothing anyone could do to keep me here. I'd rather die attempting another escape than stay another day in this country."

Evangelia leaned forward and patted his arm. "I know you're beside yourself with hurt and bitterness, Theo," she said trying to reason with him, "but you're so thin and weak. You've got to get your strength back."

"Dear old friend," said Theodorakis, "can you imagine what I would have been like if you hadn't sent me food parcels each day? But I couldn't eat while others starved. There were so many sick and hungry youngsters in Carcelli, I had to share what you sent, just eating enough myself to survive."

Evangelia nodded. "Now I understand. When I saw you in this state, I thought the food had never reached you. You're down to skin and bone."

"Evangelia, the only thing I ever looked forward to in that hell hole was your food. It was the only joy that made the day pass more quickly."

"Were you forced to do any hard labour?" I asked.

The old man let out a forced laugh. "You won't believe this but I was assigned to do some gardening and do you know where? There's a wide ditch on the edge of the prison grounds and right by that ditch, beneath the grass that I had to cut each day, lie the bodies of those sixty generals and politicians and aristocrats who were shot

327

that November night in 1974: the bodies of so many friends with whom I'd dined and joked. Every day, I walked on their graves.

When they arrested me at Jigjiga," Theo continued, his face suddenly twisting into a painful grimace, "I shared a filthy, vermin-infested cell with one of the slain minister's daughters. I recognized her immediately. Seeing how she was being treated, my fatherly advice to her was to surrender her only weapon—her body. When the guard walked in, she stood up and with loathing walked towards him. Recognizing the mentality of the man— proud of his manhood and possessing a high degree of chauvinism, she had to gratify his sensual appetite. No matter how degrading and immoral it was for a woman of her standing, she was compelled to stoop to the level of a prostitute. The border was but a few yards away and her only guarantee of crossing it was to satisfy his needs; the alternatives she knew only too well. Beaten and molested, she would be escorted to the mouldy prisons of Addis Ababa only to be faced eventually with a firing squad. I heard the next day that she had 'escaped' during the night. Sadly, others were compelled to follow her footsteps in order to earn their freedom."

Pavlos reached into the cocktail cabinet for a glass and poured out a finger of the 'medicinal' whisky. "We're saving this for illnesses and special occasions. I think this is one of them," he said, handing Theodorakis the glass. The old man sipped it cautiously, savouring the fiery liquid as it slid down his throat.

"What about members of the royal family?" Lukas interposed. "Did you see any of them?"

Theodorakis nodded. "They're in separate quarters, isolated from the rest, but I did see the Emperor's eldest daughter, Tenagne Work, being marched around by armed wardens. She's a pitiful sight—a frail old woman. Half a dozen of her relatives are also languishing in there. I don't think there's any chance of any of them ever being released. It looks as if they're being punished for all the other family members the authorities couldn't get their hands on."

We all fell silent for a moment. "But seriously now," said Pavlos. "What are your plans? You're surely not going to be stupid enough to attempt another escape, are you?"

"That, my good friends, is what I came here for," replied Theodorakis. "I know I'm already in your debt and it's not easy for me to approach you again, but who can I turn to but old and trusted friends? I need five thousand Birr. There's an Italian who's going to undertake a mission close to the Sudanese Border and for a fee, he'll take me on as his assistant. I'll pay back every cent, once I reach my destination." The old man looked at them appealingly.

Pavlos and Lukas exchanged glances. "I wish we could help," said Pavlos, speaking for them both. "But I'm afraid, Theo, we gave you all we could spare for your last attempt. As it is we're only just able to make ends meet, selling our valuables bit by bit. God knows how long we'll be able to survive."

The old man nodded. "I felt bad asking you, but I didn't have anyone else to turn to. Come to think of it, though, I have a couple of rings myself that I could sell. It's just that I need the money by the end of the week."

"I'll give you the name of the person who bought most of our things if you like," Lukas offered. "He's about the only reliable one to help you right now. He's a decent man and will never take advantage of a desperate situation.

329

But I still feel it's unwise to attempt another escape so soon after your release."

Theodorakis was adamant. "It's now or never. If I don't go through with it, I'll rot and die in this place, waiting for people to take decisions. No, if I can't be a free man, I'd rather be dead."

After he had left, Pavlos returned to the sitting room and sat, hunched over, deep in thought. As Lukas and I entered, he looked up. "Do you know how many times I've thought I'd reached the stage where I couldn't take another day of waiting?" he asked. "Over the past five years, the idea of being smuggled out across the border must have crossed my mind at least a hundred times. But the thought of something going wrong and never seeing Venetia and the children again has always made me think twice. Not that I care two hoots about losing my own life, it's not that. They've been faced with so many hardships due to my absence, I owe it to them to stay alive. To inflict upon them the added trauma of my imprisonment or death would be too much, don't you agree?"

"Of course, Pavlos," I said. "Having waited so long, going through all the proper channels, it would be absurd to think otherwise now."

"What do you say, Lukas?" he asked, turning to his brother. "If things don't work out, do you think we might be forced to look for alternative ways of getting out?"

Lukas who had debated the issue with himself a million times, had an answer ready. "How could we, Pavlos? We have to think of Mother. In her condition there's little chance she would survive an escape. If we were caught, I, for one, as an Ethiopian national, would be shot on the spot. They wouldn't be as lenient with me as they were with Theo."

"We've been badly influenced by Theo's visit," said Pavlos, getting up and throwing his jacket over his shoulder. "I'm going out for some fresh air. Suddenly I feel I'm suffocating."

* * *

Holy Week was coming to an end and with all the last-minute preparations for Easter, our problems and worries were pushed to one side. We concentrated, instead, on building up the right spirit for the religious celebration. Easter was of equal importance to both the Ethiopian and the Greek Orthodox Churches and once more we attended midnight Mass as a complete family. Curfew had been lifted for the occasion and I was eagerly waiting to receive the blessed Holy Light that the bishop would bring down from the altar.

On that crisp April night with the fresh smell of orange and lemon blossom in the air, the few expatriate families still residing in Addis congregated in the familiar yard of Saint Frumendios Church to participate in the Easter service. In the past, the churchyard had regularly been packed with more than three thousand parishioners; now numbers were down to less than eighty. Pulling up her coat hood to keep out the cool night air, Lukas hugged Gabby tightly.

"I'm so grateful to have you both here," he whispered to me again. "This will give me the strength to carry on fighting until we're all together again."

The gloomy yard was gradually coming to life as, holding out their candles, everyone in turn received the Holy Light. It was customary to keep the wick burning and carry the flame home bringing with it renewed life. It was with that hope that we carefully carried our Easter torches home that night. Evangelia was waiting patiently for our return: it was nearly 3 o'clock in the morning and the dinner table was set with a white starched tablecloth and red candles, ready to be lit from the Holy Flame.

"*Christos Anesti!*" we cried, kissing her. "Christ has risen!" The bare dining room grew suddenly warm and radiant from the vivid glow of the candles.

"Let's get the hot broth on the table. You must be ready for it," said Evangelia, wheeling herself towards the kitchen. She was as anxious as the rest of us to break the fast we had all been observing for the past fifty days. The simmering broth, made from liver, kidneys, spring onions and parsley, was ready to be served. I quickly added the egg and lemon sauce Evangelia had prepared and sprinkled some fresh dill into the bubbling pot. As I served, Pavlos popped the cork of a red Gouder wine and filled everyone's glasses.

Evangelia raised her eyes to the ceiling and, with trembling voice led us into singing '*Christos Anesti*"— Christ has risen from the dead. At the end of the hymn, she lowered her eyes and made her own plea to the Almighty. "...good health to my children and grandchildren, and may the holy light fall upon those blocking our way..." Raising her glass, she made a toast, "To absent friends..." she said hoarsely, her lips quivering. "... may we join them soon."

Pavlos looked down at his dish. "Will such a time ever come? When will we wake up from this nightmare?" His question remained unanswered as everyone concentrated on the broth.

* * *

My two-week leave was soon over. No matter how hard we tried to stretch the days from six in the morning until well after midnight, it was impossible to catch up on everything that had happened during the seventeen months of our separation.

The night before my departure, Pavlos returned from the Olympiacos with some heartening news to take back to Nairobi. Theodorakis had succceeded in escaping to Khartoum! He had apparently crossed the border together with another Greek, Marino, our local baker. Marino, who had had some training as a nurse in his younger days, had painted his four-wheel drive baker's van white, embellished it with a red cross on each side and the pair of them had driven across the country from one control point to another, posing as medical personnel.

"Didn't anyone rumble them? Surely someone must have suspected?" said Lukas.

"No one," laughed Pavlos. "Apparently, they looked very convincing. They were carrying a whole case of medicines and disposable syringes. They told the check points that there was a meningitis epidemic and they'd been sent out to give preventative injections. They said they were just the advance group and a whole convoy of the International Red Cross would soon be on its way. To reinforce their story, they injected everyone they came across with distilled water or something similarly harmless."

"I can't believe it," laughed Lukas. "And they got away with it?"

"Yes. They had the border police completely convinced they were on a secret mission to avoid spreading panic and warned them they had to keep quiet about it because the Government would be upset if anything leaked out. They crossed into Sudan on camel back, without the slightest difficulty, then headed straight for Khartoum."

"I'm glad he made it! If he'd failed again, he'd have ended up in a mental hospital," said Lukas.

"What I can't understand is, why they wouldn't grant him an exit visa?" I asked. "He didn't have any outstanding debts with the tax bureau, did he?"

Lukas shook his head. "His biggest problem was his property. After nationalization, landlords were permitted to keep just one house, the rest had to be turned over to the Government. Theo tried to get permission to sell but his request was rejected: dwellings could not be sold until the law was gazetted. What could he do? He had no source of income, so he made a dash for the border. No one can blame him."

"But couldn't he have relinquished his property for a visa?" asked Evangelia.

Pavlos shrugged his shoulders. "He tried, Mother. He knocked on every government door. They flatly refused to discuss the issue—just like us. He had to wait."

"We all know there's no one around to make decisions these days, but this is preposterous!" cried Evangelia. "It all boils down to one thing. Son, you're wasting your time running from one Ministry to another," she said, turning to Lukas. "I doubt very much if they'll ever let us go."

My heart lurched. "Please don't say that," I begged her. "They've given Lukas some hope, at least for you. Don't get discouraged now."

"For the sake of my sons, I'll try. But I can't say I have much faith."

"What shall we do then, Mother?" Lukas' temper

flared. "Just give up trying and wait to die?" he shouted.

"I'm sorry, son." Evangelia gripped his arm, realising too late that her words were badly timed.

"Don't let me go off tomorrow leaving you all in this state," I pleaded. "We have our faith to help us survive this state of affairs. Please, don't let's lose the only thing we have left."

"You're right, my Child," Evangelia took a deep breath and sighed. "We mustn't lose faith."

Two weeks after my return from Addis, I was beckoned out of a meeting to answer an urgent telephone call. It was Lukas, bubbling with excitement. His mother had been given permission to leave.

"I can't believe it!" I screamed. "When can she travel?"

"She'd better leave immediately. Her exit visa expires in ten days and if we delay, we'll have to start the whole process over again. Is there any chance of you coming to pick her up?"

I looked at my calendar. It was Wednesday, 29 April 1980. I could take the next day's flight to Addis. Friday, 1 May was a holiday so I could accompany Evangelia to Athens on Friday and catch the Saturday night flight back to Nairobi, arriving early on Sunday morning. The timing was perfect, so long as I could get a day off.

"Can you hold on a minute. I have to get permission from my boss to take a day's leave. If he agrees, I'll be on tomorrow's flight." Within seconds I was back on the phone, a wide smile on my face. "Okay!" I yelled. "Get Mother ready to fly out on Friday, direct to Athens. I'll be there tomorrow. I love you!" I replaced the receiver and put my head down between my knees.

"Are you alright?" asked Joy, a colleague who shared the office.

335

"I'm fine, never better. I just feel a little faint. All this excitement has drained the oxygen from my brain."

"Nothing that a good cup of coffee won't cure," she said, bringing me a cup from her desk. A few sips and I was on my feet again, hurrying back to the meeting. It was difficult to concentrate on what was going on. I had to call Laki and ask him to buy me a ticket; I had to ask my mother to come and stay with Gabby; I had to shop for Addis; cancel my dental appointment; pack—there were so many things to arrange in just a few hours. The flight left at 6.15 the following morning and I had to be on it.

"Mellina," my boss's voice interrupted my thoughts. "Send in Joy. You'd better leave early today. You've got a busy weekend ahead of you."

I barely paused to express my gratitude.

It was still dark when the plane began taxi-ing down the runway. For once, it was on time. I fastened my seat belt and closed my eyes for the first time since Lukas's telephone call.

"Ladies and Gentleman, we have landed in Addis Ababa, Ethiopia. Welcome to thirteen months of sunshine!" came the hostess' voice over the loudspeaker. I couldn't believe we were there already. I must have slept throughout the flight.

I filled out my entrance card, declared the foreign currency I had brought with me and trembled at how the military dictatorship would react to my return. For the first time, it hit me that the airport had been renamed Addis Ababa Airport—Haile Selassie I International being stripped off soon after the revolution. I was escorted to a grim, cement floor hangar-type arrival lounge, the white walls decorated with three huge idealized portraits of Karl Marx, Vladimir Lenin and Friedrich Engels. It was cold and uninviting. The baggage carousel was out of order and my suitcase arrived on top of a trailer and was manually thrown in through a side door. Before I could pick it up, the friendly porter, who had seen me off a few weeks before, rushed up and helped me with my luggage. Flinging my hand luggage on his back, he wheeled the rest of my belongings towards a stern looking customs officer.

"He's the best one," the porter mumbled under his breath. "The rest will tear your baggage apart and confiscate all food stuffs."

As it turned out, I passed through without any hassles.

Lukas was standing at the barrier. "You look terrible," he said, taking me in his arms and guiding me towards the car.

"Don't worry about my looks, sweetheart," I smiled. "I'll take care of them later. I'm here to carry out 'mission impossible'."

By 9.30 next morning, relaxed after a good night's sleep in my husband's arms, I was ready to travel with Evangelia to Greece. Minutes before we left the house, she emerged from her bedroom clasping the icon of the Virgin Mary.

"I want you to take great care of this, Mellina," she said, entrusting her most valued possession to my care. "We came together from Karpathos in 1926 and now, after fifty-four years, we're going back."

"But, Mother," I said, looking at all the rings, necklaces and bracelets strapped to the frame. "You've left all these pieces of jewellery on the Madonna. What if they stop us at the airport? They'll accuse us of smuggling."

For years, the icon had drawn worshippers from all over Ethiopia to the Fanouris home to celebrate the annual

Feast of the Virgin Mary on the 7th of September. Every year since Pavlos' birth, Evangelia had kept her vow and performed an all-night vigil on the eve of the Feast. Gradually others had joined her, coming to fulfil their vows. Evangelia had always provided refreshment for the visitors, although her change in circumstances had limited her once-generous hospitality to a cup of tea. Over the years, people whose prayers had been answered had come laden with diamonds, gold and silver. Now I had to explain to the Ethiopian customs how this had come about. I felt panic skitter through me but Evangelia was supremely calm and confident.

"She's survived fires and wars," she whispered softly to herself. "She'll go through the customs."

As Evangelia eased herself out of her wheelchair and into the front seat of the car, a sobbing Askala fell to the ground and began kissing her feet. "You've been more than a mother to me," she wept. "I'll never forget the good bread we have eaten together. Go in peace, Mama, and may God bless you."

"And you, Askala," Evangelia's voice was choked by sobs. "You have got to take my place now. Look after my boys; I'm leaving them in your care." The two old women hugged one another, painful tears flowing down their cheeks.

"I'll pray night and day that they will follow you and I'll do my duty as long as I'm permitted to. My prayers to Gabriel will not go unanswered," Askala cried, as the car pulled slowly away.

"Really, Mother, you're acting as if we were still kids and not near-grandpas," Pavlos teased Evangelia, trying to dispel the tension that was building up.

"This is too painful for me, far too painful." Evangelia

wiped her eyes. "I came here a young girl in my early twenties, now I'm leaving an old woman. I can't even walk! I'm leaving behind a lifetime of friends and memories" She glanced in the direction of Gulele. "I dread to think how they'll get me onto the aircraft."

"They'll carry you in your wheelchair, Mother," Pavlos assured her. "You have nothing to worry about."

We had barely unloaded the bags from the car when an airline official came out of the terminal pushing a wheelchair in our direction. He helped Evangelia settle into it and prepared to wheel her straight through to the departure lounge. "Your daughter will complete the formalities. You needn't be bothered with that," he said kindly.

"But I haven't kissed my boys goodbye," Evangelia panicked, trying to slow him down.

The official called Pavlos and Lukas over. "Can you hurry please. We have to get your mother through quickly. She'll be the first to board."

Before Evangelia had a chance to become over-emotional, final kisses had been exchanged and she was whisked away.

"That was quick!" I exclaimed. "They sure are in a hurry!"

"We made the arrangements yesterday," said Lukas. "The doctor told us she wasn't to get too worked up as it would be too much of a strain on her heart. The attendant knew that, which is why he speeded things up."

"Smart thinking," I smiled. "Well, I'd better go and clear our things through customs. I'll call you the minute I'm back in Nairobi on Sunday morning and tell you about the trip."

He nodded without replying. We embraced quickly.

"Tell Venetia and the kids how much I love them," Pavlos whispered as he kissed my cheek.

There was a lump in my throat again. "Don't ever give up. You'll be the next ones to leave." I turned and walked quickly away, feeling their loneliness and isolation.

I had placed the icon in my briefcase and was carrying it as hand luggage. "What have you got in there?" asked the customs officer.

"Just an icon of the Virgin Mary," I replied, my heart thumping.

"Icons are treasures of Ethiopia. It is forbidden to take them out of the country," he snapped. "Open it."

"This is not an Ethiopian icon, sir," I said, unfolding the embroidered tablecloth in which Evangelia had wrapped it. "My mother-in-law brought this icon with her from Greece in 1926."

I waited for the officer's reaction when he saw the jewels, but he appeared not to notice them. His eyes were fixed on the face of the Madonna. "Isn't this the same icon at which my wife and I worshipped about three years ago on the night of the 7th of September?" he asked. My hopes began to rise.

"Yes, sir, I'm sure it is," I replied. I related the icon's history, beginning with Pavlos' miraculous birth.

"Yes, I know all about it," he said. "Through our prayers, the Virgin saved our little boy's vision. In fact, my wife and I had offered a pair of eyes carved from gold…"

"Would these be them?" I asked fiddling among the ornaments.

"Good heavens! I believe they are," he said, picking them up and examining them. Slowly he placed them back on the icon and carefully covered them with the cloth.

"Please put it back in your briefcase," he whispered. Lifting his eyes to meet mine he cleared his throat. "Where is the old lady?" he asked. "I should like to go and wish her a safe journey."

I pointed towards the departure lounge. "You can't miss her. She's in a wheelchair."

With passports and boarding passes in one hand and the briefcase in the other, I walked briskly across the tarmac towards the aircraft. They had already wheeled Evangelia out and had her waiting at the bottom of the steps. She kept turning her head to check that I was following. Two attendants were arguing as to how the chair should be lifted into the aircraft and I watched as they picked it up, one on each side, and then put it down again. In another attempt, one lifted the front and the other the back, but again it was no use. There was obviously no way they could carry Evangelia in the wheelchair up the steps. In a panic, I started running towards the plane, envisaging that there was going to be an accident.

"We'll have to carry her up," one of the young men told me as I arrived panting.

"If that's the only way, then why don't you both give her a chair lift with her arms round your necks," I suggested. That, too, was impossible; the steps were too narrow

"Put me down!" cried Evangelia, losing her patience. "If someone can support me on the left hand side where the fracture is, then I shall try and push myself up on the right side."

Through sheer will-power, Evangelia dragged herself up that staircase step by step. When she reached the door she was on her knees, unable to straighten up. Following anxiously behind, I called to the bewildered attendant,

"Help her up slowly and give her the crutches."

Once she had her crutches, Evangelia straightened herself, took a step and collapsed into the first seat. "I can't breathe," she gasped. "Have you got my medicine?"

I plunged into my handbag and fished out the heart stimulant the doctor had prescribed. Counting out ten drops into a cup, I quickly added some water and placed it to her lips, praying to God not to let things go wrong now.

"I'll be alright," she whispered, once she had swallowed the liquid. I dabbed her face and neck with cologne and rubbed her arms and legs to stimulate her circulation. "I'm feeling better. I really am. Come, sit down and relax. I know this has been just as difficult for you."

The rest of the passengers boarded the plane and soon the engines were revving and we were taking off. Evangelia had asked for a window seat. Without uttering a word, she watched the land she would never see again drift out of sight. The aircraft swung slowly to the left on its northbound journey and the whole city of Addis Ababa was spread below us. I saw Evangelia's eyes searching for Gulele beyond the outskirts of the city. Suddenly the cemetry came into full view.

She lifted her hand and waved sadly, "Goodbye, Manoli. Goodbye, Sophia. I know I'm deserting you both, but my heart and soul will always remain with you."

"We have a long way to go, Mother," I patted her arm. "Shall I recline your seat a little? You might like to close your eyes and rest."

"It's alright, my child. I'll rest in a little while. For as long as we're flying over Ethiopian territory, I'd like to look down and recall some of the happy and sad times we've lived through. Memories are all I'm taking with

342

me."

I left her to reminisce in peace, silently gazing out of the window in a world of her own. It was only after the plane had landed at Athens airport that she finally looked up, suddenly aware that life had to go on and that a large number of children and grandchildren were anxiously waiting to welcome her. As the Fanouris clan bustled round Evangelia's wheelchair, all trying to hug and kiss her at once, Venetia slid her arm into mine.

"Now, Mellina. What's in store for our husbands? Will they ever come home?"

PART FIVE

Addis Ababa

A whole year had passed to the day since Evangelia left for Athens. Officialdom had kept Lukas and Pavlos on a string, making promises that were never kept. Their courage and morale dropped dangerously low until Lukas found it increasingly difficult to write to Mellina: there was nothing to say. Without talking to or consulting each other, Lukas and Pavlos came to the conclusion that they were both doomed and the sooner they accepted it the better. Independently, they both wrote similar letters to their wives, telling them to dismiss them from their lives and start again. In return, they each received an irate missive from their partners.

"Venetia is so mad with me I wish I'd never written what I did," Pavlos confided in Lukas.

"Why? What did you say to make her so mad?"

"Well, I was so depressed last week, I told her she'd better write me off completely and carry on with their lives without me. Hell, what can I do from here? She's having problems with the girls as they need a father's guidance. Young Manoli is now a practising architect in Rodos and

346

needs my help to start him up in business. What can I give him, except some fatherly advice now and then? He needs me around. It's just pointless. I might as well be dead. I just told them to write me off."

Lukas nodded despondently. "I went one step further. I told Mellina I'd give her a divorce if she wanted it, so she'd be free to marry someone else and reconstruct her life. She can't wait around for ever."

"I bet she was as mad as hell!" Pavlos managed a smile.

"Mad! She's coming next week to tell me off in person. I don't know if I want her to see me in such a state. Anyway, what good will a brief visit do? It will only make things worse when it's time for her to go back again."

"Don't complain! You don't know how lucky you are that Mellina can come in and out. I'd give anything to see Venetia right now—even if it were only for a few days. If she had a UN pass, I wouldn't hesitate for a second but if she came on a visit now, they'd never let her leave again."

"You have a point there. But being together again will only delay what's inevitable."

"And what's that?"

"You know very well. She'll just have to start another life with someone else."

Lukas was emotionally torn. He desperately wanted to see Mellina and Gabby. His daughter was growing fast and he felt cheated not being able to enjoy her development, but it was a dull pain he was learning to live with. Having them there, touching them, would be like opening an old wound, which would have to heal all over again.

* * *

347

The following week, Gabby and I arrived. I was angry, but I waited until we were alone in the apartment before I broached the subject. "If you still love me," I said, the tears welling, "then you'll never mention divorce again. Unless, of course," I hesitated, lowering my eyes and inspecting the tear mark on my skirt, "unless, you've met someone else."

It had never occurred to Lukas that I might interpret his gesture in such a way.

"Of course not," he reassured me. "I'm only suggesting this to relieve you of a bond which doesn't appear to have any future. We're in a situation which is dragging on and on—like gangrene. It's eating us up, killing all our hopes and aspirations, leaving only rotten feelings inside."

"If that's the only problem, then we don't need to discuss the matter any further. We're going to see this gangrene through together. We've got to put our heads together and think of a way out. How long are you going to sit and wait for the Ethiopians to take a decision?" I demanded angrily.

Our argument carried on for several days. It was only Gabby's presence, demanding her father's attention, which introduced some intervals of calm. When Gabby asked him to play "horsey", Lukas dropped everything. Every moment they spent together was precious, to both of them.

A few days before Gabby and I were due to leave, Lukas received yet another negative response from the Foreign Ministry. He tried hard to conceal his feelings, but the thought of being separated from us again was too much for him. Suddenly, all the pent-up emotions came

348

gushing out. "I can't take it any longer! I've reached the end of my tether," he yelled. "I can't hold onto the knot any longer. I've got to get out."

Pavlos looked at him in disbelief. "Well, I never thought I'd hear those words from your mouth, Lukas. I reached that point months ago, but I didn't dare utter a word in case I discouraged you from pursuing your course. I can't stand it any longer either, so what are we going to do?"

My eyes widened. So they had finally come round to it. My stomach knotted as I thought what could happen. "How will you do it?" I asked, tremulously.

"I think we've reached the point where we don't care any more. We just do not care," yelled Lukas emphatically.

"I know of a trader who could help us," said Pavlos, his hopes beginning to rise. "He's approached me many times, saying that he could take us over the border to Djibouti. Maybe the time has come to go and find him."

Lukas was almost feverish. He paced up and down the room. "I think you should go and make contact right away, Pavlos. There's nothing stopping us now." He turned to me as I sat chewing my nails nervously. "You've got to be brave, sweetheart. I'm completely useless to both you and Gabby in this situation. I can't provide for you; I'm not there when you need me." He sat down heavily, putting his arms around me. "I can't see any other alternative, I really can't. Even death would be better than this. At least this slow torture, just rotting away here without hope, would be over once and for all."

What he was saying was hard to accept, but seeing the desperation in his eyes, I couldn't oppose him. His life had lost all meaning. I had to get used to the idea that they were going to attempt an escape and if they were killed in the process, then as the Greeks said, *'I tan i epi tas.'* 'Better dead in freedom than alive in captivity.'

When Pavlos returned home for lunch, there was a sparkle in his eyes for the first time in years. "I missed Abu Sitta. He left this morning for Djibouti, but he'll be back in six weeks' time. Apparently his price is ten thousand Birr—cash in hand. It's too high. We don't have anything like that kind of money, but we'll have to see what else of value we have to sell," he said, his voice tinged with excitement.

"We'll find something," said Lukas, casting his eyes round the room. "We're down to heavy furniture and carpets, but I think we can sell off a few pieces without appearing too conspicuous and attracting the attention of the *kebele.*"

Up to now I had kept out of their discussions, wanting neither to encourage nor discourage them, but I felt it was time to get off the fence. "I'll leave you all the money I brought with me," I said quietly. "It's not much, but it will help."

Lukas squeezed my hand gratefully.

"We'd better not mention this to anyone," Pavlos cautioned. "We've got to keep it completely secret. You know how rumours travel. We don't want a hint of it reaching any official ears."

No one had an appetite for lunch. Mama Askala came in and wrinkled her nose in disapproval. "What's this?" she demanded. "I've spent the whole morning cooking and you've hardly touched a thing."

"It was delicious, Mama Askala, but none of us are hungry, really!"

"You're getting the same food for dinner and I'll carry

on serving it until it's finished," she scolded us like children. "As if this were the time to waste food," she muttered, disappearing into the kitchen. A minute later she returned and, ignoring the rest of us, placed a piece of cake in front of Gabby. "Here *coucoush*," she bent close to Gabby, using the pet name she had given her. "You appreciate my food, so you, and only you, are entitled to a piece of my cake."

We all laughed. Our loving, bossy Askala always managed to make her point. "I've prepared some very special *berbere* with garlic and all the spices, specially blended for you," she added, turning to me. "I want you to divide it up between you, your mother and Electra, okay? But use it sparingly, I don't know when I'll be able to send you some more."

"I'll probably be back again," I replied.

"No, my sweet child. I think this will be your last visit here." Turning away abruptly, she hurried back to the kitchen.

* * *

At the airport, Gabby was difficult. "I don't want to leave Daddy!" she cried, pushing me aside with a kick to reinforce her statement.

"I'll be joining you later, Honey," said Lukas, picking her up and placing her in my arms. I looked into his eyes, wondering if we would ever again be able to hear music together and see the colours of a rainbow. I opened my mouth to say something, but nothing came out. I tried a second time. Lukas placed his finger over my lips.

"Don't say anything. I know you'll all pray for our safety and that's all we need right now. Now, off you go."

Gabby allowed me to put her down and slowly guide her away, waving to her Daddy until we were out of sight. From the aircraft window, we spotted the two lonely figures on the waving base, waiting for the flight to take off. Gabby started to cry. "I don't want to leave them here," she sobbed, tears streaming down her cherubic face. "Please, let's take them with us. I want them to come." She began to scream and kick.

"Please, Baby, don't cry," I said, taking her in my arms, trying to soothe her.

"No, no," she screeched, becoming hysterical. Clutching her fists tightly, she began to pound on my chest, screaming and shouting, "You're a bad, bad Mummy, a very bad Mummy!"

"Why, sweetheart?" I asked, trying to calm her.

"You're leaving Daddy behind. Look! He's all alone with Uncle Pavlos. He's all alone!" she screamed, arching her back and flailing her arms and legs wildly. "Why don't you take him with us to Nairobi? Why?"

I felt an unbearable ache in my throat that tightened with every breath I took. I was petrified that if I tried to speak I would choke. Suddenly, something in me snapped and all the frustration and sorrow that had been suppressed for so long, erupted. "There's nothing I can do! Nothing!" I shouted, losing the self-control I had tried so hard to maintain. Putting my fingers through my hair, I pulled as hard as I could, wanting to inflict as much physical pain as possible to ease the pang in my heart. I tore and tugged, sobbing and crying repeatedly, "There's... nothing... I can d-do. Noth... I c-can..."

Stunned by my reaction, Gabby stopped crying and nestling close, put her arms round my neck and rested her head on my chest. "It's alright, Mummy. I'm here. Don't

352

cry…" She looked up to see if her words of comfort were having any effect.

"I love Daddy very much," I whispered, hugging her tightly. "But there's nothing I can do to bring him home." Then, as if my outburst had suddenly cleared my mind of all its preconceived ideas, I stopped. The same inner vision I had experienced when Lukas had proposed to me, flashed before my eyes. Of course there was something I could do. The time had come when it was up to me to stand by him in his time of need. I had to find a way to help him. We should have set aside our doubts and organised Lukas' escape long before. I returned to Nairobi with my mind in a turmoil.

Aspa and Michael had come to the airport with Laki, anxious for news.

"They've given up, Michael. They can't take any more. They're looking for ways of getting out," I said, as we drove towards the city.

In the game park to our left, shy impala grazed peacefully. A *matatu* passed us, music blaring from the cab, its passengers crammed like sardines, waved and smiled at Gabby. Lukas, Ethiopia, the awful loneliness, their desperation—the whole thing seemed unreal.

"What possibilities are they considering?" asked Michael.

"There's apparently this trader who transports goods to and from Djibouti. He can hide them among his merchandise and help them cross over the border."

"Good Lord! I hope it's not Abu Sitta. He's the biggest crook ever. I've heard he takes people's money and then turns them over to the police at the first checkpoint, claiming it was just bad luck. He's said to work hand-inglove with the authorities."

"Oh, my God! I believe that was his name. Are you sure? Michael, we've got to warn them." I told them of Pavlos' plans.

"You'd better call them as soon as you get home, but make sure you speak in some sort of code. You don't know who's listening in."

Dropping the bags in the hallway, Laki and I rushed to the telephone. I called the Addis operator, but there was no reply.

"Try the supervisor," urged Laki.

"I'm sorry, caller, but all the Addis lines have been out of order since yesterday due to heavy rainfall," the supervisor told me.

"Can you tell me how soon we'll be able to get through," I pressed him.

"It's difficult to say, Madam. You might try again later this evening or maybe tomorrow. Technicians from both sides are doing all they can to repair the lines. If you give me your number, I'll try and call you as soon as we can connect you."

"Look, there's no need to panic," said Laki, the minute I had replaced the receiver. "It's not as if they've already made plans to take up this guy's offer. They've only tried to contact him. Didn't you say Pavlos couldn't find him?"

"Yes, but now he'll know who they are and if he does turn people in, he'll be bound to tell the authorities he's been contacted. Then they'll have someone watching them."

"Relax. You said he won't be back for six weeks. Even if we don't get through till tomorrow, there's still plenty of time to warn them to keep away from this character. It was a blessing Michael had heard of him."

A familiar blue Mercedes pulled up in front of our door. My nephews ran in to greet us followed by Electra and Byron. "It's good to have you back, Sis." Electra kissed me. "But from the way you look, you didn't leave Lukas in a very good state, did you?"

I shook my head. "No, things are not good."

"Chin up, Mellina," said Byron. "I have some good news for you." He looked at Electra and smiled. She nodded.

"We've been waiting for your return. Byron has something to tell you."

"Well, for goodness sake, out with it!"

"Just four days ago, I found out there is a British pilot in town who's undertaken several rescue missions in war-stricken countries. Purely by coincidence, I was introduced to him at a cocktail party a couple of days ago. In passing, I asked him if it were possible for him to carry out a rescue mission in Ethiopia and he appeared to be interested. He wants to see us tomorrow night and talk things over."

"Byron, that sounds incredible!" I exclaimed. "If he's prepared to do it, when could he go?"

"He's here for two weeks before he flies to London to carry out a government contract to deliver some aircraft to West Germany. That will take approximately one week. He says he could be available during the second week in June."

"That gives us exactly four weeks to work out the details," Laki calculated quickly.

The telephone rang. It was the exchange. "We're trying your call to Addis," said the operator. "Replace your receiver. We'll call you back when we've made contact." A few minutes of silence followed, during which I thought rapidly how to word my message. The 'phone rang again. "You're through to Addis. Speak up, please."

"Hi, Honey." I raised my voice.

"What's up?" asked Lukas anxiously. "Did everything go alright? Gabby's fine, isn't she?"

"All's well. We had a good trip and we're home safely. It's just that I forgot to sign the traveller's cheques before I left. I'm sorry, darling. You can't use them." I kept my fingers crossed that he was getting the message.

"But..." he started. Then he paused for a second, remembering that he had watched me studiously sign each one that very morning.

"So, I can't use them?" he asked, dragging his words to give him time to think.

"It only occurred to me that I hadn't signed them when a fellow passenger asked me on arrival in Nairobi where to cash her cheques."

"Not to worry," he replied. "It just means Pavlos and I can't buy that second-hand car from Djibouti that was offered to us, I suppose?"

"No, I'm sorry. Looking back, it wasn't in very good condition anyway and would have given you endless trouble."

"You're right. Maybe it was just as well that you didn't sign the cheques. What do I tell the guy with the car though?"

"Tell him you've changed your mind and you can't take the risk."

"Yes, yes," Lukas replied, getting his thoughts straightened out. "But now what do we do for transport?"

"Don't worry. Byron has just told me of another opportunity that's come up which sounds a much better proposition. I'll let you know the minute something is

356

arranged."

"Fine! I'll be waiting to hear from you."

Before we had time to say any more, the line was cut. It didn't matter. Lukas had got the message.

Chapter Thirty

Addis Ababa

"What was all that about?" asked Pavlos as Lukas replaced the receiver.

"They must obviously know something about Abu Sitta that we're not aware of. It was Mellina telling us to abort the idea of using him. From what I could gather, she must have met someone either on the flight or at Nairobi airport who put her off. I'm sure she'll explain in more detail in a letter."

"So, what in hell do we do in the meantime?" asked Pavlos, an angry red flush rising in his face.

"Well, it looks as if there might be an alternative— using someone in Nairobi. It might be safer and more reliable. We'll have to wait and see what it's all about. It sounds as though the ball has started rolling."

The men decided Lukas should continue his daily visits to the ministries, keeping up the pretence of trying to obtain exit visas, in order to avoid suspicion. In the meatime, they went ahead with their plans to sell some of the furniture. The Nairobi option would be financed from that end, but if it failed, they would have to have ready cash for alternative endeavours. Every day, they took something into town to sell.

While they were sorting out saleable items, Lukas came across some Maria Theresa coins in one of his mother's sewing baskets. He decided to take them along to the Armenian shopkeeper, who had bought their silverware and jewellery. The old man was extremely nervous, greeting Lukas shiftily, while continually glancing towards the door whenever anyone passed. Examining the coins hastily, he scooped them up and took them into the back of the shop.

"Is something wrong, Mr. Zerkerjian?" asked Lukas when he returned.

The old man leaned forward over the counter. "I've just heard bad news about a fellow goldsmith, Mr. Merzian. He's been killed," he confided.

"What? He was here just last week. I saw him. What happened? Where was he killed?"

"Ssh!" Zerkerjian waved his hand in front of his lips. "I don't want anyone to overhear us. You never know how it could be interpreted. Come behind to my workshop," he whispered.

Lukas followed the old man into the back. His worktable was covered in gold dust and bits of gold nuggets piled in one corner waiting to be melted down and mixed with various alloys. He sat down, pushing aside the bracelets he was working on and waving Lukas to a seat. Placing one elbow on the table, he rested his head on his hand.

"We had heard that Merzian was trying to find a way of escaping from the country, but none of us really believed he would take the chance. Well, just over a week ago he told some friends he was going down to Kulubi to

359

fulfil a vow to Saint Gabriel. It turned out that some trader had promised to take him across the border to Djibouti. We don't know any details, but it's reported that he was shot resisting arrest just outside Harrar."

Lukas felt himself breaking out in a cold sweat. It must have been Abu Sitta! He must have been the one taking Merzian out. The timing was perfect. It was last week that he had left for Djibouti. Poor old man! He was seventy years old and had probably wanted to live out the rest of his days with his daughters who had emigrated to the United States.

"He was widowed three years ago," Mr. Zerkerjian echoed Lukas' thoughts. "He felt very lonely without his wife—God rest his soul. He'd lost interest in his work and was pretty miserable. They refused him an exit visa because of a tax dispute."

Lukas shook his head sadly. "That could have been Pavlos and me," he thought. "It's easy to say anything is better than this depressing, living death, but when you're up against it, when you come face to face with the end, life is sweet."

* * *

Nairobi

"Mellina, we're going to be late!" Byron called from his car, honking the horn outside our maisonette.

"I'm ready!" I shouted from an upstairs window. "I'm through putting Gabby to bed." Leaving the babysitter in charge, I picked up my bag and ran to the car.

"We've got ten minutes to reach the aero-club," said Byron, reversing out of the driveway. "You know what these Brits are like: they're so punctual and correct, I'll bet you anything he'll look at his watch the minute he sees us."

Byron rapidly negotiated the heavy Hurlingham traffic and sped out past the towering turrets of Kenyatta Hospital, looking for all the world like a fortress overlooking the city. As we turned into Wilson Airport, I glimpsed dozens of small light aircraft parked in front of the enormous hangars which lined the perimeter of the airfield. Most of them were owned by private companies who ran safari trips. Kenya Airways scheduled internal flights also landed there.

We arrived at the club a few minutes before the appointed time, our tyres crunching on the gravel as we turned into the car park. It was a low, grey stone building with bougainvillea creeping up the walls. To one side, separated from the airfield by a high pallisade was a small, sparkling, aquamarine pool. While Byron parked the car, I walked ahead into the reception area of the club, where a brown leather sofa and a few armchairs were arranged around a coffee table. The sole occupant was a man in his early thirties, wearing a khaki safari suit with a brown and gold patterned silk scarf tucked into the neck. His legs were crossed and he was sitting, totally relaxed, sipping a cold beer. He obviously wasn't waiting for anyone.

"I don't think he's arrived yet," I whispered to Byron as he joined me.

"That's him over there," he said, pointing towards the man.

"But, he looks completely disinterested in us," I said.

Byron grinned. "Watch," he whispered in Greek. "He's calculating the time to the last second. He's drinking his beer, wiping his mouth and now he's looking at his watch.

What did I tell you? He's getting up. Our appointment was for seven thirty and it's precisely that time now."

The pilot strode over to us and extended his hand. "Good evening. Captain Brian Carrington. Pleased to make your acquaintance."

Byron introduced me. "It is Mellina's husband who is trapped in Ethiopia," he said.

"I see." Clenching his fist, Captain Carrington pressed his nose against it as he considered his next words carefully. "I have undertaken many rescue missions and quite successfully, too. But, I do like to give each one very careful consideration."

He put his hands behind his back and walked to and fro for several minutes as if in deep thought. I looked at Byron, my eyebrows raised. I wondered what he could be considering. We hadn't had a chance to open our mouths. He closed his eyes and rubbed his forehead until, as if coming out of a trance, he began to bombard us with questions. Why were we so anxious to get them out? Had they committed any crime? Were they in any way disabled? Could they cross mountains on foot if the need arose? Where could they travel to without being at risk? What radar systems did the Ethiopians use? The questions were endless. He was obviously extremely thorough, which was presumably why he had been so successful, but some of the questions were impossible to answer. We knew nothing, for instance, about airspace regulations.

Finally, he took us into a room where there was a huge aerial map of East Africa. Pointing to a relatively flat section of land between two mountainous regions near the Kenyan border, he announced, "Right there! If they can get there I'll pick them up."

I had no idea whether he knew the area or had just

362

picked the nearest piece of flat land on the map, but he seemed extremely sure of himself.

"I shall be using a small light aircraft that can, without any danger, land on rough land. In fact, if you step outside, I'll show you the exact model I'll be using." He led us through a back door onto the tarmac of the airfield. Several small planes were parked nearby and he walked over to a red and cream four-seater. "This is the only type of light aircraft that will stand up to landing on rough ground. You see it has a strong support beam beneath the wing, stretching right across."

Totally ignorant in these matters, I looked blankly at the plane just praying that it would fly my husband to safety. Byron, who was more mechanically-minded, made several technical enquiries. As we walked slowly back to the clubhouse I heard Byron pose the critical question— how much would the mission cost?

"Well," Carrington hesitated, slowing to a standstill. This was a matter he wanted to discuss out of earshot. "I will, of course, have to make precise and accurate calculations, but, as a preliminary figure, give or take a few thousand, I would estimate a minimum of fifty thousand dollars."

Byron and I froze in our steps. The blood drained from my face. I turned and looked at him. Surely he meant fifty thousand Kenya shillings, which would be approximately five and a half thousand dollars. My brain raced. If we appealed to our relatives, I was sure they would help. We could pay them back when Lukas was working again.

Byron's voice interrupted my thoughts. "Did you say United States dollars or was it English pounds?"

"No. My fee is in US dollars. It's still just a rough estimate, you understand. Any such mission is extremely risky. I have to consider my life, my reputation and my aircraft.

My heart stood still. How could we possibly find that kind of money?

"So," he was continuing, "you find out whether your people can reach the spot I indicated on the map, and when I return to Nairobi in three weeks' time, we can go from there. The time, the place, must be exact, you understand."

Byron consulted his calendar. "Now, let's see. That will be around 21st June."

"Precisely. I can be here a day or so before and go in on the weekend of that week. The money must be deposited in my foreign account in London and confirmation received, the week prior to my arrival." He took out a visiting card, wrote his home telephone number on the back and handed it to Byron. "I'll be waiting to hear from you." He shook hands and walked outside to his car.

"The timing's bad," I said, as we slowly followed Carrington out to the car park. "The rainy season will be in full swing. How on earth will this guy be able to land in the middle of nowhere without previously inspecting the ground?"

"I don't think you should worry about rain. He's only going over the border and I doubt if there'll have been any heavy rains there. It's mostly desert around that region; it's the Ethiopian highlands that get the heavy rainfall."

"You may be right, but what's the point of discussing such details, when the most important factor right now is his fee. We'll never be able to raise that kind of money. In fact, I doubt very much if we can put together a tenth of that amount."

Byron opened the car door for me. "Listen, everyone is

going to help. I'm sure Venetia's brother will be only too happy to help get Pavlos out. And what about Kostas? He's often written to you asking what he could do to help. Surely, he can chip in something."

"He's got good intentions, but he has kids in school and college. He only earns a salary; he's not a businessman."

"Well, let's try and find out what we can raise, before we say anything to Lukas and Pavlos."

"Wait a minute!" I suddenly remembered the money I had inherited from my godfather, Evangelos. He had left each of his nephews and nieces a thousand pounds. It would help. "He roasted for ten years in the Congo to earn that money and never enjoyed it. I know he'd have been pleased to know it will go towards rescuing Lukas."

"There you are," Byron exclaimed, trying to boost my spirits. "You've already identified one source of money. There'll be others."

* * *

On my way to the office the next morning, I stopped outside the Panafric Hotel, where a friend waited for a lift. "Hi, Mellina," Erica greeted me with her usual cheerful smile. I pulled out into the stream of traffic, stopping a little further on at a red traffic light. Erica turned and looked at me. "There's a disturbing aura around you this morning, Mellina," she remarked. "Is something wrong?"

Erica could pick up signals like a radio receiver. In fact, it was this extra sensitivity in her that had first brought us together. She had come to my office one morning, collecting contributions towards the funeral arrangements of a colleague who had recently died. I dug into my bag and produced several notes—perhaps a little more than I could afford, but Anna Maria had left behind two young children who were having to return to Chile with their grandparents.

"My heart goes out to those children," I had said, "especially the baby. She's only two and to grow up without a mother is terrible."

"But she'll be watching and guiding them from where she is," said Erica. "The soul never dies. Anna Maria has just crossed over to the other side."

I looked up at her and felt that she knew things that I desperately needed answers to. After Dad died, I strongly believed that he was in another place, maybe better than this earth that we lived on. But where? Erica guessed immediately what was going through my mind.

"You've lost someone close to you, haven't you?" she asked.

"Yes," I said, looking away. It was always painful to talk about my father. "I lost my Dad three years ago, but I still can't accept his death. I feel he's around us the whole time."

"And so he is." She sounded so sure of what she was saying. "But tell me, you're a little psychic, aren't you?"

I thought for a moment. "I guess so. I do feel certain things and sometimes know what's going to happen, but my father was the psychic one. He used to pick up signals from miles away and was never wrong."

"You've taken after him, but you need to develop your powers."

"No way!" I laughed. "I'm scared. I feel it's better to leave such metaphysical phenomena alone."

Erica smiled. "Look, I have to be going now but maybe some day, over a cup of coffee, we could discuss the subject at more length."

The next day, as I drove past the Panafric, I spotted her waiting at the side of the road and stopped. "Do you need a ride?" I asked. She accepted, explaining that a colleague usually gave her a lift, but possibly there was something wrong as he was late.

"I pass here every morning," I said, "so if ever you need a ride, just wave me down."

"Thanks a million. Actually, I do need to be more punctual. My boss is an early bird, so if you do pass this early, it would suit me perfectly."

Our friendship had started with daily superficial chats on the fourteen-kilometre drive to work, gradually building up to sharing one another's worries and problems. We talked about anything from children's emotional development to single parenthood, the revolution in Ethiopia, nationalisation, and the forced separation of two people who wanted to be together. Our daily conversations were more therapeutic than visiting an analyst. They helped me to recognise and deal with my problems, gave me courage and confidence, and strengthened my faith in the future.

"Well, is there something wrong?" Erica repeated her question, seeing I was lost in a world of my own.

"Oh! Sorry, Erica. My mind's been racing to the four corners of the earth," I apologised.

"You've been quiet for a good five minutes, which is far too long for you," she laughed.

"Gee, I am sorry," I repeated. "I was thinking who I might contact for money." I had told Erica the previous day I was going to meet the pilot. "He wants fifty thousand dollars!" I said.

"For the love of Christ, where can you find so much

367

money?"

"That's what I'm debating. It's completely beyond our means."

"I don't believe this guy can be genuine somehow."

"Well, we really don't have much choice. And what's worse, we only have a few weeks to come up with the cash."

Erica was silent for a minute. "Something else is going to come up, something more positive. I don't feel this is the right man." Deep down I agreed with her, but where would we find another Brian Carrington.

"It's time I introduced you to Margaret," said Erica.

"Who's Margaret?"

"She's a spiritual channeler. You know," she hastened to explain, "a physical presence on earth acting as a channel of communication; disembodied entities talk through her. A wonderful person! She's always running around helping people and I know she'll be only too happy to guide you in the right direction."

"I'm scared, Erica. What if she says we shouldn't attempt any rescue missions."

"I'll give her a call and see if she's got a few minutes for us."

"Wait! How much does she charge for a session? I might not be able to afford it."

"She never accepts payment. She believes she would lose her power if she took any money. She gets fulfillment just by helping others."

I drove into the small car park outside my office and we each went our separate ways. When we met for coffee later, Erica had already set up the meeting. Margaret was free that afternoon and had asked us to go directly to her house after work.

368

A tall, beautiful woman in her middle thirties, opened the door. Her long, black hair reached down to her waist and she had sparkling, green eyes. "Come right in and pour yourselves a cup of tea. I'll be right with you," she said, hurrying back towards what looked like a study.

"She's probably seeing someone else," whispered Erica. "She can never turn anyone away."

"It must be very tiring for her," I said, searching out an empty seat in the far corner of the room. Each of the three armchairs within reach was occupied by a sleeping cat and I didn't want to disturb them. Erica poured me a cup of tea and brought it across.

"Margaret loves animals. The number of creatures she has in the garden is unbelievable. Anything that can crawl, swim or fly seems to find sanctuary here."

We had just finished sipping our tea when the study door opened and a grey-haired woman emerged. "Now, you mustn't worry. Everything will be just fine," we heard Margaret assure the old lady. "If you feel you want to talk to someone, come back at any time. Alright?" She opened the door and walked her to the gate.

"Dear old lady, all alone, with no one to care for her," she explained briefly when she returned. "Now," she said, turning to me, "It's a pleasure to meet you."

"The pleasure's mine," I smiled, suddenly feeling rather nervous. "I'm sorry for disturbing you. I know you must be extremely busy."

"I'm never too busy when it comes to helping someone and, from the look in your eyes, I can see that you are worried."

I opened my mouth ready to pour out my troubles, but she raised her hand and stopped me. "You don't have to tell me. I know! Don't have faith in the one who made

369

promises. He won't keep them. Try other solutions. His method would have been too risky." She was about to continue when the telephone rang. She got up to answer it and then turned to us apologetically. "I'm sorry, my son has just called from school. He's finished early and has to be picked up." Erica and I stood up to leave. "If you need my help," she looked at me, "you know where to find me. I really don't mind being disturbed."

Once we were outside, I turned to Erica in disbelief. "How on earth did she know what was on my mind? Did you mention anything to her?"

"Not at all. I told you, Mellina, she's a medium. I've known Margaret for five years now and I've never had cause to doubt her powers.

The month of June came and went with no sign of Brian Carrington. Although Lukas had said there wasn't a chance in a million of reaching the rendezvous spot in safety, we had still hoped to work something out. We tried calling Carrington's London home, but there was never any reply, until one day in the second week of July a female voice answered. Byron asked to speak to Carrington, only to be told that he was in the Bahamas and was not expected back for several weeks. He had apparently left for the West Indies immediately after returning from Kenya.

"He obviously abandoned the idea as soon as he left Nairobi," said Byron bitterly.

"He could have told us," I cried.

"Not everyone who looks like a gentleman is one."

"You can say that again!" But, I consoled myself, Margaret had warned me!

Chapter Thirty One

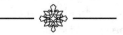

A couple of weeks after our disappointment, I had a call from Aspa. "Michael and I have something to tell you, but it's not something I can discuss over the phone," she said excitedly.

"Something wrong?" I asked. I had developed a tendency to be pessimistic about everything.

"No...but it's important. I think it's worth your while to come right over."

"What's up?" asked Laki as I put the phone down.

"I don't quite know, but Aspa wants me to go over right away."

"I'll come with you then. Let's go."

Gabby had to be collected from school, so Laki rang Electra to ask her to pick her up and take her home with her. We sped across town through the lush green suburbs of Nairobi, the carefully-tended gardens a riot of colour. Even along the roadside, scarlet poinsettia bushes vyed with coral-red hibiscus and the delicately-scented mimosa for space, whilst the purple heads of the towering jacaranda waved above us. Laki tried to gain my attention by pointing out some of the more spectacular blooms, but I was too preoccupied trying to guess what lay in store. I felt a growing excitement.

At the sound of Laki's horn, both Michael and Aspa appeared at their front door.

"Okay, what's happening?" I said, looking Aspa straight in the eye.

She smiled. "Come in. We'll tell you all about it. Can I get you something to drink?" She looked from Laki to me.

"Maybe later," we replied simultaneously.

Aspa looked at Michael, "You tell them."

"Go ahead," he smiled. "I know you're bursting."

"Listen, guys," she said, taking a deep breath. "Michael has found a pilot who's going to Ethiopia to train some helicopter engineers. When he's completed his contract, he's agreed, on his way out of Ethiopia, to land at some mutually agreed spot, pick up Lukas and Pavlos and fly them back to Nairobi."

"What!" I screamed. "This is unbelievable."

"It's the best way to get them out without any unnecessary risks," said Michael.

"But how did you find this guy?" asked Laki.

Michael told us how it had happened purely by chance. He had gone to Wilson airport to charter a small aircraft to fly some tourists to Turkana. The regular pilot was away and he was introduced to a temporary pilot who was being employed for the trip. Michael was told he could only make the flight once as he was scheduled to depart for Ethiopia on a contract. At the mention of Ethiopia, Michael studied the pilot with renewed interest. He was an open, affable sort of man, so he decided to take the plunge. Drawing him on one side, he explained Lukas' situation and told him he was looking for someone to undertake a rescue mission.

"Would you believe it, he just said he would do it, without even batting an eyelid," Michael concluded his story.

"When is he going?" asked Laki.

"In two weeks' time, around the 16th to 18th of July."

"Well, that'll give us some time to alert Lukas, so that he and Pavlos can make the necessary preparations."

"Right, but not a word to anyone," Michael warned. "We mustn't jeopardise this guy's future. He didn't even talk about money. If he does carry it off, it will be largely due to the kindness of his heart and his wish to help two fellow human beings."

"Rest assured," said Laki. "We won't breathe a word. We don't even want to know his name."

"Now," Aspa repeated her offer, "anyone for a drink?"

"Yes, please, and make it a double whisky," laughed Laki.

Refreshments in hand, we sat down at the dining room table to work out a detailed plan. The first priority was to find out how far Lukas and Pavlos could travel towards the Kenyan border, accepting that their petrol was rationed and they had to obtain travel passes. Next, we had to find a spot where a light plane could safely land, preferably on a stretch of open land or, better still, murrum road. We had to have the details as soon as possible. It was decided that letters were too slow and that I had to telephone Lukas.

"But, for heaven's sake, Mellina, give and take messages in code or it could end disastrously," urged Michael. Coming out to the car to wave us off, he pecked me on the cheek, "Keep us in the picture, won't you. Let's hope this time we can pull something off."

I didn't want to get too excited, but I couldn't control the butterflies in my stomach. By eleven that night, a call had been put through to Addis. The telephone rang and

373

rang but no one answered. "Shall I disconnect you? There's no reply," the Addis operator announced.

"No, please, let it ring a few more times. They're probably asleep." I knew after curfew, there was nowhere else they could be except their beds.

The receiver clicked. "Hello," I heard Lukas reply groggily at the other end.

"Sweetheart, it's me!" I yelled. A dry "Yes" came through.

"Lukas, are you alright?"

"Yes," he mumbled, "but I'm still asleep. Give me a few seconds to splash some cold water on my face."

Pavlos, who had obviously been woken up too, picked up the receiver. "You guys sure pick the right time to call," he said, filling in time until Lukas returned.

"It's important, Pavlos. Are you fully awake? Can you make sense of what I'm saying?"

"Try me."

"A doctor will be coming to Addis in about two weeks and both you and Lukas should go and get a check-up."

"Where's he coming from?" asked Pavlos.

"Nairobi," I replied. "The minute he lands he'll contact you."

"Gotcha!"

"Now, you know the two canaries you want to send to Gabby from around Lake Arbaminch, well, he can pick them up on his way back to Nairobi as he'll be flying his own plane. But you'll have to let him know where exactly he can pick them up from."

"Yes," he hesitated, "but there's no way we can contact anyone in Arbaminch to get any details."

"All right then. Find out how far you can go and let us know, okay?"

"Fine, here's Lukas. He wants a word with you." Pavlos handed him the receiver.

"Do you think Gabby will get the canaries in time for her birthday?" he asked. He had been listening on the phone in the bedroom.

"God willing, yes!" I replied. "She'll be thrilled. It will be the best present she's ever received."

"Okay, Honey, that's great. May I ask one favour? Please don't call us again at such an unearthly hour. We had trouble waking up."

"What do you mean 'unearthly'? It's only 11.15."

"But you forget we're in bed by eight o'clock. We can't go out and we've no women, no alcohol and no television to keep us occupied. What else is there to do around here?"

"Okay," I laughed. "I'll try and call you before 8.00 p.m. in future. But from now on, one of you had better be home at that time, there might be more details cropping up. The doctor has a busy schedule, and if you miss this opportunity, where will you get your check up?"

"Tell the doctor our symptoms and emphasise that we're extremely sick. We need medical attention as soon as possible."

"Don't worry. After he's examined you, we're sure you'll be on the road to recovery. Hold tight now. Don't despair. I'd better leave you now. I love you."

"Me, too," he replied. "It's only this love that keeps me going."

* * *

Addis Ababa

Lukas leaned back in the heavy armchair and looked at Pavlos. Had it been a dream or had they really called from Nairobi? No, it had happened alright. He leapt up, suddenly wide awake, and went to put some coffee on.

"Okay, let's try and decode what Mellina has just said," he said, sitting down again.

Pavlos reached for a cigarette, tapping it on the table before he put it to his lips. "It looks as if a contact is coming to Addis and will probably brief us first-hand about what we're to do."

"Yes, but she said something about picking up two canaries—which are us, of course. It sounds as though someone, flying his own plane, is maybe coming on official business and is intending to take us back with him to Nairobi when he's finished. Presumably he needs to know where he can land to pick us up without being spotted."

"Well, it can't be somewhere too close to Addis or they'll pick him up on the radar. I suppose that's why she was hinting about Lake Arbaminch."

"But that's impossible," said Lukas. "It's over 250 miles on dirt roads. Even if we could get the petrol, we'd be stopped by patrols."

"Well, somehow we're going to have to find out how far we can drive without being stopped, but how?"

"I have an idea!" exclaimed Lukas, suddenly remembering. He had received an invitation from Tollis Koutruvis, First Secretary at the Greek Embassy, to go down to Langano for a long weekend. "I could accept and once we were down there, we could probably drive on as far as Awassa. We'd be travelling in a car with diplomatic plates so no one would ask for permits at the checkpoints."

"Brilliant!" cried Pavlos. "You'd better accept fast before Tollis invites someone else in your place, and ask him if I can come along too."

* * *

The trip to Langano was uneventful. As Lukas had predicted, the police were only interested in the driver's permit, ignoring the passengers. Pavlos noted down the exact location of all the control points, which had doubled since Lukas and Mellina had travelled that road.

"The lake region of this country is one of the most beautiful areas I have ever visited," Tollis remarked as they approached Lake Zwai.

Seizing the opportunity, Lukas interposed. "There's a steep hill beyond Lake Langano, towards Lake Awassa, where you can see all five lakes at once. It's a magnificent sight."

"That's something I'd like to see very much. I've brought my wide-angle lens with me and that's a photograph I have to take." Lukas grinned at Pavlos. It had almost been too easy. This was their chance to scan the area for a suitable landing site.

After they had pitched the tents and started the camp fires for dinner, Lukas and Tollis strolled down to the edge of the lake. Tollis reintroduced the Awassa trip. "How about making an early start in the morning? We might even spot some game on the way."

"That would be great," said Lukas. "The lakes will be all the colours of the rainbow at that time of the morning—pink, blue and yellow. The most spectacular thing, though, is the sight of the pelicans flying over from Lake

Margarita to Lake Abiata for their morning feed. They resemble a huge white cloud."

"Why's that?" asked Tollis. "Why the morning move from one lake to another?"

"Lake Margarita is formed in a volcanic crater. No fish can live in the water because it's so alkaline, but it's a perfect habitat and breeding ground for pelicans and other species. They fly over to Abiata every morning, fill up, and by mid-day, they're on their way back carrying food for their young."

"That's fascinating. I can't wait to take some photographs."

By 5:45 the next morning, they had parked the car at the top of the hill and were waiting for dawn to break. Beneath them, the vast dark plains stretched into the distance, even darker patches indicating where the lakes lay. A faint light in the east outlined the black bulk of the surrounding mountains and hills. Within fifteen minutes the whole landscape would come to life, transforming the dull grey of the lakes into sparkling silver splashed with crimson and pink and, finally, into a deep blue. By the time the sun had risen over the eastern lakes, Tollis had finished his first roll of film, capturing the magnificent transformation.

Lukas pointed out the different lakes to him. "That's Zwai in the distance. To the left is Abiata, to the right, Langano. Here is Awassa and that one furthest away is Margarita."

"What's that white cloud over Lake Awassa?" Tollis asked.

"That must be the first flight of pelicans."

"I'd like to photograph them at close quarters. Let's go up to the lake."

It was the opportunity Pavlos and Lukas had been waiting for. The road was in reasonable shape with several stretches of straight, pothole-free tarmac. A few kilometres from the lake, there was a road block where a soldier signalled them to stop.

"Where do you think you're going?" he demanded.

"We're going to observe the bird life at Lake Awassa," Lukas answered in Amharic.

"No one is allowed beyond this point unless they have a special permit from the Dergue. This is a restricted military zone. Now reverse your car and drive back."

"Is there a training camp here?" Pavlos asked, as Tollis reversed and drove back towards Langano. Lukas looked around for signs of a military base and just before the town of Awassa, he spotted a few small aircraft in the distance.

"It must be a small airforce base," he said, pointing towards the planes.

Tollis still had his mind on pelicans. "I wanted to photograph those birds," he said with disappointment.

"Let's try Lake Abiata then," suggested Lukas. "There might not be quite so many birds there, but I'm sure we'll find plenty of different species to photograph."

Their scouting trip over, Lukas sat back and mulled over what they had discovered. If there was to be a pick-up, it would have to be half-way between Langano and Awassa. There was no way they could go any further. The other complication was the military base—an air base at that! It could make the operation extremely dangerous.

Back at the Langano camp, Pavlos and Lukas decided to go for a stroll to work up an appetite for lunch. "It's going to be dangerous," said Pavlos, once they were out of earshot. "Our only chance will be if the pilot's on a cleared flight schedule and reports that he's having to force-land due to a mechanical fault. He can pick us up and be away again in a few minutes. I think it's the only way we can pull it off."

"Did you make a note of possible, clear stretches of road, where he could land?"

"Sure. There are one or two possibilities before you reach Awassa."

They walked back to camp.

Dropped off outside their building, the two brothers had barely made it to the lift when they heard the faint ring of a telephone coming from one of the apartments. It could have been anyone's, but something told Lukas it was theirs. Dropping his bags, Lukas ran up the three flights two steps at a time, leaning heavily on the door to regain his breath. He fumbled in the dark to find the switch for the stair light, cursing the architect who had chosen to site it in some obscure corner of the landing. The key? Where was the key? He dug deep into his trouser pocket. Had Pavlos locked up when they left? Gratefully he felt the cold metal on the familiar leather ring. He thanked God the caller was persistent.

"I'm coming! Don't hang up!" he shouted as he ran towards the phone. "Yes," he breathed into the mouthpiece.

"Hi, Honey! You sound a bit out of breath." It was Mellina.

"You sure time your calls well. We're just this minute back from a weekend at Langano."

"I'm glad you guys had a break. How was the road?"

"Pretty good, but a little wet up to Shashemani. We took an early morning ride down towards Awassa, but unfortunately we just couldn't go up to the lake."

"Oh? What was the problem?"

380

"A herd of wild buffaloes was blocking the road."

"What buffaloes?" was her immediate reaction. Then she stopped for a second. "Oh. I see. You were scared they might charge, so you turned back?"

"Right!" She had got the message.

"What a shame you couldn't go further down."

"There was no way—absolutely none!"

There was a short silence while Mellina passed the information on to someone standing beside her. Lukas waited for a reply.

"Did you at least manage to find a good stretch of road?"

"Yes. Until we met up with the buffaloes, the road was fairly clear."

"Was the road winding? I know how you get car sick. Or were there some good straight stretches?"

"No, there were quite a few good stretches, some at least five to six kilometres. The best piece of road was a few kilometres before we met up with the buffaloes."

"Were there any telephone wires or electricity cables to spoil the scenery?"

"Nothing too close. Pavlos took some notes so that he could give you precise details for the tourists you'll be sending from Nairobi."

"We'll let you know when we need them. In the meantime, just sit tight and pray the rains won't prevent you from enjoying another weekend in Langano. The lower altitude is good for your health."

"You can say that again!"

* * *

Nairobi

"That's not very good news." Michael was pensive. "If they can't go beyond Awassa, the pilot will have to land soon after Langano, which will be risky. Langano is only 180 kilometres south of Addis and I doubt if he could make a diversion from an authorized flight plan without the Ethiopians becoming suspicious. Still, there's no way we can plan it on any other route. I've got a meeting with Robert the day after tomorrow. I'll have to discuss the details with him then."

I looked at him with my eyebrows raised.

"I'm sorry. That's the pilot. It's about time we identified him by his name," he smiled. "Now, to go back to the original plan. Time is running out: Robert is scheduled to leave at the end of the week if he gets final clearance from Ethiopia."

"What clearance?" I asked, feeling sudden misgivings.

"Well, he's been given verbal and written assurances that he'll get clearance from the Civil Aviation authorities, but so far nothing has reached Nairobi."

"They probably have to get the go-ahead from the Dergue itself," I said. "No one dares move a finger without the green light from the highest authority."

"I've heard there's also a shortage of fuel for aircraft in Addis. They might find it a little embarrassing to quote the real reason for the delay and prefer to blame it on the clearance procedure."

"What if the clearance never comes?" I asked, ready to be pessimistic.

"The contracts for the training are signed. Clearance is only a formality to set the wheels rolling."

We waited anxiously as the days ran into weeks. The clearance never came. At the beginning of August, Robert received a message stating that his contract was being postponed for a "few weeks only", due to a shortage of fuel in the country which would be alleviated "shortly". I dreaded telling Lukas. The fuel shortage was just a sham; there would always be a fuel shortage in the country, as long as the struggle over Eritrea and the Ogaden continued. The war against the Eritrean Liberation Front had been going on for twenty-six years, it was not going to stop overnight.

In the second week of August, Robert asked to meet Michael at the Norfolk Hotel in the city centre. It was a balmy night and Michael noticed there was a new moon as he strode into the Delamere bar and ordered a cold lager. The bar was a popular meeting place for the town's youth and became extremely crowded as the night wore on. However, this early in the evening it was still possible to get a seat. He nibbled at some macademia nuts and waited. On the dot of eight, Robert joined him and they went in to dinner. The Ibis Grill, overlooking the exotic gardens of the old colonial hotel, was congested with wealthy tourists, most of them American or German. Michael led the way to a reserved, candlelit table and glanced at the menu.

After they had ordered, Robert leaned forward. "Something's come up." His sentence was drowned by the in-house pianist striking up. He tried again. "It concerns your people in Addis…"

Over a meal he couldn't recall eating, Michael listened to Robert's plan. He told him how that morning he had bumped into an old acquaintance who had just flown in some royalty from one of the Gulf states. He was eager to do some freelance flying while his employers were on a three-week safari. Tyrone Goodman was a reputable and skilled pilot with many years' experience and over a glass of beer at the Aero Club, Robert had casually mentioned the plight of the Fanouris brothers. Tyron had been sceptical, but had asked for more details.

"I would offer to get them out myself, but that would be risking my pilot's licence and my kids' future," said Robert. "But Tyrone has no ties. He might just take it on."

"How can we find out?" asked Michael.

"Why don't we ask him now," said Robert, wiping his mouth and standing up. "He's just come in." A man of medium build with ash blond hair and a short clipped moustache strode towards their table. He was wearing a casual safari jacket with an open-necked shirt, khaki trousers and sand-coloured desert boots. "May I introduce Captain Tyrone Goodman," said Robert.

Michael shook his hand. "Won't you join us for a meal?"

"No, thank you, I already ate in my room, but I will accept a cup of coffee." His accent was almost undefinable—a strange cross between English and American, with a slight Kenyan twang. It was the voice of an adventurer who had travelled the world, smoothed and moulded by a dozen different cultures. Michael pulled up an empty chair and invited him to sit down. "Before you say anything," Tyrone started, "Robert's filled me in on the situation and I've decided, I'm going in." He said it as though he were going round the corner to pick up a packet of cigarettes.

Michael hurriedly chewed the piece of steak he had just inserted into his mouth and swallowed hard. "Did I hear you correctly?" he asked.

"Yep. I've been playing with the idea ever since Robert mentioned it and my mind's made up. I've been in some sticky situations myself and I know what it's like. It sounds like they're going through hell. This will be nothing compared with 'Nam, I can tell you."

"You don't know what this means to us all," said Michael. "We didn't know how to tell them that another mission had been called off."

"No problem, but you'd better contact them right away and get me the exact details of where they can drive to and when. It's crucial they find a good stretch of road for me to land on. It's going to be risky as I won't be on an authorized flight, so we have to work it all out precisely. What I need is road maps—detailed road maps. Aerial maps won't do for this job."

"I'm sure we can find road maps somewhere," said Michael, confidently.

"Don't think so," said Robert with a shake of his head. "I've tried to get hold of some of those Michelin maps, but they all seem to be out of stock."

"Okay, I'll see what I can do," said Michael. "Mellina, the wife of one of the guys you're going to rescue, should be able to help. She's got a lot of connections with people who used to travel from Addis to Nairobi by road. Of course that was before the revolution, but I'm sure the roads haven't changed."

"Sounds good, and I know the US Mapping Mission has also produced some great maps. If we could get our hands on those, that would be A-OK."

* * *

The telephone rang a few minutes before midnight. I was engrossed in a late-night television movie and must have answered it automatically, putting the receiver to my

385

ear. It was only when I heard Aspa's voice saying, "You had better listen and listen carefully," that I registered what I was doing and jumped up to turn off the set. "Are you with me?" she asked.

"I'm sorry. I am now."

"Michael has just come back from having dinner with Robert and you won't believe this. He's found a pilot who's going in to rescue Lukas and Pavlos."

"You mean the clearance finally came through?" I shrieked.

"No, they've decided on a different approach. I can't say very much tonight, but what they desperately need is maps. We'll try and see what's available in town, but see what you can do from your end."

"First thing tomorrow morning. If I get anything, I'll call you right away."

"Now listen, Mellina, not a word to anyone. Secrecy is of the utmost importance. You must find a way of camouflaging the real reason for needing the maps. Use any excuse."

"Okay, but I'm sure they'll guess."

"It's up to you to convince them that they're needed for another purpose. I can't stress enough the importance of caution."

"I understand."

"You can tell Laki, but only Laki, okay?"

The next morning, while I was trying to figure out who was the best person to contact for maps, my office door was flung open and there stood Laki, tanned from a recent safari, full of bounce and vigour. "Hi, Sis! I was on my way to the rifle range at Limuru, when I decided I could spare a few minutes to have a cup of coffee with you."

"You couldn't have chosen a better time. Talk of

telepathy," I laughed, picking up my purse. We walked across to the cafeteria and took our coffee to a table outside under the acacia trees. There was a plop as a tiny frog, disturbed by our presence, leapt into the pool nearby.

"I know you've got something important to tell me," he said, looking up from his first sip of coffee. In a low voice, I related the happenings of the previous evening. Laki's eyes sparkled. "Finally, we seem to be heading towards a workable plan. Hallelujah!" It was hard to conceal his excitement. Before we had time to discuss the maps, Carl and Teresa joined us with their coffees and hot samosas.

"What a surprise to see you here, Laki," said Carl, sitting down. "You both look excited. Any good news about Lukas?"

Laki and I looked at one another. Noting our hesitation, Carl looked a little hurt. "Look, we've been friends for long enough now. What? Three years? You can trust us!"

I winced, feeling rather ashamed. Over the past three years, Carl and Teresa had stood by us like siblings. I thought back to the night when Gabby was burning with fever and Mum and I were in a panic. It was Carl who had come to the rescue at 2 o'clock in the morning, insisting that he drive her to the hospital. His prompt action had saved her life: it had been scarlet fever.

"You promise you won't breathe a word to anyone?" I asked them dramatically.

They both raised their right hand. "Scouts honour," they smiled.

I told them the plan. "The only problem is we urgently need a map of Ethiopia and…"

"Why didn't you say so before," Carl interrupted. "I can get one for you in an instant. Jones, in my office, has a

387

pilot's licence and flies up to Turkana nearly every weekend. I've seen several maps in his office and I know he'll spare me one. I'll be back in a flash." Before we had finished our coffee, he had returned with a rolled map tucked under his arm. "Here, take it. He doesn't need this one. He's got another."

I unfurled it and saw that it was a detailed, large-scale map of northern Kenya and southern Ethiopia. It would probably do. Laki immediately offered to cancel his shoot and deliver the map to Michael. He raced into town, zigzaging from one lane to the next, hoping to catch him before he went to lunch. He was just leaving his office as Laki pulled up.

"Hey, Michael, over here," he waved. "I was just coming to see you."

"Laki, good to see you. Has Mellina talked to you?"

"Sure. In fact, I have something for you."

Michael was on his way to meet Tyrone and invited Laki to join him. They weaved through the lunchtime traffic, out past the city park and the burgeoning industrial area, until they turned right at the Nyayo sports stadium and headed up the Langata Road towards the airport.
"Mellina asked me to give you this," said Laki, feeling for the map on the back seat behind him.

"Wow! That was quick work! How on earth did she get her hands on this?"

"A friend got it for her."

"I hope she didn't tell anyone what she needed it for?" said Michael anxiously.

"No, no! It happened to be a spare one lying around in one of the offices." Laki skimmed over the question.

Michael was engrossed in the map. "It might do, unless he needs a more detailed one. We'll see what he thinks."

They stopped outside the offices of one of the charter companies. It was refreshingly cool inside after their sticky drive in the midday heat. Laki followed Michael along a high, airy corridor until he stopped outside the last door. His knock was answered with a hearty, "Come on in. It's open."

Tyrone put down the pen he was writing with and stood up to shake hands with Laki. Michael introduced him and then got down to business. "We've got one map here." He spread it out on an empty table at the side of the room. Tyrone switched on an overhead lamp and bent over it. His eyes swivelled from side to side as he studied it carefully.

"Hmm! It's not bad, but I need more details of the main road, tarmac, dry-weather roads and murrum roads." He reached out and picked up a red felt-tip pen from his desk. "Can I mark it or do you have to return it?" he asked.

"No, it's okay. It's ours to keep. Go ahead," said Laki.

He quickly scanned the map again and then without hesitation, leaned over and marked the flight path he was going to take in and out of Ethiopia. "That, gentlemen, is the route I shall take. I shall have to dump fuel somewhere on the way up to enable me to refuel for the return trip," he said, marking an 'X' on the border and circling it with a flourish. "Yes, sirree," he said, dropping the pen, "I think we're going to pull it off, but I do need a better map."

"May I call my sister from here," asked Laki, a sudden thought striking him.

"Sure, go ahead. Just dial 9 first for an outside line."

Laki had remembered that Andrew Somerson, a friend of his who worked at UNEP, was the last person he knew to cross the Ethiopian border by car. He was sure to have maps. He instructed Mellina to contact him and ask to borrow them. He turned to Tyrone. "If Mellina manages to get her hands on those maps, I can bring them over tonight."

"That's fine. We shouldn't really lose any time. I'll be ready to go in about a week. That will be…," he flipped thought the calendar on his desk. "…let me see, yep, I can probably fly up to Loyangalani on Saturday, 5 September, sleep there, set out just before dawn on Sunday, the 6th, fly to the appointed place about 6.00 a.m., pick them up and return to Nairobi for a slap-up Sunday lunch." He turned to his two companions, smiling broadly. "Well, that's about the size of it, gentlemen. But I need those maps."

"Hopefully we'll see you tonight then," said Laki, shaking his hand at the door. "He appears very confident," he commented to Michael, as they walked down the corridor and out into the heat of the midday sun.

"Let's keep our fingers crossed."

* * *

Andrew was writing a report and had a deadline to meet. He heard me talking to his secretary. "It's alright, Jane," he called. "Let Mellina in. I can spare her a few minutes."

I knew he was busy so I went straight to the point. "Andrew, do you have any detailed maps of Ethiopia I can borrow? You must have used them when you came down from Addis," I asked, fidgetting with my wedding band a little nervously.

"Yes, I think I kept them," he said, going to his filing cabinet and flipping through the hanging compartments.

"They might be a little torn but they're probably still usable, although I must admit I didn't think anyone would be needing them in the foreseeable future. I can't imagine anyone wanting to attempt such a trip at the present time. Ah, here we are." He adjusted his reading glasses to examine the maps. "Yes. Michelin maps of Ethiopia." He pulled them out and handed them to me. "They're excellent maps—show every bump and lump."

"Thanks a million, Andrew. You just don't know what these mean to me." I blushed a deep red. I was not supposed to even hint at my reason for wanting them.

"Don't say a word, Mellina. I don't want to know. Good luck!"

"I could kiss you, Andrew!" I blushed even deeper.

"Well, what are you waiting for," he smiled, offering me his cheek. "I'll accept a kiss from you any time."

* * *

"Fantastic! Just what we need." Tyrone was delighted. "This is exactly the map I was looking for." He spread it out on the table. "Now we're set. Call Addis and ask when is the best weekend to implement this mission—and see if they can manage to be on this stretch of road on a Sunday morning around 6.00 a.m. before there's any traffic about." He circled a point between Langano and the Lake Awassa road block. "So, the ball is in your court now. I shall wait to hear from you. Incidentally, when do I get to meet the wife? I'd like to reassure her that I really will be going through with this."

"Let's leave it until you're ready to leave. These people have waited three years for this reunion and have gone through countless disappointments. Let's finalize the plans from Addis first," Michael replied.

Tyrone nodded. "Then I'll wait to hear from you," he said.

* * *

"Well, Sis," smiled Laki as he entered the house and made himself comfortable in an armchair, "he's ready to go. We just have to get in touch with Lukas and work out a suitable day. Tyrone suggests a weekend, preferably a Sunday. If the guys in Addis have enough fuel to get down to Langano, he could go this coming weekend."

My stomach began to churn. Now that our goal was in sight, I began to think of everything that could go wrong. The initial plan was not too dangerous but this pilot would be flying illegally over Ethiopian territory. "What if they mistake him for an enemy plane from Somalia," I said, "especially as the registration number is in Arabic. They could shoot him down."

Laki looked at me earnestly. "Mellina, we've been through all that. Look, I understand your having second thoughts, but it's a chance we have to take."

"If only there was someone to tell us if we're doing the right thing. You know we really are gambling with their lives. Do we have a right to do that? What if it fails?"

"If we want to save them, we don't have any other option. Now, stop all this negative thinking and start thinking positively," said Laki sharply.

I sat silently for a moment. If there was only someone I could turn to, someone who could read the future and could reassure us all would be well. And then it came to me. Of course! She had said if I were troubled, I could go to her any time. "I'll go to see Margaret!" I cried, jumping up from my seat.

Mum's face lit up, "My God! Why didn't you think of her before?" she exclaimed.

I ran out to my car and drove straight to Margaret's house, only to be told by the uniformed security guard at the gate that she was out with *"Bwana"* and he didn't know when they would be back. Disappointed, I sat for a few moments wondering what to do. Seeing my dilemma, the guard called, "Wait one moment, Mama, I call housegirl."

He ran up the drive, reappearing a few minutes later with a rotund, pleasant-faced *ayah* in a blue and white striped polyester dress and spotless white apron. "*Jambo*, Mama," she called. "*Habari*?"

"*Jambo! Mzuri sana*" I returned her greeting. "Do you know when *Memsahib* and *Bwana* will be back?"

"They not tell me, but I get roast and potatoes in oven. They are here for dinner."

"I wanted to see Mrs. Cartwright; it's quite urgent."

"Then you write note and she call when she come back," she suggested.

I hurriedly scribbled a note and handed it to the *ayah*, stressing the importance of her not forgetting to give it to Margaret. "I don't forget, Mama," she smiled.

When I returned home, my mother was bathing Gabby and from the commotion coming from upstairs, I gathered all her dolls had joined her for a swim and she was refusing to get out.

"I'm waiting for my mummy," I could hear her arguing.

"Mummy's here," I called. "Let's have you dried and downstairs for dinner, shall we?"

"Can I feed my babies, too?" she asked, as I appeared

393

with a towel at the bathroom door.

"You can bring your favourite baby, but we don't have enough food for the whole group."

"Any luck?" asked Mum, taking the towel and wrapping it round her grand-daughter.

"Margaret wasn't home, but I'm sure she'll call me," I replied.

The dinner table was in chaos with Gabby attempting to feed herself and her entire entourage of dolls, when there was an unexpected ring at the door. Mum parted the curtains to see who it was.

"It's a couple I don't know," she announced, going to unlock the door. "Maybe they've got the wrong house."

"Is this Mellina's house?" I heard a familiar voice enquire. It was Margaret. I left Gabby and hurried to the door. "We found it quite easily. I must say Erica's directions were very precise," she said, looking directly at me. "I knew from the tone in your note that you needed to see me urgently. I knew it couldn't wait until morning, so I came right away with my husband."

"I really didn't want to disturb your dinner…"

"Nonsense," she interrupted me with a smile. "That can wait. Your problem is more urgent."

"Sorry about the mess," I said as her eyes fell on Gabby and her four dinner guests.

"Don't worry, my dear. I've been through all that with my own three. This is the fun of growing up."

"Okay, Honey," I turned to Gabby. "Wash your hands and off you go upstairs. You need to put those babies to sleep." By some miracle, she instantly obeyed and went up to her bedroom. My mother followed to ensure she stayed there.

"Now, we don't have too much time…" Margaret's

words trailed off as her eyes searched the room. Her gaze rested on the staircase lights. "Those lights are too bright for me," she said, raising a hand to shade her eyes. "Could you possibly switch them off and maybe I could have a candle here." She pointed to the centre of the table in front of her.

I rummaged in a drawer for one and lit it. Margaret focussed her gaze on the flame for a few seconds before turning to address me. A serene, glassy look had come over her face, as though she were a different person from the one who had just entered my home. I looked questioningly at her husband, who had seated himself in our rocking chair. He gently nodded his head and smiled, lifting his right hand slowly as an indication that I should relax. Everything was okay.

I wondered if she were in a trance, but before I had time to speculate further, she turned to me and in a sort of different voice said, "It's about your husband, isn't it?"

"Yes," I whispered, feeling suddenly choked and wanting to cough and clear my throat.

The room was totally silent but for the sound of our breathing. Margaret sat perfectly still lost in meditation for what seemed like an age, though it must have only been for a few minutes. Then, almost in a monotone, carefully measuring every word, she began to speak. It was like a rehearsed recitation.

"Yes. A difficult and dangerous mission lies ahead, which must be undertaken within the next three weeks. Then and only then is there a chance for success. A large bird with steel wings will fly in and pick them up on a clear road very near water. There will be soldiers who will obstruct and try to prevent their leaving. A military plane will be instructed to force them to land. But they will fly beyond the clouds to freedom."

She stopped, concentrating once more on the burning candle. I was sure they could both hear the thumping of my heart. Had she actually mentioned freedom? "You do believe in 'the other side', don't you?" she asked.

"You mean to where our departed loved ones have gone?"

"Yes. That's right," she whispered.

"Yes, of course. That's where my father is. Or that's where I want to believe he is."

"He is there, Mellina. The message he wishes to pass on to you is that he'll be with your husband on the selected day, with Manoli. Together, they will guide their children to safety."

The mention of my father brought back the choking sensation. Tears began trickling down my cheeks. Even from there, Dad was trying to lend a helping hand.

"Who's Manoli?" Margaret asked.

"He's my father-in-law," I replied, wiping my eyes.

"You have good spirits on the other side." Margaret stopped for a moment and then continued. "Not very tall with black shining hair. Only a little grey at the temples. Fun-loving personality." A detailed description of my father followed, leaving me in no doubt that Margaret was actually seeing and communicating with him. She breathed deeply two or three times and then slowly stood up. "Our supper will be getting cold, Tim," she said, turning to her husband. "I think we have to be going."

I started to thank her, but she raised her hand to stop me. "Don't say anything now. Come and tell me all about it when it's over, then we'll celebrate. Alright? But don't forget: whatever has to be done must be accomplished within the next three weeks. Otherwise it will be too late."

Chapter Thirty Two

Addis Ababa

It was ten days since Lukas had last heard from Mellina. Throughout the city, celebrations were being organised for the seventh anniversary of the Revolution on September 12.

Pavlos was growing sceptical about the "doctor's" visit. "I can't see anyone coming out here on official business at the moment. Everything's at a standstill, what with the anniversary celebrations coupled with the Ethiopian New Year, I doubt if anyone will be working this week."

Lukas remained optimistic. "I'm sure they're just finalizing details. I've a feeling we won't have to wait long now. What's worrying me is the lack of petrol. I've only managed to save a few litres and we need to take enough for the return trip in case anything goes wrong."

"My God, you're right!" exclaimed Pavlos. "I'm so anxious to get out of this place, I never thought of that."

The petrol problem seemed insoluble. The men had plenty of friends they could approach, but they were loathe to implicate them in their escape. Lukas was increasingly worried that the green light might come through from Nairobi any day and they wouldn't have enough petrol to reach the appointed place. He began to have a recurring nightmare in which they ran out of fuel on the road to Langano, they pushed and pushed until the sweat poured from them, then they would see in the distance the rescue plane swoop down and, waving and shouting madly, they would watch as it disappeared into the clouds without them.

"I'm going to church to light a candle," said Lukas, feeling the need to get out in the fresh air. These days they walked everywhere or crammed into a small *seicento*, if one happened to be heading in the direction they wanted to go.

"I think I'll come with you," said Pavlos. "We can ask Askala to stay by the phone in case Mellina calls."

As they paused for breath at the top of Churchill Road, someone honked behind them. Thinking they were obstructing the driver's path, they moved to one side. "Hey, Lukas, Pavlos," a voice called. "Jump in. Let me give you a lift."

It was Stephanos, an old Ethiopian friend. Lukas and he had attended university together and their friendship had remained firm over the years. With their imminent escape in view, Lukas was trying to avoid contact with friends, in case the *kebele* tried to make something of their association. It was people like Stephanos in particular he wanted to protect. This was his country and his future depended on forgetting the past and concentrating on building a new socialist state with new ideas. Old friends whose property and livelihood had been nationalized and who were bent on escape should be part of that forgotten past. It was painful to sever friendships in this way, but it was for their own good.

"Thanks for the offer, but we're only walking to the Greek Church and we're almost there," Lukas called back.

"Don't argue with me. Jump in," Stephanos insisted. A queue of traffic was building up behind him, so the brothers decided to comply. "And why may I ask are you walking? Where's your car?" he asked.

"It's parked at home. Not a drop of petrol to run it. Useless bit of junk, a car is, without the precious liquid," Lukas replied.

"Look. I'm due to fill up my car today but, having been on official business all last week, I haven't used my last week's quota yet. I've got two jerrycans in the back. Let's go and get it."

"How much are you allowed—ten litres?" asked Pavlos, quoting the normal resident's allowance.

"No, my friend, I'm one of the lucky ones. Because I work on agricultural projects and do a lot of mileage, I'm allowed seventy litres a week. So, now you know why I'm so generous with this week's supply," he laughed.

It was too good to be true. Lukas dived into his pocket to check how much money he had. Out of the corner of his eye, he saw Pavlos doing the same. He touched his money clip and felt a few notes, praying they were red ten Birr notes and not single green ones. Pavlos seemed happy enough.

"That's very kind of you, Stephanos. Are you sure you can spare it?"

"Sure I can, otherwise I wouldn't offer. Let's go fill up those cans," he said, smiling.

Lukas could barely contain his excitement. Seventy litres! That meant they had one hundred in all—enough to cover the distance there and, God forbid, back. He tried hard to hide his jubilation.

"Just make sure I get my cans back as soon as you fill your car," Stephanos was saying. "I shall be off to Assela this week, so I'll need them."

"No problem, you can have them tonight. We'll drop them off at your house," said Lukas.

"Why bother?" said Stephanos as they pulled into the garage. "We can just as easily drive back to your place now, fill up the car and I can take my cans back home with me." He leapt out and removing the containers from the boot, told the attendant to fill them up. Lukas thought quickly. If the security guard saw Stephanos helping them fill up the car, he could identify him to the *kebele* if there was an inquiry about their escape. Stephanos might be accused of being an accomplice. No. It was too risky.

"I have a better idea," he said. "We're near our church. We can borrow some containers from our priest and transfer the petrol."

"Okay, that's fine by me. It will save time, I suppose."

Lukas heaved a sigh of relief.

"What took you so long?" scolded Mama Askala when they burst into the apartment full of high spirits. "They've called three times from Nairobi. Now, just sit and wait; Mellina said she was going to call again in about an hour."

"Wow! She must really be missing me," said Lukas, putting his arm playfully round the old woman's shoulders.

"It's no good for young couples to be separated for so long," Askala continued, shaking her head.

"Are you trying to tell me something I don't know? Maybe that she's dropped me for someone else?" quipped Lukas. "Aha! I detect a funny little smile, Mama Askala. Maybe you know something?"

"God forbid!" she said, shaking his arm off. "What

400

kind of talk is this? My Mellina would never do anything like that. She's moulded from good paste." Her tone softened. Then she turned to glare at Lukas. "And don't you go putting words into my mouth, you Rascal."

"You wait and see," he teased, infuriating the old woman. "I'm going to tell her you suspect something the minute she calls."

"Don't you dare," she shouted, picking up her wooden spoon and pushing Lukas towards the door. "You're not too old to get a hiding, you know," she chuckled.

She disappeared into the kitchen and Lukas sat down to think. Askala was another problem. How could they leave her behind? She was part of the family. What if she were tortured for information about them? How could they live with that knowledge? Askala had been with the family for forty-five years. She was too old to get another job, too set in her ways. They had all long ago agreed that they must leave her financially independent when they left and the brothers had set a goal of five thousand Birr, the equivalent of ten years' wage at her present salary, to see her through her old age. It had been difficult to raise. Lukas had had to part with several precious items, including his family signet ring bearing the emblem of Saint George killing the dragon. All he had left was his gold wedding band, which he had resigned himself to selling too if the need arose.

The telephone rang, interrupting his thoughts, and he leapt to answer it. From the three beeps before the line opened, he knew it was the call they were expecting. Very faintly, he could hear Mellina conversing with the telephone operator.

"I'm trying to connect you. Hold on please. Mr. Lukas, are you holding?"

"Yes I am."

"Then go ahead please. Nairobi calling."

Lukas took a deep breath. "How are you, Sweetheart? We've been waiting for you to call. We were getting pretty worried."

Mellina lost no time in coming to the point. "We had a few loose ends to tie up and had to be certain of some details before we called you," she replied. "Now, listen. The plans have changed. The doctor is coming directly from Nairobi, picking up the canaries and then flying straight back. Can you get the birds down beyond the lake, where you usually go camping?"

"Yes, of course, we can. When?"

"When is it most suitable to you? It has to be as soon as possible and preferably a Sunday morning."

Lukas covered the mouthpiece and turned to Pavlos, who was waiting impatiently to hear what was being arranged. "They want to know when's the most suitable day for us to go down to Langano," he whispered, fearing that Askala, who was fluent in Greek, would overhear.

"Well, Saturday 12 September, is a national holiday. Everyone will be preoccupied with the celebrations. That might be the best day, or even the Sunday," he replied.

Lukas nodded. It was perfect. No one bothered to check passes during major celebrations. "This weekend is as good as any. Everyone's involved in the anniversary celebrations. In fact, we can even legitimately take a few days break. Everything here will be closed."

There was silence for a moment as Mellina held consultations. "Fine. Then this weekend it is. I'm turning you over to Laki who will give you all the details. Okay?" There was a catch in Mellina's voice. Sensing her tremulousness, Lukas' heart began to race. If all went well,

402

he would be holding her in his arms in less than five days' time.

"Take the details down, Lukas," Laki spoke slowly and clearly so as not to make any mistakes. "The doctor will be coming on OYZ XXI, green and black lettering, around 6 a.m. on Sunday morning. You will have to be parked on the main road facing the direction in which the wind is blowing with both your boot and bonnet open. That will be the signal that the road is clear for him to land. If there's any danger, boot and bonnet should be closed. He will land and pick up the canaries. Have you got it?"

"Yes, I have, but is it alright if we also deliver Jeannie at the same time? Gabby's been longing for her little pet."

"I'll let you know, but I don't think there will be any problem. We'll call you about the final arrangements on Friday. Okay?"

"We'll be here. Let's hope the phones won't be out of order."

"We'll all keep our fingers crossed. By the way, have you got enough fuel?"

"Yes, I think we're alright. Just pray for us."

Lukas hung up. He sat for a moment, trying to absorb all that had transpired. It was unbelievable to think that their life in Ethiopia was finally drawing to a close. He looked around the room; despite everything they had sold, the apartment was still overflowing with the memorabilia of a lifetime. It was difficult to leave it all behind, but their belongings were, after all, only material things. It was their lives that had to be saved. Jeannie jumped into his lap and began licking his face.

"It's alright, little one," he fondled her ears. "We won't leave you behind. You'll be fine."

Askala poked her head round the door, making sure

only half her face was visible. "Your dinner is getting cold," she called. Lukas wondered if she knew what was going on. She was not stupid. He thought he detected a certain sadness in her eyes, but as ever she never allowed her feelings to show. "Come on then. I'm not going to reheat the soup again!"

* * *

Nairobi

I stared at the ash blonde hair and the clear, twinkling eyes. They were set a little too close above a prominent nose so that he had the look of some kind of bird of prey, but there was a firmness about his chin which gave one confidence. I extended my hand and introduced myself. It was the first time I had come face to face with the man who was going to rescue my husband.

"I'm very pleased to meet you. I'm Mellina Fanouris."

"Pleased to make your acquaitance, Mrs. F.," Tyrone crushed my fingers in a tight handshake. "You'll be having dinner with your husband on Sunday night, I promise you that," he assured me.

"I really hope so," I mumbled, my voice slightly quivering. "You are our last hope. If this attempt fails then we might as well write them off as doomed!

"No! Please, don't mention failure. I hate the word! Now, come over here and let me explain the plan in detail."

Tyrone led me towards a large table with various maps sprawled all over the place. He switched on a lamp and adjusted it at a slight angle so that the bulb focused on the map I had been able to get from Andrew. Red and blue lines had been drawn with thick markers. With unfailing patience he went over the route with me, explaining in detail the entire operation. "I suppose arrangements have already been made for visas to be issued upon entry," he concluded.

"Oh! yes," I replied. "Michael and Laki have taken care of those details. We shall have them ready on arrival. The Kenyan authorities have been most efficient and helpful. One last thing," I hastened to add, "will it be all right if my husband brought our little dachshund along?"

"No problem. The dog comes too. I presume her vaccinations are up to date?"

I nodded.

"We're all set then! I'll be touching base with you on Friday.

After such excitement, it was difficult to go back to the office and concentrate on what I was doing. Picking up a mistake in one of the drafts I had prepared that morning, a sympathetic boss dropped the letter on my desk and looked me straight in the eye.

"That's not like you, Mellina. Anything bothering you? I feel you're not yourself these days. Something I can help with?"

I shook my head. "Thanks, I'm fine. I'll snap out of it in a day or so."

"I know you must be thinking about your husband. I'll never know why in heaven's name, he doesn't just climb on a camel and cross the border."

I smiled. "One of these days he might do just that."

"I hope so! I can't have you so melancholy. My work is suffering," he said, his eyes twinkling.

The telephone interrupted our banter. It was a long distance call from Greece. My boss motioned me to carry on and retired to his office, closing the door behind him. I could just faintly make out the voice of Litsa, one of Pavlos' daughters.

"Hello, sweetie-pie," I tried to greet her calmly.

"We haven't received any letters from my father for the last two weeks and we're really worried. He mentioned in his last letter something about the time nearing for the two canaries to fly away. Please, Mellina, tell us that our interpretation is correct. Is something being arranged?"

"Yes, sweetie, it is." I had to tell them. They were just as involved and suffering just as much as we were. They were entitled to know. "You guys had better go to your nearest church and get down on your knees and pray as you've never prayed before."

"When is D-Day?" she asked.

"Sunday."

"You mean in three days time? This coming Sunday?" Her voice rose with excitement.

"Yes. That's right."

"We haven't seen Dad and Uncle Lukas in six years. Oh, my God. Are they really getting out at last?" Feeling she was becoming over-emotional, I asked to speak to her mother, but was told she was out.

"Hold on a minute. I hear someone at the door. It might be her." There was silence for a few moments while she ran to check. I quickly constructed what I was going to tell Venetia. I had to weigh my sentences carefully. "Yes, it's Mum!" Litsa's voice came through. "She's just getting her breath back. She'll talk to you in a second. Is there anything at all we can do to help out from this end?"

Before I had chance to reply, Venetia snatched the phone excitedly from her daughter. "Mellina, tell me, please. Tell me it's true. Tell me I'm not dreaming?" she pleaded.

"Venetia! It's a dangerous mission. We've both got to be brave. We've got to pray everything will work out."

"I'm on the next plane to Nairobi. I can't sit here and wait. I've got to be there."

"Yes, Venetia, you're right, but we've got to be realistic. What if something goes wrong? It's very risky."

"With the situation as it is, things couldn't be much worse. We can't share our lives. We can't enjoy our kids together. They're buried alive in Ethiopia, as good as dead. We've got to take the risk."

"Alright. Then we take it. I'll expect you on the next flight out of Athens." Litsa was already checking the airline schedules. The next available flight arrived early on Sunday morning.

"If everything goes according to plan, when do you expect our men, God willing, to be in Nairobi?" asked Venetia.

"From the sound of things, about 6 p.m. Sunday evening. Maybe earlier."

"That's fine. It will just give me time to recuperate from the flight. I want to look my best for my Pavlos."

"Okay. We'll pick you up on Sunday morning."

I hung up, wondering if I'd done the right thing. My mouth was dry. I hated to be too optimistic. It invited disaster.

"Mellina, can we send this urgent cable," Mr. Shaw's welcome voice interrupted my creeping fears.

Arriving home after work on Friday evening, I found Michael and Aspa waiting for me. "There's some good news and some bad news," Aspa started.

"Give me the bad news first," I said, fearing the worst.

"Tyrone has to use another plane. His own is being serviced and won't be cleared for flying by tomorrow, so we've got to call Addis and give them the new registration numbers."

I let my breath out slowly. "And what's the good news?"

"He's leaving for the border on schedule at mid-day tomorrow."

Suddenly the financial side of it all struck me. Money had not even received a mention so far. "Hasn't this guy asked for any money in advance?" I asked.

"No, not a cent. We brought the subject up again at our last meeting, but he just doesn't appear to want to discuss money at this point. His exact words were that he was grossly overpaid by his royal employers and didn't want to discuss the matter further."

"Well, Venetia is arriving on Sunday morning and she's bringing money with her. Having a wealthy brother at times like this has its advantages. She'll bring a foreign currency cheque from a respectable bank in Switzerland."

"That's fine. I'm sure Tyrone can cash any cheque from a Swiss bank in the Gulf."

"I'll be able to chip in my share too. There's my godfather's inheritance and I can sell my diamond wedding band and bracelet. They're the last two precious items of jewellery I have left, but who cares? I'm just grateful I have them available."

That night we transmitted the new details to the waiting "canaries" and confirmed that the plan was going ahead.

"We'll be waiting at the rendezvous point from 7.00 a.m.," said Lukas. "We'll set off from camp at six, as soon as curfew is lifted. What about Jeannie? Did you ask? She's sensing that something is going on and won't leave my lap."

"Bring her along, it's okay. The doctor will look at her."

"*Hasta mañana* then, until Sunday!"

Chapter Thirty Three

Addis Ababa

Sensing his apprehensiveness, Jeannie nuzzled close to Lukas, burying her head beneath his arm. For weeks, he had been torn between having her put down and finding her a good home. With the mass exodus of expatriates, there were few animal lovers left who would choose to fill a dog's bowl while starving beggars scavenged in trash cans. "It's alright," he comforted his faithful companion, stroking her affectionately. "You're coming too."

Now their escape was imminent, the time, which had dragged for so many years, was flying by. Lukas fiddled aimlessly with the cash they had managed to amass for Mama Askala, but no matter how many times he counted it, the sum remained depressingly low. He looked down at his wedding band, twisting it indecisively. It was the only thing left of any value. He compressed his lips, nodding to himself; it would have to go.

"Penny for your thoughts," Pavlos pounced on him from behind. Lukas leapt in the air. "You're jumpy! Something on your mind?"

"We've got our final directives from Nairobi," he

breathed, looking round for Askala. "We'll be leaving for Langano tomorrow afternoon to rendezvous at the agreed spot early on Sunday morning. An overnight bag is all we're allowed to carry. We have to leave all our I.D. papers and passports behind; it would be fatal if they were found in our possession. Lastly, Jeannie will be flying first class— on my lap."

"Then, we won't be needing this," said Pavlos, taking a wad of notes from his pocket and slapping it on the table. "From the look of things it couldn't have happened at a better moment. Here's to Askala's retirement fund."

Lukas' eyes widened. "Where did you get all this?" he asked. It probably wasn't as much as it seemed, but after months of scrounging for pennies, it looked like a fortune.

"A debtor from the bookshop days suddenly decided it was time to settle his old account," he grinned.

Lukas laughed. "Well, maybe the tides are turning. A few seconds ago I was contemplating selling my only bond with Mellina! This little miracle has saved me a good deal of emotional torment."

September 11th was the beginning of the Ethiopian New Year. Although the people's enthusiasm for celebrating feasts had been subdued, fires were still being lit all over the city. The two men leaned on the balcony of the apartment and watched as the flames illuminated the dark streets. Close at hand, they could see shadowy figures leaping across blazing twigs, enacting an ancient ritual. By leaping the flames three times, they invoked kismet and hoped to shake off any future obstacles that may lay ahead. In the past, old and worn household effects and clothes were tossed on the fires and new ones acquired. Years of war, drought and ensuing poverty, had destroyed the custom, compelling the Ethiopians to cling

411

to whatever they were fortunate enough to possess.

"I've been dreading to ask this question," said Pavlos, turning away from the spectacle. "But what if the escape fails and we're caught."

Lukas, prompted by the sight of the Ethiopian ritual, had been reflecting on his own destiny. He looked calmly at Pavlos. "I, for one, will accept it as fate. Come on man, we've been stripped of our wealth, our dignity, our self-respect and treated like common criminals. Is there anything left to live for? I'd rather die and have it over with."

Pavlos nodded. "You're right. I've been thinking the same. Venetia and Mellina will have to learn to live without us. It's better that way than living this half existence—neither married nor unmarried. A short, sharp clean break is better by far."

"Let's tackle a more immediate issue," said Lukas, changing the subject. "How are we going to keep the truth from Askala. She's already suspicious."

"We'll just have to act as though it's a weekend trip and we'll be back on Monday. It's hard but it's for her own good."

All Saturday morning the sound of the Seventh Anniversary celebrations penetrated the flat, as the massive parade marched through the city towards Revolution Square. At regular intervals, a military band would strike up, the music interspersed with cheers, loud hailer speeches and gun salutes. Through the open windows of surrounding apartments, military music blared from radios tuned in to the government station. As lunchtime approached, peace began to prevail. The brothers ate a hasty meal and were soon ready to depart, their bags packed with basic essentials, leaving behind wardrobes stuffed with clothes. Lukas took his bible from his bedside table and placed it on top of a freshly-laundered shirt, pulling the zipper shut.

"Close your eyes and walk out. There's no looking back now," he told himself as he walked from the room. "We're in your hands now, Lord," he prayed, crossing himself.

He found Pavlos raiding the refrigerator. "Something for the road," he said, handing Lukas a plastic container filled with cheese and salami.

"That's not nearly enough!" exclaimed Askala, catching them in the act. "Do you think I would let you go off without preparing some food?" She handed them a basket full of goodies.

Lukas turned and hugged the old woman tightly. "We love you, Mama Askala. You've been like a mother to us."

"Well, I gave my word to your Mama, didn't I?" she laughed. A little flushed, she twisted herself free from his grip. "Steady on. You've taken my breath away, you rascal."

"You're not through yet." Pavlos pushed Lukas aside and clasped her in his arms. "No kiss for me?"

"You boys are acting mighty funny!" she looked questioningly from one to the other.

"We shan't ever forget your caring…" Lukas' words died as his throat tightened.

"You'd better be on your way," she shook her head. "I don't know what's got into you. But I know I'll feel uneasy if darkness creeps up on you while you're on the road."

Lukas picked up Jeannie, slung his bag over his shoulder and took a last look round the apartment. "Lock up after us, Mama Askala. We have a key."

"I'll be in on Monday to dust and clean. Tomorrow I'm visiting relatives in Entoto."

413

"Take some tangerines from the fridge to give them," he called back.

"I'll do no such thing! The price of fruit has hit the ceiling and you're wanting to give it away. When will you learn to economise?" She shook her finger at him as he entered the lift. "Now be off with you."

"When do we expect you back?" asked the guard politely, as he opened the garage door.

"If this jalopy doesn't leave us stranded, we'll be back in a couple of days," joked Pavlos.

"*Melcome menged*," he called after them. "Have a safe journey!"

The timing of their departure was perfect. The streets of Addis were deserted, the crowd having dispersed the minute the parade was over. Only a few drunken stragglers were sleeping off their over-indulgence in the shade of some jacaranda trees. A couple of empty paper bags, lifted by the breeze, drifted across Revolution Square as the brothers crossed where, only hours before, the might of the Ethiopian regime had been gathered. Unchallenged, they drove out beyond the city limits and on to the road to Langano and freedom.

* * *

Nairobi

The City Market closed early on Saturday afternoon, so I had a limited time to complete my purchases. Thinking of Lukas' spartan diet, I rushed from one shop to the next to give him a home-coming to remember— tender *filet mignon* and bacon rinds rolled into luscious tournedos from the butcher, avocados and mangoes from the greengrocer, fresh flaky croissants from the French patisserie. They were all commodities that even gold could not buy in Ethiopia.

Street boys tugged at my sleeve, begging for shillings, while their companions eyed me up as a pocket-picking prospect. Aware of their game, I laughed, tossing them some coins. Suddenly, nothing bothered me. All around everything appeared more colourful and beautiful. I looked at the banks of exotic flowers stuffed into tin containers; the Birds of Paradise seemed almost alive with their pointed green 'beaks' and feathery orange and purple tufts. My enthusiasm for flower arranging was suddenly rekindled and I hastily gathered an armful of zebra grass, pink Cymbidium orchids and scarlet heart-shaped anthuriums, imagining them artistically angled on a piece of twisted driftwood. For so long, I had lacked the incentive to add these touches of beauty and femininity to our home but now, hopefully, it was all going to change. My light-heartedness couldn't be restrained. I danced from stall to stall, attracting quizzical glances from the vendors I regularly patronised.

"Something extraordinary happening?" an Indian stall owner asked, twisting his hands in a common gesture of query.

"I'm expecting someone special," I sang.

"Oh, Mister Right's turned up?" he shook his head sagely. "May I suggest, then, some fresh passion fruit? The juice is a boost for energy and the seeds act as a natural tranquilizer if they are munched after too much exertion." He grinned, baring his stained teeth.

"Cheeky bugger," I mumbled under my breath. Sex, I wanted to tell him, was the last thing on my mind. Instead, I buried my head in my shopping basket and moved on.

415

"*Memsahib*. A taste of Lamu mangoes and you'll never yearn for another," cried a Swahili from the coast, juggling the fruit in his hands.

"Don't listen to him," shouted another selling papayas. "Try these. Sweetened to perfection and tasting like honey."

"Over here," a local Kikuyu beckoned me. "Fresh *madafu* from Mombasa. Its sweet water will quench your thirst and clean your kidneys."

Before I had a chance to object, the top of the coconut had been hacked off and I was left with no option but to gulp down the colourless liquid. Time was running short. Ignoring all other pleas, I elbowed my way out and hurried back home.

Gabby and her friends were playing with their dolls in the garden. With my arms full of shopping, I kicked open the kitchen door and was in the process of unloading it when the telephone rang. My mother answered it upstairs. "Mellina, it's for you," she called down a little anxiously.

It was Aspa. From the tone of her voice, I knew, instantly, there was something wrong. "If you're standing, you had better sit down," she whispered. My head began buzzing. I could feel my pulse racing and a prickle of sweat in my palms. "The mission's been aborted," she said, gulping back her tears. "I'm really sorry."

"No!" I screamed, running my fingers through my hair and tearing at it. "It can't be true!" I shrieked, losing control.

My mother was by my side in an instant, cradling me in her arms. "You've got to be brave, Honey—for Gabby's sake. How will she react if she sees you in this state?"

"I can't take any more," I cried. "Tyrone gave me his word, he promised." I beat my fists against the wall.

"Mellina," Aspa tried to reason with me. "It wasn't his fault. He sprung an oil leak before reaching the border and radioed the base that he'd been forced to turn back."

Laki had just arrived. Hearing the commotion, he dashed into the room and dived for the receiver as it slipped from my fingers. "Mellina's beyond herself," he said, resuming the disrupted conversation. "I gather the mission's been aborted. At this point, is there anything we can do? Lukas should have left Addis by now, but they may not have reached Langano yet. I suggest we call the Bekele Molla Hotel and leave a message that the doctor's on an emergency and won't be joining them for the weekend. They'll understand. If anyone can get the message through, it's you Aspa. You're strong under pressure. I'll leave it to you."

I accepted the handkerchief my mother offered me and collapsed into a chair. I could visualize a deserted road with two forlorn figures looking anxiously skywards, trusting in a deliverance that would never come. They would never be able to handle another disappointment.

"Sis," Laki turned to me. "In all fairness, we knew Tyrone wasn't flying his own plane. We should have been prepared for mechanical problems. What we've got to do now is warn Lukas not to be caught hanging about near the rendezvous spot, or the whole mission will be in jeopardy. Now," he gently lifted my chin, "go throw some water on your face and let's put on our thinking caps."

Breathing deeply, I tried to pull myself together. "Let's try calling the house first," I cleared my throat. "There's a slim chance they might still be there."

Askala was quick to answer. "They've left for Dire-Dawa," she said. "Didn't you know they were going out of town?"

417

"How stupid of me," I forced a silly giggle. "Of course I knew. Incidentally," I tried to sound casual, "what time did they leave?"

"About an hour and a half ago." She paused for a moment to think. "Yes, it was around 3.30 p.m. Is something wrong? You don't sound yourself."

"I'm fine, Mama Askala. It's a bad line," I lied. "I'll call back in a few days."

I looked at my watch. It was six-thirty. They must be almost at Langano. I turned to Laki. "I hope Aspa manages to get through… Oh, my God," the thought suddenly struck me. "How am I going to handle Venetia?"

"We should warn her before she leaves Athens," said Laki. "It will be devastating for her to find out when she arrives."

I nodded, picking up the receiver again to place a call to Athens. No one answered. Venetia was probably on her way to the airport.

At eight o'clock the telephone rang. Laki sprang to answer it. "It's Tyrone," he hissed, cupping the mouthpiece with his hand. We all gathered round, desperate for news. "It was sheer bad luck," Laki spoke down the line. "Yes, they should have reached Langano by now. Aspa's trying to leave a message for them." There was an extended silence as Laki listened to Tyrone. A look of concern came over his face. "I don't know how we can possibly pull it off," he said finally. "I'll have to get back to you. Where are you calling from? Okay, I'll page you at the Norfolk Hotel."

Laki put the receiver down and turned to fill us in on the conversation. "He's barely landed and he wants to change his shirt and fly straight back! He says his own plane will be cleared for take-off by early morning."

418

I shook my head. "It's crazy. If Tyrone leaves at 8.00 a.m., it will be mid-day before he reaches them. They'll be parked dangerously close to a military base. It would be madness to push their luck for more than an hour or two at the most. They'll be caught," I lamented.

"What if we succeed in getting word to them?" Laki looked up hopefully. "We still have time to warn them and set a new pick-up time."

Throughout the night we tried, pleading with operators, supervisors and technicians that it was a matter of life and death that we be connected. Finally, a sympathetic operator regretted that the line beyond Pontemaki—a village only a few kilometres from Langano—was dead. Any cherished hope of warning them was abandoned.

I crept into Gabby's room to gaze at her sleeping peacefully, unaware of the drama going on around her. A tear trickled down my cheek. Tomorrow Lukas should have been holding her in his arms—instead his hopes would be dashed once more. What had my innocent child done to grow up without a father? I opened the medicine cabinet and noted nervously that my supply of valium had almost gone. I quickly swallowed one of the tiny pills. If Lukas was dragged away for ever, I knew I would become addicted to their calming effect.

Chapter Thirty Four

Langano

The wheels of the Mercedes churned up the powdery sand as Lukas sought a suitable parking spot close to the shore. They had reached Langano in record time, sailing through the checkpoints with no problems. They had decided not to check into a bungalow so as not to get the Hotel manager into trouble. Hidden among thorn trees and flowering hibiscus bushes, a safe distance from the crowds who were setting up tents and gathering logs for their fires, they felt inconspicuously safe for the night. But as darkness fell, the aroma of juicy steaks sizzling over glowing coals began to waft towards them, tantalizing their appetites.

"What if we slipped in for a hot meal," suggested Lukas, listening to his rumbling stomach. "There are plenty of people around and with the generator off at 10.00 p.m. I don't think we'll be recognised by candle light."

"The camp is fairly full," said Pavlos, quickly scanning the number of tents already erected. "We're lucky so many people have taken advantage of the long weekend to come down." He rubbed his chin in contemplation. "Yes, it's too crowded for anyone to notice us, I think we'll take the chance. A sip of hot soup would be warming."

But as dinner time approached, the idea of food became less tempting. It was not worth taking the risk so they decided to settle for stale bread and cold cuts in anticipation of something better the following day. Jeannie was not so easily placated. She refused the salami she was offered and sniffed around, waiting for her favourite tit-bit—a banana.

"I've never come across a dog before that prefers fruit to meat." Pavlos shook his head, munching the rejected appetizer. Eyes transfixed, tail wagging with a slight tremor in her front legs, the little dachshund waited patiently while Lukas peeled the banana. Piece by piece she gulped it down, licking her chops in anticipation of more.

Sleep was an impossibility. Nervousness coupled with mixed emotions about leaving behind the country they loved and a lifetime of friends, forced them both to toss and turn.   Lukas sat up. "I have just the remedy for a situation like this." He fumbled in the picnic basket. "I threw in the last quarter bottle of whisky for an emergency." He took a swig and offered the bottle to Pavlos. The effect was better than they had bargained for. Being unused to spirits, which they literally only imbibed for medicinal purposes, the gulps were enough to knock them out. Dirty jokes which had been repeated umpteen times became hilarious, transforming mild titters into uproarious laughter. The perils ahead lost all significance as they sank into oblivion.

Jeannie's fussing woke Lukas up and sleepily he looked at his watch. It was quarter to six already. He grabbed his jacket and jerked the car door open. The gush of crisp air slapped Pavlos awake. "What's going on?" he cried, jumping up.

"It's time we were away. I've already spied a few early bird watchers, focussing their zoom lenses in our direction. I don't want to end up in a photograph album alongside crown cranes and crocodiles. Come on. Let's get moving."

Jeannie picked that precise moment to be mischievous. Sniffing out lizards and chasing squirrels was far more fun than she had ever experienced. Ears flapping, her tail rigid with excitement, she totally ignored Lukas' hushed calls until he resorted to guile. Creeping behind a bush, he imitated the mating call of a guinea fowl. The response was spontaneous. The dachshund raced round the bush to find to her disappointment, not the speckled bird, but Lukas' large hand, which seized and leashed her securely.

"That's enough, girl," he panted, stooping to pick her up.

The smoky blue shadows of daybreak leisurely unfolded to expose the first blushes of sunrise. Dawn came with dramatic African suddenness—a silent explosion of red and gold with ribbons of apricot fanning out across the curve of the eastern horizon. It was time to leave. The road to Awassa was deserted. In the distance, clusters of white wings flapped in preparation for their flight across to the nourishing aquatic environs of Abiata. The lake was rich with tilapia and fresh water annelid worms, but it was the tarantula spiders, hanging in massive dew-dropped spheres on the tips of spiky branches, which were the pelicans favourite dish. With Pavlos at the wheel, Lukas focussed his attention on the spectacle before them. The first flight of pelicans had taken off and were soaring across the lightening sky from south to north.

In contrast, a single black bird flew parallel to the car.

"This guy obviously intends to get his fill in Awassa while everyone else is away," Lukas jested, mainly to break the silence. But the sight of the bird had somehow disturbed him. He began to feel uneasy. "Stop being so superstitious," he rebuked himself. So what if it was a black bird: the azure sky was dotted with them. But the emotion persisted. His throat was dry. A vein on his temple began to throb and he frowned as his gaze concentrated on a knuckle-shaped rock on the horizon. That was it: the old woman. What had she predicted so many years ago? His memory was hazy, but slowly fragments of the puzzle began falling into place.

It was when he was a teenager walking home from school. An old beggar woman, squatting in the dirt, had stopped him with outstretched hands. He had pulled out a small coin and was about to toss it into the jagged tin she held, when she raised her head and fixed him with a penetrating stare. As if in a trance, she cleared her parched throat and whispered, "Turn that coin into a paper note and I'll tell thy fortune."

He had accepted the bargain. Swatting the hungry flies feasting on the opaque mucous globules at the corners of her eyes, she took the green bill from his hand and held it up, blocking out the sun. It became translucent with his future engrained upon it.

"Thy destiny shines brightly, lavished with riches and expensive objects. But be warned, my son. Sinister clouds are gathering, awaiting the moment to smother our beloved land. When this country's strongest tree falls and the sun scorches its roots, many nests will drop to the ground crushing newly-hatched eggs. Blood will flow in the streets and the shrieks of mother birds will chill the air. When this," she said, scooping up a handful of dust, "has quenched its thirst, forcing the seed of the Meskel flower to crack the earth and burst its buds, reawakening the dead earth with garlands of yellow, birds in cages will be freed to fly to their mates. Beware the feathers of black crows. Only the ones white as hail, fluffy as dove down, will lead the way to freedom."

Lukas shuddered at the recollection. Emperor Haile Selassie's deposition, the Red Terror and the sequence of events that had followed had compelled them to gamble with their lives. So far, the prediction had been exact. No, he tossed aside his pessimistic fears, he was going to interpret the last part his way. Meskel daisies and the indigo bird were heralds of the Ethiopian New Year and the end of the rainy season. It was but a few days before the ground would be splashed with garlands of yellow. Surely that was close enough to fulfil her prophecy?

"We're here." Pavlos swerved off the road and switched off the engine. "We're in good time." He shivered, pulling his jacket collar closer to his neck. "Is something bothering you?" He turned to Lukas. "You seem a bit pale."

"Nothing that a cup of coffee can't cure," replied Lukas, reaching for the thermos flask and pouring out two steaming cups. Pavlos reached into the picnic basket and offered him a biscuit. Lukas declined. His stomach felt like a quivering jelly, but he dare not impart his forebodings.

As they had been instructed, they parked the car facing the wind with the boot and bonnet open. The birds had gone and the air was perfectly still. In the silence that surrounded them, the distant drone of an aircraft engine suddenly made them alert. Lukas felt the skin on his arms and the nape of his neck turn to goose pimples. He glanced

424

at his watch, it was exactly 8.30 a.m.

"What precision!" he yelled, his heart thumping. "Trust an Englishman to be punctual."

As the sound grew louder, they strained their eyes to identify the registration number that was engraved on their minds. The plane circled once and pushed its flaps down to descend, but as it banked, the tricolour flag, symbol of the Ethiopian Airforce, came distinctly into view. It landed at the airbase.

"We were rather too optimistic," said Lukas, disappointed.

The sun, now almost vertical in the sky, beat down mercilessly. They had deliberately chosen that stretch of road because there were no obstacles and, especially, no trees. Now, the lack of shade took its toll. Anxious not to miss their means of deliverance, they took it in turns to scan the pitiless blue sky while the scorching sun blistered their faces. Inside the car was like an oven and offered no respite from the heat. The minutes and then the hours ticked by.

"I could have been mistaken about the time." Lukas searched for an excuse. "The line was bad."

"Something's wrong," said Pavlos. "What are we to do?"

Lukas stared at the horizon, the old woman's prophecy still ringing in his ears. How could he tell Pavlos? He would think he had finally lost his sanity. Instead, he picked up his New English Bible and snapped it open at random. One particular verse caught his eye, here was their answer.

"For there is still a vision for the appointed time.

At the destined hour, it will come in breathless haste,

It will not fail.

425

If it delays, wait for it;

For when it comes will be no time to linger."
(Habakkuk 2, verse 2)

"Let's go back," he called out to Pavlos. "This wasn't the right time. Here, read this." He handed him the creed. "There's no point hanging around. We have to reach Addis before curfew or we're done for."

Pavlos blinked and shook the drops of sweat from his brow. "We can still make it if we wait until 3.00 p.m." He clenched his fists and struck the side of the car. "Damn it, this day would have been perfect. Everyone's off the roads, celebrating another successful year for the Dergue. If we lose this chance, we'll be buried here."

Lukas' confidence wavered. For a moment he had convinced himself that only the timing was wrong. Suddenly, he felt utterly and totally depressed. In silence, they retraced the long road to Addis.

* * *

Nairobi

The Olympic flight from Athens arrived at exactly 6.15 a.m.

"What do we tell Venetia?" I cast around for some suggestions.

"Tell her the truth. There was engine trouble and that the pilot is ready to go as soon as we've made the necessary arrangements. What other explanation can you give?" said Laki.

The passengers started emerging, one by one gathering round the conveyor belt to identify their luggage. Standing by the exit, I searched for Venetia's greying hair, usually drawn up into a bun on top of her head, but failed to spot her. Then, from somewhere among the travellers descending the stairs into the terminal, I heard someone calling my name.

"Aunt Mellina, over here." I turned sharply to see Mary, Pavlos' youngest daughter, waving at me.

"Hello, Poppet," I called. "Where's your Mum?"

"Right there!" She pointed to a fashionably dressed woman with beautiful, flowing auburn hair, wheeling a trolley towards us. I gasped. Mary laughed, noting my surprise. She hurried over to where we were waiting. "We made her change her looks for Dad. Six years is a long time to be separated."

"I'm glad you came with your mother," I said, giving her a hug and a kiss.

"My uncle gave me the ticket as a present. He felt I'd suffered more than the others from Dad being away, so here I am."

Mary was a youngster of seven when she left Addis. Now, she was a blossoming thirteen-year-old whose development Pavlos had only seen from photographs. "What time will they be arriving?" she asked.

"There's been a delay." I tried to sound casual. "We'll talk about it when you come through customs."

Having cleared their baggage, they both emerged. Venetia and I embraced each other. "Mary tells me there's a delay. The mission's not off, is it?" she asked, panic in her voice.

"No, no! There was some engine trouble, but Tyrone is going back to get them." It was not important to say when.

"Oh!" She suddenly looked drained. Once in the car, speeding home, the questions started. "You mean right this minute they are waiting to be picked up?"

"Yes!" I burst out crying. "There was no way we could warn them."

"Oh, my Lord! What do we do now?"

"We'll have to wait for them to get back to Addis and make fresh arrangements. The pilot is set to leave right away, but we've got to see when it's feasible for them to go down to Awassa again."

"I'm just grateful I'm here," she said. "At least I can share the anxiety with you."

Just after four in the afternoon, we began calling Addis. A new direct dialling system had been installed and we called systematically every half hour. At 7 p.m. there was still no reply.

"What if they were arrested?" said Venetia.

"Give them some time." Laki interrupted his dialling. "They probably hung on until the last minute. We'll start worrying after ten o'clock."

By 7.20, I couldn't wait any longer so I decided to try again. The first ring had barely finished when a gruff, dry voice answered. "Sweetheart," I yelled. "You're back…" I couldn't utter another word. Laki grabbed the receiver.

"Lukas, are you both safe? Thank God. Listen, the doctor had an oil leak and had to turn back. How soon can you return to the same spot? Come on, man. Don't give up on us now… What do you mean you don't think you've got the strength for another attempt?… Come on, Lukas, you've got to force yourselves—it's now or never. You've got to make one last effort. Okay, let me speak to Pavlos." He motioned Venetia to come to the phone. "Their morale is shattered, Venetia, but your presence here is God sent. We're relying on you to force them to take one more chance," he whispered. "Yes, Pavlos," he shouted down the line. "Someone here wants to talk to

428

you." He passed the phone to Venetia.

"Honey! I came out to meet you. No, don't ask any questions. Just be on that plane, please, I've waited for this moment for a long time now and I can't wait any longer…" Her voice broke. She handed the receiver back to Laki.

"Now!" Laki recommenced his conversation. "How soon can you get down again? Right. Stand by, then, for further instructions. I'll call the doctor and get straight back to you." He hung up and immediately called Tyrone at the Norfolk Hotel. A pager fetched him out of the restaurant. "They're back, Tyrone. They'll try and get some fuel tomorrow and probably be able to go down on Tuesday. How does that fit in with your schedule? Perfect. Okay, I'll tell them. Tuesday, 15 September, pick up time 1.00 p.m. Fine: I'll confirm once I've called them back."

Without pausing to brief us, his finger was once more dialling Addis. "Lukas? Tuesday, 1.00 p.m. He'll be there. As it's lunchtime, there shouldn't be much traffic on the road. Remember the signal for danger? Okay. The registration will be the one we gave you originally, have you still got it? Fine. God be with you." He sat back in the chair, breathing a sigh of relief. "This time I'm going with Tyrone. There's nothing either of you can say to dissuade me, so please don't try."

* * *

Addis Ababa

Pavlos' pallid face had turned a healthy pink and broken out in a sweat. "I can't believe it, Venetia is in

429

Nairobi! That's the quickest acting tonic I've ever taken. I'd better go and take a cold shower."

Driving back from Langano, not a word had passed between them, each buried in his own depressing thoughts. Taking his eyes off the road for a second, Lukas turned to look at his brother whose face had turned a sickly grey, his forehead was furrowed and his eyes had lost all their lustre. A hunched, beaten figure, he looked at least ten years older. Lukas felt bitter and disappointed for both of them and by the time he turned into their street, he had resigned himself to giving up.

The guard at their apartment block greeted them with surprise. "Why are you back so soon?"

Pavlos stirred himself. "I told you this old jalopy might leave us stranded. Well, it very nearly did."

A few minutes after they entered the apartment, the telephone rang and the cloud lifted. With renewed vigour, they began planning how to acquire more fuel. Pavlos returned from his shower, wearing a clean shirt with a pat of cologne on his freshly-shaven face.

"I'm ready to drive straight back," he grinned.

"To Venetia's waiting arms," Lukas retorted. "Now, where do we get this fuel from?"

On Monday, their ration card entitled them to ten litres. They still had a jerrycan containing twenty litres in the car boot which was enough for the journey down.

"We'll have to find another thirty litres to be on the safe side," said Pavlos. He stopped. Lukas knew he meant for the return trip if the mission aborted again, but he refrained from voicing the negative consideration.

Early on Monday morning, they hurried to the petrol station. The queue was already a mile long but that was nothing new. They couldn't remember the number of

430

times they had waited in line for hours to get their ration, often to be told, when their turn came, that the fuel had run out and they should go to another garage. Lukas prayed that wouldn't happen today.

As the time for offices to open approached, many drivers abandoned the queue, hoping to try their luck later. Finally, as Lukas eased the car alongside a pump, an attendant came over and asked for their card. Lukas recognized him immediately. Before the Revolution, he had worked at the service station to which the Fanouris' took all their private cars and business delivery vans. "Fesseha, how are you?" called Lukas, getting out of the car.

"*Geta* Lukas! I haven't seen you in years. Where have the good old days gone when we used to fill up your cars to our heart's content?"

"It does seem ages ago," Lukas nodded in agreement. "But how come you're working here? We thought the Dergue had appointed its own people to control the distribution of fuel."

"I don't know. Maybe they liked my face," he laughed. "They assigned me here only recently."

Lukas wanted desperately to ask for more fuel, but he was terrified of jeopardizing the boy's future. Fesseha reset the metre and started to fill the tank. "Ten litres a week is nothing these days, it's barely enough to coat the petrol tank," he joked. Then he stopped and glancing round, asked Lukas. "You wouldn't, by any chance, want a little extra would you?"

Lukas inhaled deeply. "Who doesn't want more? But, I wouldn't want to get you into trouble."

"How much do you want? As long as the money is correct at the end of the day, they won't know how many

431

cards I've signed."

"Fesseha, only if you're absolutely positive that you won't be affected."

"*Geta* Lukas, we've been friends for many years. I made a small fortune from all the tips you used to give me and I'll never forget that. No, I'm going to fill her up."

Lukas wanted to embrace him. Instead, he turned out his pockets and gave him all the money he had left. With luck, they wouldn't be needing any Birr after tomorrow.

Fesseha's eyes widened. "You don't have to give me all this—really."

"We're all going through difficult times, Fesseha, and I'm sure every cent counts. Spend it in good health and may God repay you for your kindness."

The next stop was the *kebele*. "I issued you with a permit only a few days ago," the senior officer shouted.

"But we didn't make it beyond Modjo. Our car broke down and we had to come back," Lukas argued.

"Your pass is valid for a week. Use that one."

"But, sir, you know how strict the officers on the roadblocks are. They will only make us turn back if they see the permit is wrongly dated."

The officer frowned. "Oh, alright," he said irritably. "I suppose I'll have to give you a new one. I heard you were back last night. This time, I hope you'll make it."

"With your heartfelt wishes we can't but succeed," Lukas murmured, bowing low as the permit was handed to him. "And I hope I never set eyes on you again," he muttered inwardly.

Askala, taking advantage of their absence, didn't turn up on Monday. Lukas was glad as it made their departure a lot easier. He checked that the money they had left for her was still in the bureau where he had hidden it. They

432

would ring her from Kenya and tell her about it.

At 6 a.m. on Tuesday, 15 September they crossed Revolution Square once more. People who had long distances to walk to work were on the streets already. Pavlos glanced at the huge portraits of Marx, Engels and Lenin glaring down at them as they drove speedily out of the city. Once out in the open countryside, Lukas slowed down. If they drove steadily they would arrive at the rendenzvous point around mid-day; if they arrived too early, they might arouse suspicion. It was, after all, a working day and they couldn't claim to be picnicking or sight-seeing. The risks of being caught were far greater than on Sunday. They were in the hands of fate.

* * *

Nairobi

Laki was all set to leave when Venetia and I called round at his house on my way to the office. He had to be at Wilson Airport by 8.30 a.m. as they were scheduled to take off at nine. I put my arms round him and looked him straight in the eye. He was so much like Dad with his love for danger and adventure, but I wanted to make sure he wasn't going to take any unnecessary risks.

"Laki, promise me that you won't fly into Ethiopia with Tyrone. Promise me."

"Please don't, Sis. I have to do what I think is right. Don't make me break a promise. At this point the plan is for me to stay at the border with the fuel, okay? But the plans could change."

"Laki, if I lose a husband, I don't want to lose a brother as well. Swear to me on Dad's soul, you won't do it."

"Speaking of Dad, guess what I saw in my dream last night?" he smiled, brushing aside my pleas. "I saw him in a long white robe, chanting away at the top of his voice like he used to when he was very happy. He looked at me and said, 'Go ahead, Son. The road's clear.' I know deep in my heart that he'll be there with us. I feel it in my bones. Things will work out today."

"I don't know what to say, but, please, please, you've got to stay at the border so that if anything does go wrong, Carl can send a back-up service to help you." Only the previous day I had decided to bring Carl and Teresa up-to-date with events. He had immediately come up with the idea of a back-up so that in case anything went wrong, Jones, his colleague, could be ready for take-off at an hour's notice.

I handed Laki a small icon that Dad had given me when I first left home as a child. "May it bring you all safely home," I said softly.

"I'm off," he called to Mum.

"Hold on. I'll be right there." She dashed out, wiping her hands on a towel and handed him a coolbox containing sandwiches and cold beers for the trip. As he climbed into his car, Mum made the sign of the cross over his head. After he had gone, in age-old tradition, she fetched a jug of water and poured it where the car had been standing, to wish him a smooth journey.

"We'd better pour a whole bucketful this time, " I said trying to make light of the situation. "Enough for the return trip too." She didn't hesitate to comply!

Leaving Venetia with her, I climbed back into my own car to drive out to UNEP. Mum waved me off. "Take it easy. You're shaking like a leaf."

"I'll try. I'll call you later."

Carl was waiting for me in my office, a broad grin on his face. "Everything is set. We've got plane and pilot standing by. Did Laki get off alright?"

"Yes. They're leaving at nine."

"Fine. Call me if you hear anything. Teresa and I will wait for you to join us for lunch at the cafeteria." Lunch was the last thing I wanted, but I thanked him anyway. Left to myself, I gazed out of the window at a cloudless blue sky, wondering where they all were.

"Come on, Mellina, snap out of it. Are you going to spend all day gazing out of the window?" It was my boss.

"I'm sorry. My mind was wandering. I didn't have a very good night."

"I'm sorry," his voice softened. "Want to go home and rest?"

"Rest? Home? No, no, I'm fine, thank you. I'd much rather be here and get on with some work. The time will pass much more quickly."

"That's my girl. Then, let's get started on this report. Think you'll have it ready by the time I get back from lunch?"

With a deadline to meet, there was no time for day-dreaming. At one o'clock the phone rang. It was Teresa, waiting for me at the cafeteria. I quickly finished typing, stapled the pages together and placed the report on my boss's desk.

"We've ordered you a nice hot curry. You usually like it," Teresa greeted me, as I joined them at a partly-shaded table on the terrace. I ate mechanically, my mind elsewhere. If only 4.30 would come. All I wanted to do was go home and wait for news.

The Cessna 310 took off at exactly 9.30 a.m.

"I have a good feeling about today," said Tyrone, smiling.

"Me, too," Laki replied. He gazed down as the plane skimmed over Nairobi Game Park, gaining height. Graceful giraffe were snipping tender leaves and spiky thorns, while ostrich and wildebeeste chewed the cud closer to the ground. Here and there black and white zebra-striped minibuses, owned by Nairobi tour operators, kicked up the early morning dust as they sought to thrill their customers with a lion kill or startled rhino. The grassland gradually gave way to a neat cultivated patchwork as the plane sped north over lime-green tea plantations, interspersed with plots of maize and banana trees. Ahead, Laki could just make out the snowy peaks of Mount Kenya. He glanced at the control panel. They had reached an altitude of 13,000 feet and were cruising at two hundred miles an hour.

"Yes, I feel we'll pull it off this time," Tyrone said confidently. "But we'll need all the luck we can get. It's going to be tricky, the area being so mountainous and with no beacons to guide me. I'll have to stay alert and be extremely careful."

"I know you'll manage, Tyrone. I have complete confidence in your judgement and your experience," Laki assured him.

"You know I'm not doing this for money, don't you?" Tyrone looked at him.

"How can you possibly be doing it for money, when you're charging us less than the going rate for a straight forward charter, let alone a rescue mission where you're putting your own life on the line."

"Sometimes you get a gut feeling that you've just got to do something. That's how I felt about this job. I mean, the lives those guys have been forced to lead is hard to believe. Ifelt I had to do something to help." Tyrone was an extraordinary human being. He was risking his aircraft, his reputation and his life for two people he had never met. Laki didn't know how they would ever be able to express their gratitude.

"Feel like coming in all the way?" he asked Laki as the sparse vegetation began to change and the green hills of Marsabit came into view. It was the last stop before the Ethiopian border.

"Sure! Let's go!" Laki pushed the pleading image of Mellina to the back of his mind.

The plan was to offload the fuel at Marsabit, making the plane lighter and safer. Landing on a road in the middle of the bush was difficult enough without having to worry about six twenty-litre cans of highly-explosive aircraft fuel sitting in the cabin. Marsabit was a notoriously difficult airstrip. Aircraft had to approach between two hills and then suddenly drop down onto the runway. Tyrone veered slightly east so that he had a straight approach. He clenched his teeth as he began the descent.

"Pilots avoid this landing strip like the plague, but in this case..." he concentrated on his manoevring, "it's imperative to land."

As he touched down on the raw, red earth, a huge billowing cloud of dust enveloped the plane. It was some minutes after the propellers stopped thrashing before the cloud settled and they could emerge. The strip was deserted. The men carried the fuel cans to a nearby

437

wooden shelter which had been erected to shade waiting passengers from the sun, but there was nowhere to lock away the precious fuel for the return trip.

"This rather complicates matters." Tyrone thought hard. "There's no security here. I'm sorry, but it might be better to revert to our original plan and have you wait here, Laki, to guard the fuel. Then, I'd also be much lighter going in. In fact, I suggest that we offload everything—coolboxes, food, the lot." Seeing Laki's disappointed face, he hastened to add. "It makes sense for you to stay, really. If I'm not back in exactly three hours, you'll know I've met with trouble and you'll have to get help."

Laki nodded. "You're right, it is more practical if I stay. If we're not back in Nairobi by six o'clock, Carl will send the plane that's on stand-by. So, if something does happen, it's better that I stay and meet them. The only thing is, what happens if anyone queries my presence here?" he asked.

"No problem. Just say I dropped you off to go and pick up some tourists from Loyangalani and that I'll be back to pick you up." Tyrone climbed back into his seat. Engines on, warm up, thumbs up. He took off at 11.30 a.m. Allowing him three hours to fly in and out, Laki was to expect him no later than three o'clock

Once in the air, his radio on, Tyrone picked up a welcome signal. "This is Swiss Air flight SR 282. Request permission to fly over Ethiopian airspace."

"Permission granted. You may proceed," the reply came through loud and clear.

"This is my chance in a million," thought Tyrone. "I'll fly in close behind the Swiss plane and hope to confuse Addis's Air Traffic Control into identifying two aircraft as one." He looked down at the desert landscape. Ahead were the Ethiopian mountains, stretched out as far as the eye could see.

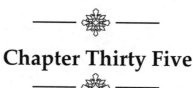

Chapter Thirty Five

Awassa

A few kilometres before the rendezvous spot, Lukas and Pavlos stopped for a drink at a small roadside cafe constructed from mud and straw. The proprietor served the hottest, best-tasting tea they had had in a long time.

"It's only 11.30," said Pavlos, looking at his watch. "We'd better take it easy and sit here for awhile rather than out on the road." They had barely sat down, when a truckload of soldiers, both Ethiopian and Cuban, passed on their way to the military base at Awassa.

"They're returning from the anniversary celebrations. They've been taking part in marches and helping with crowd control," the owner told them.

"Don't they ever stop off for a coke or a beer?" Lukas asked, fearing he might say 'yes'.

"What, them?" the owner sniggered. "Never! They're mostly Cubans and they don't spend any money. No, I make my money from the truck drivers that come up and down from Moyale and sometimes from the likes of you who come to photograph the birds. That is what you're here for, isn't it?"

"Sure." They both nearly choked on their tea.

Pavlos glanced at his watch. It was nearly noon. In case the 'doctor' was early, they decided to go wait on the road. If another truckload of soldiers came through, they would just have to think up some plausible excuse for being there. As Lukas pulled out, checking in his mirror that the road was clear, something hit the windscreen. He jerked his head back in time to glimpse a white feathery breast slide off the top of the car and fly away.

"Crazy bird!" Pavlos called after it. "You nearly killed yourself and you've sent Jeannie berserk," he laughed, trying to calm the dog. Jeannie scrabbled frantically, attempting to leap out of the window and chase after it.

"Was that a pure white bird?" asked Lukas, the old beggar's prophecy still haunting him.

"No. Only the breast was white. I think the wings were grey. It happened so fast, I couldn't make out what kind of bird it was. Why? What's wrong?" Pavlos looked at his brother puzzled.

"It's nothing. Forget it."

No sooner had they parked the car and opened the boot and bonnet than they saw, in the distance, another truck approaching. It was an army vehicle similar to the one that had passed the cafe.

"What do we do now?" cried Lukas, hurriedly shutting the boot .

"Quick! Give me the toilet roll," yelled Pavlos. "No Ethiopian disturbs anyone on the loo. Communists or not, they still have some manners." He rapidly pulled down his pants and squatted behind a small bush, exposing only the upper part of his body.

The truck trundled nearer, slowing down alongside the

car. Part of the green canvas covering the back of the truck was raised and an officer leaned out. "What's your problem? Why have you stopped here?" he demanded.

"My brother's got terrible diarrhoea. Can't stop it with anything." Lukas pointed towards Pavlos. Taking his cue, Pavlos picked up the toilet roll and waved it in the air, whilst with the other hand he clutched his stomach, feigning pain.

"I'm sorry. I hope he'll be better soon. However, you're near a restricted area, so you'd better move on fast."

"Thank you, Sir. We'll be off as soon as he can control himself."

The soldier knocked twice with his rifle on the metal support bar, signalling the driver to carry on. "*Etiopia Tikdem!*" he shouted, clenching his left fist and thrusting it skywards as the truck moved off.

Lukas raised his arm. "*Tikdem!*" he yelled in reply. "Let her come first." The time was almost five minutes to one. In the distance, Lukas heard the sound of a plane. "Pull up your pants and get here fast," he called to Pavlos.

Shading their eyes, they both watched the aircraft approach. Lukas had stretched up his hand to wave when the distinct colours of the Ethiopian flag on the tail made him quickly lower his arm. It was a one-seater reconnaissance plane. It circled once and then flew off south. The drone of its engines had only just died when the sound of a second plane approaching from the opposite direction broke the silence. The men screwed up their eyes against the glaring sunlight. Was it the same plane doubling back? Then the black letters "XXI" became visible. Lukas stared in disbelief. The sweat stood out on his forehead and began trickling into his eyes.

"Come on!" Pavlos hit him hard on the back. "He's our man. He's come to get us."

Within seconds the aircraft had swooped past them and landed in a cloud of dust a kilometre away on the road in front. With a speed they didn't believe possible, they slammed down the bonnet and boot, leapt into the car and screeched up the road, skidding to a halt beneath the wings of the plane.

The door opened and a calm voice greeted them. "Welcome, gentlemen. It's good to see you. I'm Tyrone."

Pavlos scrambled into the plane, stretching out his arms to take Jeannie. Lukas reached into the car for the bags. As he straightened up, he glanced up the tarmac road, shimmering and dancing in the heat. For a second he froze. Barely three kilometres away, he could make out the dark crawling insect shapes of an approaching army convoy. He threw the bags into the cockpit and hoisted himself up. Within seconds, they had pulled the door shut and Tyrone was revving for take-off.

"Have you seen what's ahead of us?" asked Lukas.

Tyrone smiled. "Relax."

The plane shot forward. Lukas watched with fascinated terror as the trucks grew larger. Another few hundred metres and they would be on them. Then, suddenly there was nothing in front of him but sky. Lukas turned to Pavlos and the pair of them let out a whoop.

"I know we haven't made it yet, but at least we're off the ground. I'm sorry," Lukas addressed Tyrone, "we haven't intoduced ourselves. I'm Lukas and this is my brother, Pavlos, and we sure are pleased to meet you."

Tyrone grinned. "That was pretty good timing. We took exactly fifty-seven seconds from landing to take-off. However, now you must fasten your

443

seat belts. I'm afraid we've been picked up by radar and I'll have to fly very high. You do speak Amharic, don't you?" he asked Lukas.

"Of course."

"Then you'll be kind enough to translate for me what is going on between the reconnaissance plane and the control tower in Addis."

Lukas listened carefully to the transmissions. "They've sent two reconnaissance planes to force us down."

"No need to worry about that. They're far too slow. I'm heading straight into those rain clouds. Once we're hidden in them, they'll never find us."

The three of them fell silent as the Addis control tower came through again. "Unidentified plane in Ethiopian airspace. Have you located it?"

"Still not spotted," came the reply from one of the reconnaissance planes. "Will continue surveillance."

Suddenly a thick bank of swirling mist closed around the fugitives. Fine streamers of rain spiralled down the windscreen. Lukas and Pavlos exchanged nervous glances, but they knew the impenetrable greyness was their sanctuary.

The radio crackled. "Am returning to base. Cannot find anything. Over and out."

Lukas shuffled in his seat, letting out his breath in a long, low whistle. "When did they first pick you up on radar?" he ventured.

"Oh, about twenty minutes ago. I was safe until then as I was flying an international aircraft."

"They must have sent the first reconnaissance plane from Addis at about that time to intercept you. One circled us minutes before we spotted you, then headed south."

"I know. I saw it. I swerved to keep out of sight. I was

more worried by that convoy of soldiers on the road. They were only about five kilometres away, so I decided to slow them down. I flew literally about ten feet above their heads, so they'd think I was about to crash into them. It caused a huge commotion, I can tell you. There were rifles and helmets flying in every direction. I knew it would give me time to land, pick you up and take off again before they realized what was happening."

"My God! You risked your life for us! How can we ever thank you?"

"Well, you can start by pouring me a cup of coffee and handing me one of those delicious sandwiches your wives have sent you," Tyrone grinned.

"How long before we're out of Ethiopian airspace?" asked Pavlos.

" We'll be in Marsabit in about an hour."

One more hour. What if they sent a jet from Addis, thought Lukas? It would only take about fifteen minutes to catch up with them. He tried to relax and bit into a sandwich. Bread! Real, soft bread. Not hard millet bread, but soft, buttered, pure wheat bread.

"I'd forgotten what real bread tasted like," came Pavlos' voice from the back. "To be honest, I never thought I would taste real bread again."

"Everything will change for you now," said Tyrone sympathetically. "You've got a whole new life ahead of you. You'd better believe that."

"And all thanks to you. We'll never forget this."

"A man's gotta do what a man's gotta do," he joked. "Seriously, though, sometimes there are certain things that just have to be done, that are destined. We didn't only have luck on our side today, we also had a watchful eye from someone up there." He jerked his finger upwards.

As suddenly as it had disappeared, the plane emerged from cloud into brilliant sunshine. Looking down at the miles of desert beneath them, Lukas noticed the brown landscape was spotted with gold. The meskel flower was in bloom! So the old woman's prophecy had come true. A lump rose in his throat. How ironic! To think that this was the first sight that had met his parents' eyes when they arrived in Ethiopia fifty-five years ago and now it was his last. He looked back at this final image of Ethiopia. His eyes burned as he bid farewell to gold mountainsides and green valleys.

Tyrone interrupted. "Gentlemen, you can breathe again. We will shortly be landing in Marsabit, where someone is anxiously awaiting you."

* * *

Laki's sunburnt face was tilted up towards the approaching plane. Was it Tyrone? In the short space of time since he had disembarked at Marsabit, two light aircraft had landed bringing tourists from Loyangalani. It seemed incredible that this small airstrip in a remote corner of northern Kenya could be so busy.

The first plane had landed only an hour after Tyrone had left. Its approach had sent shivers down Laki's spine, thinking yet another mission had gone wrong. Only when he saw the passengers climb out with their cameras and fishing gear did his heartbeat return to normal. Although the weather forecast had predicted rain, it had been a hot, sticky day and Laki had been forced to strip down to his shorts. With barely enough shade to protect the fuel, he had roasted in the sun for three hours. Picking up that morning's newspaper, he tried to kill time, but it was useless. He couldn't concentrate on anything.

A little after 2:30, he spotted another plane coming in to land. Suspecting it was another safari plane, touching down before the onward flight to Nairobi, he ignored it. "It's too early for Tyrone to be back yet. I'll give him another half hour or so. Then I'll start worrying," he told himself, as he paced up and down to keep busy. He glanced casually at the plane as it turned at the end of the runway. Then he stopped. There could not be another green and red tail fin like that. Throwing his cap in the air, he raced to meet it. From where he was, he could only see Tyrone's face in the cockpit. He could not make out if anyone else was with him.

The side door flew open and out leapt Jeannie, barking and zigzagging madly from side to side, overjoyed to be able to stretch her legs at last. "They've made it!" yelled Laki at the top of his voice, throwing his arms up and jumping in the air. He ran to the door of the aircraft, almost lifting out the jubilant passengers. Clapping their arms round each other, they all three hugged and kissed, tears in their eyes.

Tyrone leaned against the open doorway, a smile of satisfaction on his face. It had all been worth the risk. "Now, gentlemen," he coughed, trying to attract some attention. "If I can just temporarily interrupt this overwhelming expression of joy and happiness," he laughed, "we had better refuel and be on our way. There's more to come in Nairobi. You'd better reserve some of your energy or you'll never be able to hug your wives and children."

"There's no danger there, Tyrone," Pavlos laughed. "We've got a lot of catching up to do. They're in for a busy time."

Chapter Thirty Six

Michael and Aspa were waiting at home when I returned from work, broad smiles on their faces. "We've just come from the airport. We checked with the control tower and Tyrone's radioed that he's coming in. He estimates landing a few minutes after 6.00 p.m."

"Any passengers with him?" I asked with trepidation.

"No mention of passengers but I have this strong feeling that there's more than two on board. I've never felt more positive about anything."

"From your mouth to God's ears, Aspa. I don't think I can stand the suspense of not knowing. If something has gone wrong again, I'll just collapse."

"Well, that's why we've come to tell you that we'll go to the airport to meet them, while you stay here. You'd better take care of Venetia. Whatever happens, it will be a shock for her. Besides we don't want to cause a great commotion at the airport and upset the immigration people."

Aspa was right. Our telephone was out of order, so I told her Venetia and I would go to Byron and Electra's house in case they needed to call us. It was a beautiful afternoon and we gathered in their front garden. Their house was on the flight path to Wilson Airport, which gave us a chance to observe every flying object that passed overhead.

"What's happening?" Nicholas, my eldest nephew, asked. "You're all so nervous and why do you keep looking up at the sky the whole time?"

Nothing had been mentioned to the children, partly because we didn't want anything leaking out that would jeopardise the mission, and partly because we didn't want to involve them in all the stress. Byron took his son on one side. "Don't mention anything to the others," he whispered, implying he was confident Nicholas was old enough to handle the situation. "We're hoping that your Uncle Lukas and Pavlos will be flying in from Addis today."

Nicholas' face lit up. He had often been present when plans had been discussed and, even at ten, understood what we had been going through for so many years. The younger children gathered round, wanting to share the secret.

"Come on, Nicholas," Stavros pleaded. "Tell us." Nicholas hesitated. The toddlers, Gabby and Taki, were playing a game of hide and seek around the bushy bougainvilleas and weren't paying any attention. They were too young to understand what was going on anyway, but Stavros, he felt, could be safely let in on the secret. He whispered into his brother's ear. "But don't you dare repeat it to the kids," he admonished.

One by one small light aircraft passed over our heads. None seemed to fit the description of the one we were expecting. Then we saw it—white with a green and red tail. It passed so quickly, there was no time to identify any numbers.

"That's the one, Mellina," Electra shouted enthusiastically. "I'm sure of it."

Venetia, who had also been straining her neck, grasped my hand. Her fingers were cold. "How long before we know?" she asked, eyes shadowed with worry.

"The airport is only a few kilometres from here. They'll probably call us as soon as they land."

But instead of the phone call we were anxiously awaiting, we heard Laki's horn at the gate. It was not the double hoot he usually made, but a gentle signal of two short blasts followed by three long ones. It was a sign which sent shivers down our spines. The gates thrown back, he drove in slowly.

There were three heads in the car.

Chaos ensued as Venetia and I clutched our husbands, crying and kissing and laughing with joy. Children ran around screaming everywhere. Mary, who had run towards the car as soon as it pulled up, collapsed by her father's feet and grabbing his legs with both arms, cried, "Daddy, I never want to lose you again."

Gabby, who had been desperately scrambling through all the adult legs surrounding her father, finally found his trouser leg and tugging at him, threw up her arms in a plea to be swung up into the air. Squeezing his neck, she yelled, "Look, everybody. I have a Daddy too."

Everyone pressed forward to greet the long-awaited arrivals. Once emotions had calmed a little, Byron ran inside and brought out two bottles of chilled champagne.

"We have one last thing to do, Byron, before we celebrate our success," said Lukas. "We have to call the one we left behind, who will be waiting for our return today. We have to call Askala." He turned to me, his eyes bloodshot from tiredness and weeping. "Honey, please? I don't think I can talk to her right now. Would you do it?"

I nodded. With a lump in my throat, I dialled the familiar number. After the second ring, the receiver was picked up. "Mama Askala," I said hoarsely, coughing to clear my throat.

"Mellina, my child. They're not back yet. I'm worried."

"I know you are. That's why I'm calling you. The boys have finally reached their destination. They've reached home."

There was a long silence.

"Mama Askala," I called out, hot tears rolling down my face. "Are you there?"

"Yes, my Child. I'm here. I'm just so overwhelmed with joy. Saint Gabriel finally heard my prayers. He has granted me my last wish. Now I can die happy."

"Mama Askala, there's an envelope in the bureau drawer. Open it, it's for you," I sniffed. Afteranother short silence, I heard the crackling of an envelope being opened, followed by an exclamation.

"But…but…this is too much! There's enough here for a whole lifetime!" she cried.

"It's to make you comfortable for the rest of your life. We never want you to be deprived of anything. We're just sorry you couldn't come with the boys."

"No, don't feel sorry. This is my home. I wish to die and be buried in this land that I once loved. I'm too old for changes."

"Mama Askala, take whatever you want from the house. Anything. It's all yours."

"I only want your photographs to stick on the wall near my bed. I want to see your faces when I wake up in the morning and when I go to sleep at night. I don't need anything else. May I take them?"

451

"Of...course...you...can," I answered, barely able to speak through my tears.

"You are the only family I've ever had and you've been so good to me. I send you all my blessings. I'll never, ever forget you."

EPILOGUE

In June 1983, two years after Lukas' escape, Mellina returned to Ethiopia as a member of a UN team attending a United Nations ministerial conference. In spite of Lukas' objections, she had adamantly refused to turn down the opportunity. Fate had given her a rare chance of visiting Ethiopia again, possibly for the last time.

When Mellina arrived, Addis Ababa was in the throes of lavish preparations for the Ninth Anniversary celebrations of the Revolution. Even with two months to go, men and women were being forced to work around the clock for a pittance to decorate Revolution Square. Outside every store and hotel, youths in tattered clothes and shivering with cold were begging for food. Even as thousands of cases of whisky were being imported for the celebrations, another catastrophic famine—worse than the one which brought down Haile Selassie—was already threatening the lives of millions in Wollo, Eritrea and Tigre. The Government did eventually appeal for western aid but before the world took notice, the famine had claimed nearly three million lives.

During the only free weekend she had before the opening of the conference, Mellina went to visit Askala. It seemed strange walking down the same street after so long an absence, the street in which she had so narrowly escaped death. Recognising her, old acquaintances from the nearby bakery, vegetable stalls and houses, hastened to greet her. It was Sunday, so they could approach without fear of being spotted by a member of the *kebele*. Everyone clammered to know the details of Lukas' escape—to enquire after the family and their new home.

Mellina was touched by their concern. Askala's neighbour, *Woizero* Buzunesh, rushed out when she saw Mellina raise her hand to knock on the old woman's door. "*Yesus Christos!*" she exclaimed in Amharic. "What in heaven's name are you doing here?"

Opening the familiar door for Mellina, Buzunesh explained that Askala had been confined to bed after a severe asthma attack and was now sedated and sleeping soundly. "I don't know what your presence will do to Mama Askala. She's been calling out your name from the day she fell sick."

"I won't come in if it will make her condition worse," cried Mellina, alarmed.

"No, no. She's asleep now, but come in and sit down near her bed. I think it will do her a lot of good to see you."

Laying aside the long-promised gifts of silk scarves and woollen jumpers, Mellina looked lovingly at the white-haired old woman, her wrinkled face momentarily relaxed in sleep. Stuck to the wall beside her were the photographs of the family she had asked to keep. For nearly an hour Mellina kept her vigil. Then Askala began to stir. Groaning and grunting, she wriggled to find a more comfortable position. As she tossed, her eyes settled on Mellina. She blinked. Then, forcing herself up on one elbow, she looked enquiringly at Buzunesh.

"Am I dreaming?" she demanded.

Mellina could hold back no longer. She bent down and clasped the old woman in her arms. "I had to come back, Mama Askala. I just had to."

Askala nodded. "I knew you would, my Child. I knew you would. You've come at the right time again. Asthma will be the end of me."

"Can I fetch you some medicine?"

"No, my child. I've had the best treatment anyone could wish for," she smiled. "Thanks to the money the boys left behind, I'm being treated by the best Russian professor in town." She laughed, inducing a sudden fit of coughing.

"Lie back," Mellina ordered. "Once you're on your feet again, we'll have a lot of catching up to do. I've got so much to tell you. So many things have happened."

In the few hours they spent together, Askala related all that had happened since Lukas and Pavlos fled the country. Once the *kebele* realised that the Fanouris brothers had escaped, they sealed the apartment and placed it under twenty-four hour surveillance. Some time later, they auctioned everything left behind.

When Askala was interrogated, she stated truthfully that she had had no idea that an escape was being planned, but in her own, inimitable, fearless way, she concluded her statement by adding boldly, "What do you think you achieved by forcing them to stay in this country after you had stripped them of everything they ever possessed, especially their dignity? They had no wealth abroad. I should know. I was with the family for forty-five years. You left them with no alternative. You forced them to escape. If you want to arrest me, you can go ahead. I'm not scared to die in prison."

The authorities never bothered Askala again. She died peacefully in her sleep, two years after Mellina's visit.

During 1983, a number of political detainees were released. Among them was Mitiku Mellekot, the Deputy Minister of the Interior, who had been detained for eight

455

years without charge or trial. Sadly, there was no one to welcome him home. Abeba, having given up hope of ever seeing him again, had seized the opportunity to educate her children abroad and accepted a transfer from the UNDP. She left Ethiopia before her husband's release.

Ato Tewolde, Almaz's husband, confined solely on the grounds that he was the son-in-law of an ex-minister, survived seven years' imprisonment, but was released a broken man. Destroyed physically by poor diet and disease-ridden conditions, he emerged emaciated and covered with ugly scabs and sores. But it was his spirit, above all, that was gone. His dull, melancholy eyes betrayed a deep-rooted depression, from which he never recovered. It was as well he never found out what his wife had sacrificed in an effort to secure his release. Seeing his physical deterioration, Almaz had pleaded with the Dergue to free her husband on the grounds of ill health. When all her efforts failed, she fell at the feet of the Colonel who was handling *Ato* Tewolde's case, crying out that she would do anything to secure her husband's freedom. Taking advantage of her offer, the Colonel promised that he personally would ensure Tewolde was freed if she would agree to perform certain 'favours' in return.

Night after night, the Colonel's jeep was parked outside Almaz' house for the entire neighbourhood to see. Initially, she ensured her children were out of the way, staying overnight with a friend, but as the Colonel became more demanding, even her children became aware of what was going on. Once, finding her mother in tears after the departure of her unwelcome guest, the eldest fifteen-year-old daughter had hugged her compassionately, saying, "We know you're only doing this for Daddy. Please don't feel guilty. We all love you for it."

Allowing herself to be labelled the Colonel's whore, however, brought no results. Months passed with no mention of a pardon. "Today you've satisfied my needs like never before," the Colonel whispered in her ear as they lay together one night. "Maybe the ice is finally breaking and you're falling in love with me."

Almaz broke away, reaching for her dressing gown to cover her nakedness. Her brain was whirling with guilt and shame, fear and anger. "You said… you promised… you would get my husband freed if I slept with you. You've done nothing. What more do you want? You've taken my self-respect, I have nothing left to give. When are you going to fulfill your side of the bargain?"

"He's a political threat, you stupid bitch," yelled her lover, getting out of the bed and walking towards the shower. "Don't you understand," he said, hesitating at the door. "We'll never let him go."

Looking around her wildly, Almaz noticed the Colonel had left his automatic pistol on the bedside table. Snatching it up with shaking hands, she aimed it straight at him. "I'll blow your brains out if it's the last thing I do. I don't care if I hang for it," she screamed. But as her finger tightened round the trigger, the faces of her five children swam before her eyes. "Oh, my God!" she realised in horror. "I can't do it! My children. Who will provide for them? They've already been deprived of a father. If I hang, they'll be left at the mercy of you butchers." She let the pistol slide from her fingers, flinging herself weeping on the bed. "You've used me, you bastard," she screamed. "You've denigrated me in the eyes of my children. Get out! Get out! Never set foot in this house again."

It was the Colonel's last visit.

Ato Yohannes, Lukas' old customer, was not as lucky as

Tewolde. The receipts that Lukas had so painstakingly searched out for books he had purchased proved useless at his trial—if there was a trial. No one ever learned the truth. His family never saw him again. Throughout the three years he was imprisoned, the only indication that he was alive was the prison guards' acceptance of the food his family delivered each day. Similarly, they only learned of his death when one day a guard casually remarked that Yohannes would no longer be needing any daily rations. No other explanation was given. No one was ever told what had happened.

As if the loss of her husband was not enough, the Dergue had more in store for *Ato* Yohannes' wife. Within a few days, she received official notification that her deceased husband had left behind 'certain debts' which she had to settle. Lacking any other means of payment, she attempted to sell her one remaining asset, her house. She received a number of fair offers for the property, but each time the Dergue refused to approve the sale. Ultimately, she was forced to sell to the Government at a reduced price. When she eventually received her settlement, she found that not only had the so-called debt been deducted, but so had an additional sum for having fed her husband for three years in jail.

Shortly after Mellina's return to Nairobi in June 1983, a young Ethiopian couple finally made it to the gates of UNEP. Equipped only with the name '*Woizero* Melli' and the fact that she had previously worked with the UN in Addis Ababa, they searched from one UN office to the other until they found her. Totally exhausted, the soles of their feet swollen and cracked, they could barely stand up to greet her. They had crossed the border into Kenya on foot. Tesfu and Alem were among the lucky ones who had been given a name and a place where they could secure a meal and a bed to sleep in. Hundreds never made it. They were gunned down before they had a chance to set foot in a neighbouring country.

Those who were left of the Ethiopian royal family languished in prison until 1988, when Colonel Mengistu issued a proclamation during the 13th anniversary celebrations of the Revolution, saying that they were to be released. Princess Tenagne Work, daughter of the late Emperor, an old and frail woman of seventy-two, now leads a quiet, simple life out of the public eye in Addis Ababa. She lives in an old house that has been made available by the Dergue. Princess Sarah Gizaw and Asrate Kassa's wife and children live in the same compound. All their possessions were confiscated during the revolution, so they live like ordinary citizens—but are still deprived of freedom of movement. Although it is rumoured that friends living outside Ethiopia send them some financial support, it is the Ethiopian people themselves who pay them daily visits and offer them food.

Mellina returned to Addis once more in January 1990. With the help of her friend and neighbour Buzunesh, she managed to find Mama Akala's grave and place some white daisies upon it.

Otherwise, it was as though time had stood still. Addis had almost reverted to the way she remembered it as a child. Clusters of eucalyptus trees had sprung up, hiding the tin-roofed *tukuls*. The atmosphere in the capital was so calm that it was impossible to believe, as the foreign press reported, that the Eritrean and Tigrean troops were as close as Dessie. Just as in the days before the Emperor's deposition, only hushed rumours were circulating.

But it was no rumour that the country's youth was

being creamed off for battle fodder. While Mellina was visiting a friend, her maid came in to pour coffee with red, puffy eyes. Between sobs, she described how soldiers had gone through her neighbourhood the previous night, conscripting boys as young as 15 years of age. Those who had resisted had been beaten and thrown into the waiting trucks.Those who had tried to escape had been shot in front of their parents. The recruits were destined for training camps and the front line. The night before Mellina's departure, the dreaded trucks parked at the entrance to Askala's dead end road. By morning, the whole neighbour-hood was grieving. The muttered comments did not bode well for the regime. "Haile Selassie never harmed youngsters," said one parent. "He would warn the disloyal but never kill them. This tyrant is unrestrained by laws or religion. He snatches our children from our arms without conscience or compassion."

Yet just six weeks after Mellina's visit, in March 1990, the winds of change were already blowing. Following the dramatic events in Eastern Europe—the crumbling of the Berlin Wall, the fall of the Rumanian dictator Ceausescu and the introduction of a multi-party system in the Soviet Union—the Ethiopian Government took its own people by surprise with some astonishing moves.

Overnight, the huge portraits of Lenin, Marx and Engels which had dominated Addis Ababa's revolution square for the past sixteen years, were removed. Early morning passers-by gasped in disbelief as they watched workers dismantle the portraits, derisively dubbed 'the trinity' because they were erected in a square once dedicated to the Christian festival of the epiphany. As a further sign that the country was finally bidding farewell to its Marxist past, the word '*Wozaderawi*', meaning 'proletarian' in Amharic, had been painted out of the slogan and 'Long Live Proletarian Internationalism' adorned an arch in the square.

These symbolic moves accompanied a series of radical economic reforms announced by the ruling Workers Party Central Committee, which paved the way for a mixed economy in which state controls would disappear and the private sector would be allowed to play an 'unlimited role' in economic life. Ironically in the middle of May 1990, the Ethiopian Government announced the slashing of taxes by 30% in a move to attract foreign investments. They were thus reduced to 59% from a crippling 89%. Too late, sadly, for the Fanouris family and many others.

The changes were welcomed by students, who took to the streets to demonstrate their support waving aloft the Ethiopian flag. The red flag, the hated symbol of Ethiopia's steady economic decline, had already been abandoned. Joining the students were groups of clergy, carrying, for the first time since the revolution, portraits of Christ and the saints. Humorous speculation was that the next move would be the dismantling of the eight-ton statue of Lenin which stands astride a square outside Africa Hall and the late Emperor's Palace. The statue faced the airport and depicted Lenin in a marching pose with one foot raised. The standing joke among Ethiopians was that Lenin was poised ready to flee the country. Russians, they said, had no place in Ethiopia, even if one of them did weigh eight tons.

Nevertheless, jubilations at Mengistu's mellowing were short lived. They were tarnished by the encompassing fear that 'a leopard never changes its spots'. No matter how many concessions Mengistu was prepared to make, he was the leader who had implanted hate and terror in his people and spent most of the country's money on arms, rather than feed the starving. This was the man who had vowed to sacrifice his life for Socialism and who personally shot dead anyone who had plotted against him. Visions were still vivid of those who never re-emerged from the tree-shrouded compound of his party's headquarters where countless dissidents and army officers, blamed for defeats at the hands of the rebels, were tortured and shot. Hundreds of youth were arbitrarily snatched from their homes under the cover of darkness, savagely killed and dumped on the roadsides. In the meantime, the Ethiopian People's Revolutionary Democratic Front, the Eritrean People's Liberation Front and the Oromo Liberation Front were all scoring dramatic successes in their offensive against Mengistu's army.

Finally, on 21 May 1991, after fourteen years of brutal rule that had brought Ethiopia to the brink of annihilation, Mengistu was spotted slumped in the back seat of a car on his way to the airport and exile. He had survived ten assassination attempts but left behind him a demoralized, crumbling army, a bankrupt country and 7 million people facing starvation and death.

A few days later, on 24 May 1991, exhilarated Ethiopians rejoicing at Mengistu's flight watched government workers tear down and demolish the hated bronze statue of Lenin and rip up portraits of their President. This time it was Mengistu's turn to be branded *leba*—a thief—and a coward. The unlamented dictator is now believed to be relaxing on his ranch south of the Zimbabwean capital of Harare.

Just a few yards away from St. Stephanos Church—where in September 1973 an old man had predicted blood and turmoil as a result of a fiery sunset—and after nearly eighteen years of pain and suffering—a large crowd took the appearance of a halo surrounding the sun as a sign from God that Ethiopia's troubles were nearing their end.

* * *

This book only touches on what this nation of proud, dignified people suffered when the 1974 coup brought the era of Red Terror into their lives and made Meskel lose its historic symbolism. Through fear, they have been forced to keep their suffering silent. Some, unable to live under such conditions, escaped as refugees, while luckier ones defected and sought political asylum abroad. Today, the United States alone has given refuge to more than 100,000 Ethiopians. Among them are Tesfu and Alem. Through the assistance of the United Nations High Commissioner for Refugees, they were resettled and now lead a respectable life in America with their infant son who will have the chance of growing up in a free and democratic country. But, comfortable as their lives may be, they cannot forget the family they left behind and yearn to return to their motherland.

As for Lukas and me, it broke our hearts to witness the destruction and denigration of a people and country we loved. We would willingly have lived out our lives in a free Ethiopia, contributing to the health and wealth of that wonderful nation. But, through no choice of our own, we were forced to leave. Whatever lies ahead, a part of us will always remain behind with those warm-hearted people who shared their country with us for so many years. It is their Ethiopia that shall never be forgotten.

◦◦◦◦◦◦◦◦◦◦◦◦◦◦◦◦◦◦◦◦◦
Quotidien d'Information
en langue française
publié par le Ministère
Ethiopien de l'Information
Administration B.P. 1364
◦◦◦◦◦◦◦◦◦◦◦◦◦◦◦◦◦◦◦◦◦

Addis

Ethiopia

Dixième Année No. 4   **Lundi 25 nóv**

Décision politique du Conseil Militaire Provisoire
Communiqué officiel des exécutions

«Peuple Ethiopien,

«Comme les autres peuples de par le monde, toi aussi tu avais un pays. Comme tous les autres peuples, toi aussi tu avais des chefs. Tu n'étais inférieur à aucun peuple. Tu es doué d'un patriotisme éprouvé et de bon sens.

«Mais tes dirigeants, tels des ennemis, ont fait de toi un étranger au sein de ta mère-patrie et t'ont maintenu, divisé, dans l'oppression et l'obscurantisme. Privé des fruits de ton labeur, tu a été réduit à la mendicité. Tes cris de faim et de soif ayant été étouffés, tu a été jeté, par milliers dans des charniers. Alors que tes dirigeants vivaient dans l'opulence la plus scandaleuse, tu végétais, avec ta famille, dans la misère la plus outrageante...

«Mais tes cris et tes larmes ne sont pas restés vains. De tes souffrances et de tes privations, nous n'avons oublié aucune. Nous t'invitons à te joindre à nous dans la marche en avant vers les transformations profondes et historiques...»

Ainsi commence le communiqué du Conseil Militaire Provisoire qui a annoncé au peuple éthiopien l'exécution, samedi dernier, de soixante personnalités civiles et militaires de l'ancien régime et des membres du Conseil Militaire Provisoire dont le président, le Lieutenant Général Aman Mikaél Andom.

Le communiqué classe les personnalités exécutées en quatre catégories.

Catégorie A — Les personnalités civiles qui ont failli aux hautes responsabilités qui leur avaient été confiées. Ce sont:

1 — Le Tsehafi Tezaz Aklilou Habte Wold
2 — Le Leoul Ras Asrate Kassa
3 — Le Lidj Endalkatchew Makonnen
4 — Le Ras Mesfin Selechi
5 — Le Lieutenant-Colonel Tamerat Yiguezou
6 — Ato Akale Work Habte Wold
7 — Le Dr. Tesfayé Guebre Egzy
8 — Ato Moulatou Debebe
9 — Ato Abebe Reta
10 — Le Dedjazmatch Salomon Abreham
11 — Le Dedjazmatch Leguesse Bezou
12 — Le Dedjazmatch Sahlou Defayé
13 — Le Dedjazmatch Workineh Wolde Amanouel
14 — Le Dedjazmatch Keflé Erguetou
15 — Le Dedjazmatch Workou Enkou Selassié
16 — Le Dedjazmatch Aemero Selassié Abebe
17 — Le Dedjazmatch Kebede Ali Welé
18 — Le Colonel Salomon Kedir
19 — Le Afe Neguous Abedje Debalk
20 — Ato Nebiye Leoul Keflé
21 — Le Kegnazmatch Yilma Aboyé
22 — Ato Teguegne Yetechawork
23 — Ato Salomon Guebre Mariam
24 — Ato Haïlou Teklou
25 — Le Lidj Haïlou Desta
26 — Le Blata Admassou Reta
27 — Le Fitaourari Demes Alamereou
28 — Le Fitaourari Amdé Abera

29 — Le Fitaourari Tadesse Enkou Selassié

Catégorie B — Les Officiers supérieurs de l'Armée et de la Police de l'ancien régime qui ont manqué à leur devoir:

30 — Le Lieutenant Général Abiy Ababe
31 — Le Lieutenant Général Kebede Guebré
32 — Le Lieutenant Général Deresse Doubale
33 — Le Lieutenant Général Abebe Guemeda
34 — Le Lieutenant Général Yilma Chibechi
35 — Le Lieutenant Général Haïlé Baykedagne
36 — Le Lieutenant Général Asefa Ayene
37 — Le Lieutenant Général Belete Abebe
38 — Le Lieutenant Général Issaias Guebre Selassié
39 — Le Lieutenant Général Assefa Demessié
40 — Le Lieutenant Général Debebe Haïlé Mariam
41 — Le Major-Général Seyoum Guedle Guihorguis
42 — Le Major-Général Guachaou Kebebe
43 — Le Major-Général Tafesse Lema
44 — Le Vice-Amiral Eskender Desta
45 — Le Général de Brigade Moulouguéta Wolde Yohanes
46 — Le Général de Brigade Wendemou Abebe
47 — Le Général de Brigade Guerma Yohanes
48 — Le Colonel Yalem Zeoud Tessema
49 — Le Colonel Tasseou Modjo
50 — Le Colonel Yiguezou Yimené